TENTH EDITION

THE BRADFORD BOOK OF COLLECTOR'S PLATES

CHARLES WINTHROPE & SONS

New York   Chicago

Library of Congress Catalog Card No.
77–77526

ISBN 0-9611012-2-9

Tenth Edition

THE BRADFORD BOOK OF

COLLECTOR'S PLATES

THE OFFICIAL GUIDE TO ALL EDITIONS
TRADED ON THE WORLD'S LARGEST EXCHANGE

THE BRADFORD EXCHANGE, LTD.
Niles/Chicago, Illinois 60648

EXECUTIVE EDITOR
Barbara B. White

EDITOR
Lynn Ann Walker

ASSOCIATE EDITOR
Gerald Eckert

CONTRIBUTING EDITORS

Annick Flaxman
Thomas J. Gradel
Richard Lalich

Carolyn J. Reckert
Susanne Southwood
Anthony Sterbenc

Alyson Sulaski Wyckoff

INTERNATIONAL EDITORS

Rainer Dembach
Werner Peter

Gijsbert Rijkeboer
Jorgen Sannung

Fred Woodley

CHARLES WINTHROPE & SONS
Thomas J. Gradel, President and Publisher
New York   Chicago

Foreword

This Tenth Edition of *The Bradford Book of Collector's Plates* covers an era in the history of limited-edition collectibles that is tumultuous indeed. The period that has passed since the last publication of this book is particularly marked with both sadness for a great loss, and optimism for a promising future. As many collectors know, J. Roderick MacArthur, my father and the former Director of the Board of Governors of The Bradford Exchange, died on December 15, 1984 after a long illness. (Editor's note: please see the special tribute to J. Roderick MacArthur on page 16.)

To the end of his life, Rod MacArthur was as actively involved in the operations and plans of The Bradford Exchange as his illness would allow. He always considered the publication of this book to be one of the most important services offered to collectors, and took great care in reviewing every aspect of the collector's plate market that was reported here. As we acknowledge our tenth year of publication, we feel obliged more than ever to improve our coverage of this exciting market, to carry it forward as Rod MacArthur would have wished. As a result, the reader will find carefully reorganized, fully updated sections covering not only the history of collecting and the current state of the market, but also entirely new sections—created for beginning and veteran collector. alike—that offer suggestions for ways to enhance the pleasure of owning fine limited editions and displaying them in your home.

Also, since the current state of the market demands it, you'll find detailed and informative coverage of the international market in collector's plates, with reporting from every world trading center in which The Bradford Exchange maintains an office. More than ever before, this will give collectors in all markets the information they need to be part of an active and growing worldwide phenomenon.

Of course, the most popular features of past books, such as the full-color Gallery of Bradex-listed plates and the much-expanded artist profiles and over-the-counter sections, are still here as well. Taken as a whole, this Tenth Edition of *The Bradford Book of Collector's Plates* is certainly a fitting tribute to my father's contribution to this marketplace. But more importantly, this edition is also the most complete and useful reference work for plate collectors in publishing history.

John R. MacArthur

John R. MacArthur
Director of the Board of Governors
The Bradford Exchange

Chicago, Illinois
October, 1985

The editors acknowledge with gratitude the invaluable supplementary information supplied by:

Anna-Perenna, Inc., Klaus D. Vogt; **Arabia of Finland,** Dennis Vizenor; **Armstrong's,** Dave Armstrong; **Artists of the World,** James LaFond; **Belleek Pottery Ltd.,** Charles Thompson; **Bing & Grøndahl Copenhagen Porcelain, Inc.,** Jean Gwardyak; **Canadian Collector Plates Limited,** Robert Henderson; **Christian Bell Porcelain Ltd.,** Horst Müller; **Creative World, Ltd.,** Richard Gabbe; **Crown Parian, Ltd.,** Jim Carter; **D'Arceau-Limoges,** André Azum; **Ernst Enterprises,** Ray Ernst; **Fairmont China,** Thomas W. Hogan; **Goebel of United States,** Dieter Schneider; **Gorham Division of Textron, Inc.,** David Wrenn; **Hackett American Collectors Co.,** James Hackett; **The Hamilton Mint,** Melanie Hart; **Haviland & Co., Inc.,** Frederick Haviland; **Hibel Studio,** William Hibel; **Hutschenreuther,** Stephen S. Barnet; **Incolay Studios Inc.,** Elvin M. Bright, Sr.; **Kaiser Porcelain Co.,** Hubert E. W. Kaiser; **Kern Collectibles,** Matthew P. Brummer; **Kosta Boda U.S.A. Ltd.,** Raymond W. Zrike; **Lenox China Co.,** Karen Cohen; **Modern Masters, Ltd.,** Richard Sitarski; **Pemberton & Oakes,** John Hugunin; **Pickard China Co.,** Henry A. Pickard; **Porcelaine Georges Boyer,** Gerard Boyer; **Rasmussen Import Co.,** R. D. Rasmussen; **Reco International Corp.,** Heio Reich; **Reed & Barton Silversmiths,** Patrice Johnson; **River Shore, Ltd.,** Arch Patterson; **Roman, Inc.,** Ronald T. Jedlinski; **Rosenthal U.S.A. Limited,** Ellen S. Miller; **Royal Copenhagen Porcelain Corp.,** Ivar Ipsen; **Royal Doulton,** Paul Warner; **Royal Worcester Spode Inc.,** Joyce Hendlewich; **Schmid,** Dennis Hurst; **Svend Jensen,** Per Jensen; **Vague Shadows,** Richard Habeeb; **Viking Import House, Inc.,** Pat Owen; **Villeroy & Boch,** Ingrid Vetterl; **Wara Intercontinental Co.,** Walter A. Rautenberg; **Wedgwood, Inc.,** Jim Fulks

Plate photography by Gerald Hoos   Art direction by Mary Claire
Selected photography courtesy of *Plate World* magazine

CONTENTS

"Behind the Frozen Window," 1895 issue in the
Bing & Grøndahl *Christmas* series: the first true collector's plate.

THE INTERNATIONAL COLLECTOR'S PLATE MARKET

Introduction

Collector's plates hold a unique position in the vast world of art—and are unique even among the smaller category of limited editions. This is true because, while a collector's plate is an object clearly created for its aesthetic value and its artistic merit, it also has another important aspect. Each limited-edition plate also has the potential to be actively traded among collectors in the fast-paced secondary market.

This potential arises from the basic characteristic of all limited editions: the fact that once the edition limit is reached, production ends. The edition is then closed, never to reopen again, and the subsequent market value of plates from that edition is determined by two factors. The first is: what price collectors who already own the plate are willing to sell it for at a later date. The second is: what price collectors who want that plate are willing to pay.

Market Potential Recognized

This simple "two-sided market" idea applies to any limited edition—whether it is a plate or another form of collectible. But in the plate market *only*, that idea of exchanging sold-out issues among collectors has grown to become a worldwide phenomenon, rivaling the sophistication of some of the world's exchanges in com-

modities or foreign currencies. Today, no other art form—regardless of style, medium or popularity—is traded in a reasonably uniform market with the same frequency and volume as collector's plates. In fact, there are over 13,000 primary and secondary market transactions *every day* on the worldwide collector's plate market.

This activity has led to the recognition of collector's plates over the last decade as "the world's most-traded art." More importantly, it has led to growth in many areas of the collector's market that benefit *all* plate collectors, regardless of whether they are now—or ever intend to be—traders on the secondary market. In the ten years in which this book has been published, the opportunities for collectors to get maximum enjoyment from their hobby have vastly improved. Today, collectors' needs are met by special publications geared to their market, and special events that cater to their desire to expand their knowledge of limited-edition art and artists.

The Roots of the Modern Market

Ever clamoring for more information on new and exciting issues—as well as up-to-date market information on what they may already own—today's plate collec-

The Bradford Exchange Trading Floor in Niles, Illinois: hub of the worldwide collector's plate market.

tors have come a long way from their counterparts just ten years ago. In the early 1970's, collector's plates were just coming into their own as a recognized art form, and information was not easy to come by. Even though the concept of the limited-edition plate had actually developed just before the turn of the 20th century in Scandinavia and other parts of Europe, it took nearly 50 years for the appeal—and the trading potential—of this idea to be recognized in the U.S., and shortly thereafter, worldwide.

It also took several forward-thinking American antique and collectibles dealers in those early days to create the "spark" that would ignite the idea of back-issue trading.

First, this spark set fire to the prices of the charming blue-and-white porcelain plates that were the first true limited editions available in this country. Later, it ignited the market for plates with increasingly diverse themes and media. Eventually, as in all such growing markets, the swells and ebbs of collector preference took over what a few insightful dealers had begun, and the need for an organized market became apparent.

This, in turn, led to the creation of The Bradford Exchange, the world's first organized marketplace for the trading of limited-edition works of art. It also contributed directly to the evolution of the plate market as we know it today—where reputable plate producers, knowledgeable dealers and independent means of exchange all serve the collector's needs on several levels.

What follows is the complete story of that growth. It begins with the discovery of the remarkable beauty of porcelain in ancient China, and ends with the introduction of the most current plate issues in California, New York and South Bend, where *today's* standards for beauty in plates were confirmed right before the eyes of

thousands of collectors.

We think you will find that it is an interesting and exciting history, made even more so by the fact that it continues to be written every day, all over the world, by collectors just like you.

KONGELIG HOFLEVERANDOR

COPENHAGEN PORCELAIN
BING & GRØNDAHL
B&G

Harald Bing, co-founder of Bing & Grøndahl, circa 1895.

A Brief History of Collector's Plates

On a cold December morning in 1895, we are told, Mr. Harald Bing, director of the Danish porcelain house of Bing & Grøndahl, ordered his astonished workers to destroy the mold for the small blue-and-white plate produced to commemorate the Christmas holiday.

7

The plate was entitled "Behind the Frozen Window." With Bing's unprecedented command, it became the first known limited-edition collector's plate, and the cornerstone of what is now a worldwide market. By thus limiting the plate's supply, Mr. Bing established the essential condition where demand for a plate, if it exceeds the edition size, can create an appreciation in price.

Although the idea that the laws of supply and demand can directly affect the prices of sold-out limited editions is a relatively new one, it actually harkens back to the extreme value placed on porcelain objects when the mystery of their manufacture was first unveiled.

Contemporary Chinese porcelain artisan at work.

Birthplace of Porcelain in Ancient China

Although there is still some contention among experts in the field, the birth of porcelain—or, technically speaking, the "hard paste" variety of porcelain that requires special ingredients, kiln techniques and glazing processes to produce its enviable whiteness and translucency—occurred in ancient China, in approximately 600 A.D.

Here, near the town of Ching-te Chen, a deposit of remarkably pure kaolin clay—still the one essential ingredient for the production of fine porcelain—was first discovered. For nearly 700 years thereafter, Chinese artisans perfected their techniques of porcelain production, creating objects of breathtaking beauty that were entirely unknown to the Western world.

Trade Routes to Europe Spark Demand

But in the 14th century, as the Orient was opened to European tradesmen for the first time, these magnificent Chinese wares found increasingly greater markets among well-to-do Europeans, who were stunned by the delicacy of their manufacture.

So popular was this so-called "Chinese export" porcelain, that kings and emperors offered great rewards to any local potter who could learn to duplicate the Chinese process. Even yet, for over three centuries, the only form of porcelain the Europeans could master was the "soft paste" variety, inferior in its color, translucency and strength to the "hard paste" products of the East. And the more impossible it seemed that Europeans could create their own porcelain, the more obsessive their collecting of the Chinese porcelain became.

German Unlocks the Ancient Secret

Then in 1708, an enterprising German potter named Johann Friedrich Bottger—in an attempt to placate royalty after his attempts at alchemy (turning lead to gold) had understandably failed—took on the task of duplicating the Chinese process in earnest. The key to the process became not only the discovery of kaolin clay in Saxony, near the town of Meissen, but also a way to fire the kiln to the extreme high temperatures necessary to achieve hard-paste quality, heretofore unknown. Through an ingenious use of solar energy, the kiln was finely pushed to the required 1350 degrees Celsius, and the first true European hard-paste porcelain was born.

The factory to produce this revolutionary ware was opened in 1710, under the name of the Royal Saxon Porcelain Manufactory in Meissen (now East Germany), and remains active to this day. Within a decade of its opening, it was creating porcelain ware of equal or greater beauty than that of China. Soon, master potters trained at Meissen left to establish other factories, most often in the areas of Europe with extensive kaolin deposits nearby.

Chi-chou teapot, 12th-13th century.

Ming bowl, 15th century.

Tang ewer, 7th-10th century; Ch'ien-lung vase, 18th century.

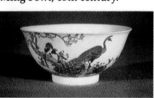

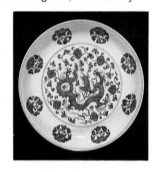
Yung-Cheng bowl, 18th century (above); Ming plate, 15th century (right).

Commemorative Plates Become Popular

By the mid-18th century, the Konigliche Porzellan-Manufaktur Berlin (KPM) and the French Royal Factory

at Sèvres were also producing fine porcelain. At roughly this period in the modern history of collecting, the idea of creating a fine porcelain plate as a decorative object, rather than just for food service, first arose.

Meissen, KPM, Sèvres and other potteries issued earthenware, china and porcelain plates honoring coronations, great battles and notable personalities of the age. The idea of porcelain being worthy of collection—which had really taken hold among the wealthy hundreds of years earlier—was now catching on throughout the populace.

Rise of the Great Ceramic Houses of Eurpoe

In the early part of the 18th century, monarchs and princes lined entire salons from floor to ceiling with exquisite porcelain wares. By the middle of that century, there were enough production facilities in Europe itself to make porcelain affordable for many levels of society other than royalty. In fact, many of the manufacturers of porcelain or bone china who are still active in today's collector's plate market established their factories in this "golden age" of European porcelain.

The oldest among Bradex-listed producers is Rörstrand, founded in Sweden in 1726 (see page 222), followed by Wedgwood of Great Britain in 1759 (page 182), Royal Copenhagen of Denmark, founded in 1775 (page 56) and Spode, founded in 1776 (page 178) in England. Royal Tettau, established in Bavaria in 1794, is the parent company of another Bradex-listed plate maker featured in this book, Royal Bayreuth (page 152).

Today's Producers Have 19th Century Origins

Because production techniques improved by leaps and bounds in the 19th century, porcelain had soon evolved from the "collectible of kings" to something the common man was proud to display in his home. Between the years of 1815 and 1898, no less than 17 producers of porcelain or fine china—whose plate issues are Bradex-listed today—opened their doors. Among them were: Arabia, Bing & Grøndahl, Haviland, Bareuther, Berlin Design, Goebel, Heinrich, Hutschenreuther, Kaiser, Rosenthal, Belleek, Royal Doulton, Fukagawa, Orrefors, Gorham, Edwin M. Knowles and Lenox.

Collecting Plates Stems from Danish Holiday Tradition

Why Bing & Grøndahl was destined to create the first true limited-edition collector's plate series, in 1895, can be explained by a look at a Danish tradition of Christmas gift-giving that existed at that time.

Among wealthy Danish landowners, it had long been the custom to distribute Christmas gifts of food to the families living on and working their lands. Eventually, these gifts developed even greater value, because they arrived on a decorative painted plate, most often of wood, that could be kept and displayed in the home long after Christmas. Families kept these plates for generations, and they were displayed not unlike the way modern collector's plates, issued in series, are today.

It was not surprising, then, that Danish porcelain

"Madonna and Child," 1908 issue in the Royal Copenhagen *Christmas* series.

houses would create decorative plates meant to be offered at Christmas, topped with the traditional gift of food. These, too, were kept and displayed in Scandinavian homes, but none were ever issued in limited editions of any kind.

That is, until Mr. Harald Bing broke tradition by breaking the mold of his 1895 Christmas plate—and started a collecting phenomenon that swept around the world.

"Winter Peace," 1910 issue in the Rosenthal *Traditional Classic Rose Christmas* series.

GROWTH OF PLATE COLLECTING

1895

1895:
First true limited-edition series, Bing & Grøndahl Christmas, introduced.

1900

1905

1908:
Royal Copenhagen Christmas Series

1910:
Rosenthal Christmas Series

1908

1910

1910-1935:
Hutschenreuther Christmas Series

1914 1914-mid-1920's: KPM Christmas Series
1915

1920

1925

1920's-1940's:
Danish and German Christmas plates continue to be held by European families, and by families of Scandinavian or German descent in the U.S.—but are not actively traded.

1930

1935

1940

1945

1947

1947:
William G. Freudenberg becomes first U.S. dealer to import and sell limited-edition collector's plates from Europe.

1949:
Pat Owen (Viking Imports) becomes first wholesaler of collector's plates, offering them to gift shops and department stores.

1949

1950

1951

1951:
Svend Jensen, a dealer, produces first back-issue price list for plates, establishing higher value for older, sold-out blue-and-white issues.

10

IN THE UNITED STATES AND EUROPE

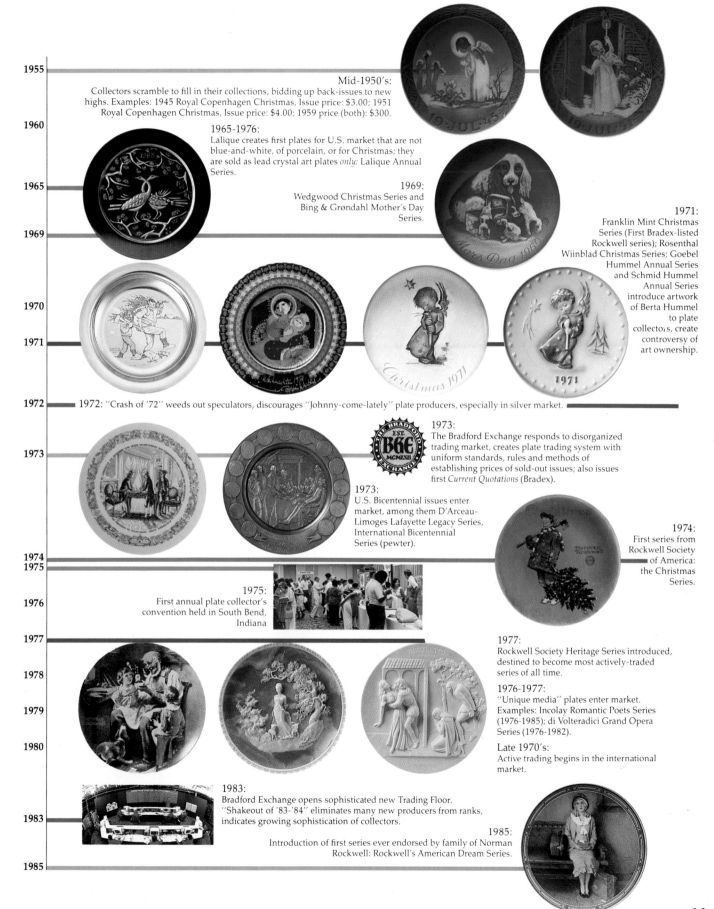

1955

1960

Mid-1950's:
Collectors scramble to fill in their collections, bidding up back-issues to new highs. Examples: 1945 Royal Copenhagen Christmas, Issue price: $3.00; 1951 Royal Copenhagen Christmas, Issue price: $4.00; 1959 price (both): $300.

1965-1976:
Lalique creates first plates for U.S. market that are not blue-and-white, of porcelain, or for Christmas; they are sold as lead crystal art plates *only:* Lalique Annual Series.

1965

1969:
Wedgwood Christmas Series and Bing & Grøndahl Mother's Day Series.

1969

1971:
Franklin Mint Christmas Series (First Bradex-listed Rockwell series); Rosenthal Wiinblad Christmas Series; Goebel Hummel Annual Series and Schmid Hummel Annual Series introduce artwork of Berta Hummel to plate collectors, create controversy of art ownership.

1970

1971

1972
1972: "Crash of '72" weeds out speculators, discourages "Johnny-come-lately" plate producers, especially in silver market.

1973

1973:
The Bradford Exchange responds to disorganized trading market, creates plate trading system with uniform standards, rules and methods of establishing prices of sold-out issues; also issues first *Current Quotations* (Bradex).

1973:
U.S. Bicentennial issues enter market, among them D'Arceau-Limoges Lafayette Legacy Series, International Bicentennial Series (pewter).

1974:
First series from Rockwell Society of America: the Christmas Series.

1974

1975

1975:
First annual plate collector's convention held in South Bend, Indiana

1976

1977

1977:
Rockwell Society Heritage Series introduced, destined to become most actively-traded series of all time.

1976-1977:
"Unique media" plates enter market. Examples: Incolay Romantic Poets Series (1976-1985); di Volteradici Grand Opera Series (1976-1982).

1978

1979

Late 1970's:
Active trading begins in the international market.

1980

1983:
Bradford Exchange opens sophisticated new Trading Floor. "Shakeout of '83-'84" eliminates many new producers from ranks, indicates growing sophistication of collectors.

1983

1985:
Introduction of first series ever endorsed by family of Norman Rockwell: Rockwell's American Dream Series.

1985

"Sunday Best" by Sandra Kuck, first issue in the *Days Gone By* series from Reco International.

PLATE COLLECTING IN THE UNITED STATES

Nineteen eighty-four and 1985 can easily be dubbed the "era of the knowledgeable collector" in the United States. The 18-month period reported in this book saw several milestone events and definitive market developments that affected the entire collecting world. Significantly, these events and developments show that collectors themselves now exert more influence on the market than perhaps at any other time in plate collecting history. And as collectors' knowledge and expertise broadens, the entire industry benefits.

The past 18 months saw the number of plate collectors in the U.S. swell to an estimated 6.4 million, an increase of more than 330,000 over the previous year's figures. Serving this huge market were more than 5,000 collectible or gift dealers, in all 50 states. And, if collectors wanted to share the excitement of collecting with friends and neighbors, there were at least 110 local clubs inviting them to do so. Not surprising, then, that in 1984 and 1985, collectors in the U.S. became aware that there is strength in numbers. When they spoke, they expected their voices to be heard.

The "Year of the Convention"

The most obvious indication of collector influence in the market was the increased number of collector conventions that opened their doors in 1984, as well as the increased scope of existing shows. In addition to the long-awaited shows in California, South Bend and Worcester, Massachusetts, collectors were treated to *new* shows in Orlando, Florida and Long Island, New York. Clearly, the collecting industry attempted to bring its new issues and artists within reach of as many collectors as possible, and record attendance at most shows proved the venture worthwhile.

The year's variety of collector events began with a fledgling show in a brand new location: Orlando, in early March, 1984. A second annual show of the same name was held there in February, 1985.

In Anaheim, California, the second annual California Plate Collectors' Convention was held in mid-March, 1984, drawing over 20,000 collectors to this much-anticipated event. Eighty-seven exhibitors and 80 artists presented their new limited-edition items to southern California's collectors, who traditionally have been among the most enthusiastic in the nation. One year later the third annual Anaheim show, held in April, 1985, had a jaunty French "April in Anaheim" theme—and was even better attended.

Both Anaheim shows featured large and active "buy and sell" events, allowing collectors to enjoy the benefits of secondary-market trading as they enjoyed the show itself. In Anaheim in 1984, more than 2,600 plates changed hands, bringing net sales for this event to more than $178,000, and in 1985, sales exceeded $165,000.

Sandra Kuck Gives Her "Sunday Best," Sweeps Awards

The Silver Chalice Awards, representing a poll of collectors' clubs all over the U.S., reflected brilliantly on Sandra Kuck in 1984, and the glow lasted well into 1985. Ms. Kuck's first issue in the *Days Gone By* series for Reco International, "Sunday Best," won the 1984 Silver Chalice for Plate of the Year, tying for that honor with "Pink Papoose," the 1984 *DeGrazia Children* issue from Artists of the World. Ms. Kuck was also named Artist of the Year in Anaheim.

Barely four months later, she was called to the podium in a repeat performance. The National Association of Limited Edition Dealers, in its 1983 Achievement Awards in South Bend, also named "Sunday Best" its Plate of the Year, and Ms. Kuck its favorite artist.

The adulation from collectors and dealers alike was particularly gratifying for the somewhat shy and modest Kuck, who had been designing limited-edition plates for Reco for some years before her portrait of two girls at an open window won collectors' hearts. In fact, so great was the impression that she made on the industry in 1984 and 1985—that she won the award for Artist of the Year again in 1985, in both Anaheim *and* South Bend—an unprecedented achievement for any artist in the collectibles world.

Silver Chalice winners for Plate of the Year in 1985 were "Abby and Lisa," first issue in the *Hibel Mother's Day* series from Knowles (under $50), and "Honeysuckle Rose," third issue in the Pickard China series *Symphony of Roses* (over $50).

Collexpo Offers New Locale, New Ideas

Meanwhile, the East Coast, with its strong concentration of avid collectors, had not had a local show in three years when Collexpo '84, billed as "The Greatest Collectible Show Ever," opened its doors in May.

The show, conveniently located at the Nassau County Coliseum in Long Island, New York, drew nearly 30,000 collectors over its three-day run. Many were existing collectors—but many were merely curious about the "fuss over collectibles," and came to see what the market had to offer.

If You Like It, You Can Buy It

At this show, many who began as browsers ended up as buyers. For the first time, show management offered attendees the opportunity to place an order for any item on display. The success of this concept led the Collector Platemakers' Guild—an independent organization of plate-producing companies—to adopt guidelines for order-taking at collector shows in the future. By 1985, all major show locations had agreed to allow collectors to order from the convention floor, following the standards set by the Guild.

South Bend Hosts Tenth Anniversary Gala

With the excitement caused by three collector shows filling the late winter and spring of 1984, some thought

East Coast collectors flock to new show, Collexpo, in 1984; The Bradford Exchange booth offers help to new and veteran collectors alike.

The appeal of collecting to all ages is apparent at the Tenth Anniversary South Bend show.

that the biggest event of all, the 10th Annual International Plate Collectors' Convention in South Bend, would be something of an anticlimax. But nothing could have been further from the truth.

In fact, this anniversary event brought together the largest group of plate producers and artists ever assembled for the benefit of collectors: 110 exhibitors and 150 artists. And it seemed as if every exhibitor had created a special collector event or seminar to mark the occasion.

Collectors themselves showed their support by turning out in record numbers for this show: over 17,000

13

enjoyed the anniversary events, in the festive atmosphere of a huge "birthday party." Veteran collectors, who had attended the first South Bend show in July, 1975, traded reminiscences and remarked on how far the plate collecting world had progressed in ten years' time.

'85 South Bend Show Looks Toward the Future

While the 10th annual show in South Bend was a time for memories, the 11th annual show was a step into the future. In 1985, the traditional excitement of new issues and favorite artists was highlighted by new presentations from industry leaders, showing their confidence in the expanding marketplace.

One of the centers of attention at the show was the new collector booth of The Bradford Exchange. Here, collectors enjoyed a three-screen video introduction to the diversity and activity of the plate market, plus a museum-quality display of landmark issues. They also received a computerized print-out of current "hot" issues, and referrals to convenient local dealers. And as ever, there were brokers on hand to attend personally to each collector's needs.

Worcester, Massachusetts Show Ends the Year

The show-going year rounded out in September with the second annual Eastern States Collectibles Show in Worcester, Massachusetts, near Boston.

Two New Faces Win "Plate of Show" Accolades

In 1984, the young artist whose work caught collectors' fancy—and earned him "Plate of Show" honors in Anaheim and South Bend—was Robert Olson, the 22-year-old creator of "Piano Moods," first issue in a series of four musical-theme plates from the Windemere Collection. In 1985, that same singular honor of two back-to-back "Plate of Show" awards went to artist Mario Fernandez' "Courtship Flight," first of the two-plate *Wings of Freedom* series produced by Fountainhead and manufactured by Pickard.

In both cases, artist *and* plate producing company were both unfamiliar enough to discount collector loyalty as a factor. Instead, the sheer appeal of the limited-edition artwork—that wonderful feeling when a collector looks at a plate and is immediately won over by a mood of joy, or grace, or tranquility—was undoubtedly the reason. This in itself was a great encouragement for the collecting world. At a time when some collectors had expressed the opinion that there was "nothing new left to collect," these two young artists proved them wrong, and reinforced the majority of collectors who find beauty in any collection, be it three plates or three hundred.

Collector World Saddened by Loss of J. Roderick MacArthur

In a year marked by general good spirits in the collecting world, there was also a note of sadness. J. Roderick MacArthur, founder and Director of the Board of Governors of The Bradford Exchange, died in December,

1984 after an extended illness (see a special tribute on Page 16, immediately following this section). He had contributed in innumerable ways to the development and growth of the plate collecting phenomenon, both for industry and collector alike.

At his death, The Bradford Exchange passed to the ownership of his children, and his son, John Roderick MacArthur, assumed the position of Director of the Board of Governors. Richard W. Tinberg was appointed President and Chief Executive Officer of The Bradford Exchange in January, 1985—pledging to build on the substantial legacy left by Rod MacArthur.

Hummel Distribution Rights Settled After Years of Controversy

In early 1985, Goebel and Schmid finally resolved a long-standing controversy over the rights to distribute limited-edition works created from the artwork of the late Sister M. I. Hummel. For many years, the rights to certain works of art had been in litigation between these two well-known producers.

Finally, early in 1985, a settlement between the two industry leaders was reached. U.S. courts ruled that Goebel and Schmid would share joint distribution of any Goebel products that depicted artwork from the period before Berta Hummel took her vows. While this long-standing litigation was somewhat confusing to collectors, it did highlight the fact that *authenticity of origin* is an important factor in the collectibles world.

Secondary Market Activity Offers Mixed Signals; Suggests Influence of "Shakeout of '83-'84"

The trading period beginning January 1, 1984 and ending June 30, 1985 showed mixed signals, suggesting that collectors are cautious but confident about the market. The Market Bradex opened the trading period at 299, and closed the period 18 months later at 237.

This decline can be traced to the fact that the 12 key-indicator series upon which the Market Bradex is based are mostly older, closed series—while the current market trend in trading shows most significant activity on back-issues of series that are still *open*. One sure proof of this trend is the fact that secondary market trading volume on The Bradford Exchange Trading Floor alone reached an all-time high in this period, posting a gain of over 180% compared with trading volume the previous year (see Page 31). And dealer trading accounted for 61% of this increase—always a sure sign of market health.

Some examples of this open-series trend in trading are big winners of the past 18-months:

	Close Price 1/1/84	Close Price 6/30/85
1981 Christian Bell *Age of Steam* "Symphony in Steam"	$100	$330
1983 di Volteradici *Ghiberti Doors* "The Adoration"	$50	$120
1979 Knowles *Gone With the Wind* "Scarlett"	$175	$230

Collectors Set New Standards

While the appeal of the artwork will usually influence a plate's success, today's collectors want something more. They want to know that a series will be completed in a timely fashion, and that the price will remain reasonable over time. They want to know that a producer will stand behind its issues, no matter what their fate in the secondary market. Most of all, they want the assurance that a producer's commitment to quality will not vary over the course of a series, or from series to series. In short, they want the respect of the industry to which they give their support.

Selectivity of New Entries Into Market Shows Growing Collector Awareness

Collectors' more careful scrutiny of new market offerings was reflected in the number of issues both listed and delisted on The Bradford Exchange *Current Quotations* in this 18-month period. While only two series were removed for lack of active trading—the Kaiser *Anniversary* series and the Lihs-Lindner *Christmas* series (both from Germany)—23 new series were added.

In Bradex order by country, these were: Christian Bell *Yesterday's Memories* (Canada); Bing and Grøndahl *Moments of Truth* and *Children's Day* (Denmark); Royal Copenhagen *Motherhood* (Denmark); D'Arceau-Limoges *Josephine and Napoleon* and *Gigi* (France); Limoges-Turgot *Peltriaux's Children of the Turn of the Century* (France); Berlin Design *Holiday Week of the Family Kappelmann* (Germany); Heinrich/Villeroy & Boch *Once Upon a Rhyme* (Germany); Königszelt Bayern *German Half-Timbered Houses* (Germany); Davenport Pottery *Toby Plate Collection* (Great Britain) and Veneto Flair *St. Mark's of Venice* (Italy).

New Bradex-listed series of U.S. origin were: Incolay *Voyage of Ulysses;* Edwin M. Knowles *Four Ancient Elements,Hibel Mother's Day,Father's Love,The King and I,Encyclopaedia Britannica Birds of Your Garden* and *Oklahoma!;* Pemberton & Oakes *Children and Pets;* Reco *Days Gone By;* Rockwell Society *Rockwell's American Dream;* Roman *A Child's Play;*and Vague Shadows *The Chieftains I.*

Famous Artists Earn Bradex Listings

For the first time, some artists who had built significant followings saw their popularity reflected in either actual or potential active trading, thus earning Bradex listing. Among these were Sandra Kuck, Frances Hook and Gregory Perillo.

Top-Trading Issues of 1984

Finally, The Bradford Exchange's announcement of the 1984 Plate of the Year and New Edition of the Year showed collectors' confidence in overall market stability. Taking top honors as the issue with the greatest secondary-market gains in 1984 was "This Is The Room That Light Made," 1983 issue in the *Rockwell's Light Campaign* series from the Rockwell Society. The New Edition of the Year award, for the greatest secondary-market gains in its year of issue, went to "Abby and Lisa," the 1984 first issue in the *Hibel Mother's Day* series from Knowles.

"Abby and Lisa" by Edna Hibel
1984 New Edition of the Year

"This Is the Room That Light Made" by Norman Rockwell
1984 Plate of the Year

Taking Responsibility for the Future

The plate collecting market in the United States—the biggest, most active and influential in the world—has now reached a stage of development that should be gratifying to both collector and producer alike. As the advanced collector learns the right questions to ask, the industry must be primed to respond in kind. Only then can the healthy growth and great diversity of the market be maintained, to the continuing benefit of all. The first ten years of the "modern market" are behind us, but the very best are yet to come.

A TRIBUTE TO
J. RODERICK MacARTHUR (1920-1984)

With the death of J. Roderick MacArthur on December 15, 1984, the collectibles industry lost one of its most energetic and innovative thinkers. MacArthur, known as "Rod" to almost everyone, was the founder of The Bradford Exchange, and was familiar to millions of collectors as its Director of the Board of Governors.

A feisty, independent leader, the white-haired MacArthur was known as a marketing genius. He was a self-made millionaire philanthropist who never gave up fighting for causes, even as he learned of his diagnosis of incurable pancreatic cancer. MacArthur conducted business up to the end.

"There's life and there's death," he once said. "We all get one crack at it, and we do the best with what we've got."

The founding of The Bradford Exchange—the world's largest trading center for limited-edition collector's plates—occurred soon after Rod MacArthur's father, the self-made insurance billionaire John D. MacArthur, asked him to take over a company, called MacMart, and make it profitable.

While at MacMart, Rod MacArthur saw the potential of limited-edition plates and realized the need for an organized marketplace. His father extended him an $80,000 line of credit to start the Bradford Galleries Exchange, Ltd., and said Rod could have the business when he erased MacMart's $500,000 debt.

When the fledgling company began to show a profit, the elder MacArthur "forgot" his deal with his son. The 77-year-old father seized Bradford's customer list and its inventory of plates. Rod MacArthur reacted by staging a "daylight raid" on his father's corporate headquarters, rounding up his own loyal employees to assist in removing the plates from the barricaded warehouse. Thereafter, Rod MacArthur commemorated this "breakaway" from his father's influence with an annual party for the entire company. And the handful of employees who had helped him achieve his independence were always invited back as guests of honor.

In 1972, the Bradford Galleries Exchange became The Bradford Exchange; since then, the company has encouraged and supported the boom in plate collecting in several ways. In 1973, Bradford began publication of the *Current Quotations,* a report on the market activity and prices of the most actively traded plate issues. In 1976, the first edition of *The Bradford Book of Collector's Plates* appeared; it has been published annually since. In 1979, MacArthur founded *Plate World* magazine to

Rod MacArthur in his many roles: at the opening of The Bradford Exchange Trading Floor (opposite page); with son John Roderick (Rick) at left; addressing collectors at South Bend (above); accepting 1981 NALED Lee Benson Award from Winnie Watson Sweet (above, right).

serve the growing collector's market. In 1983, Bradford computerized its plate-trading operation with the introduction of the "Instaquote" system. Today, this system is still unique among all other forms of trading art or collectibles.

For his many contributions to the development of plate collecting, Rod MacArthur received NALED's 1981 Lee Benson Award, one of the collecting world's highest honors.

Rod MacArthur and his father reconciled their differences before the elder MacArthur died in 1978. In his will, John D. set up a $1.5 billion charitable foundation and named Rod as director. It was Rod MacArthur's inspiration to use the foundation to fund exceptionally talented individuals—to get "the greatest minds of our time working on society's biggest problems," he said.

Since 1981, this MacArthur Fellows program has made more than 150 awards, earning international acclaim for the John D. and Catherine T. MacArthur Foundation. Rod MacArthur also directed his own foundation, the J. Roderick MacArthur Foundation.

Rod MacArthur was born on December 21, 1920 in San Francisco. He attended Rollins College in Winter Park, Florida and the University of Mexico. During World War II, he joined the civilian ambulance corps of the American Field Service and served with the French army and a French resistance unit.

MacArthur is survived by his wife Christiane, his sons Gregoire and John Roderick (Rick), and his daughter Solange. John Roderick MacArthur is the new Director of the Board of Governors of The Bradford Exchange.

"Symphony in Steam," first issue in Christian Bell's
Age of Steam series, by Theodore (Ted) Xaras.

PLATE COLLECTING IN CANADA

The Canadian market for collector's plates continued to expand in 1984 and early 1985. Though the Market Bradex dropped eight points, to close the year at 279, other measures indicate a strengthening northern market.

Thirty thousand Canadians discovered plate collecting for the first time during the year 1984. With a total collecting population estimated to exceed 750,000, the country now has more than two plate collectors per every 100 residents. The heaviest concentrations of collectors are in the most populated areas: in Ontario and in lower British Columbia.

Canadian Collectors Supported by Conventions and Clubs

Tens of thousands of collectors attended at least one Canadian plate show during 1984. Quebec, Calgary, Toronto/Durham, Vancouver and Regina all hosted conventions during the year. Total sales of plates at the "Swap 'n' Sell" events at these shows approached $200,000 (Canadian).

Plate collectors in Canada have also banded together to share information and attract more attention from plate producers. Canadians can now choose from more than 20 plate collectors' clubs, spread across six of the country's ten provinces.

Rockwell a Winner Up North, Too

Far and away the most popular plates in Canada are based on art created by the most popular artist in the U.S. Norman Rockwell's plates accounted for four of the top five primary market issues. The No. 1 seller in 1984 was "Grandpa's Treasure Chest," second in the Rockwell Society of America's *Rockwell's Light Campaign* series, issued at $29.50 (Canadian). A close second was "The Storyteller," eighth issue in the Rockwell Society *Heritage* series, issued at $29.50. The third through fifth most popular primary market plates were: "A Puzzlement," first issue in the Knowles *The King and I* series by William Chambers, at $29.50; "Evening's Ease" and "Father's Help," the fourth and third plates in the Rockwell Society *Rockwell's Light Campaign* series, both issued at $29.50.

Active and Growing Secondary Market

Secondary market strength was indicated by the interest of dealers in back issues. Twenty percent of dealer activity through The Bradford Exchange, Ltd. involved secondary market transactions. (In Canada, dealers trade through a Bradford trading system separate from the brokerage exchange that operates for individual collectors.)

The most active series on the secondary market in Canada included: the Rockwell Society's *Rediscovered Women* and *Heritage* series; Reco's *McClelland's Mother Goose* and *Days Gone By* series; Christian Bell's series *Age of Steam*; Königszelt Bayern's *Grimm's Fairy Tales*; and Knowles' *Biblical Mothers*.

Canadian Art Is Greatly Respected

Canadian collectors continue to demonstrate their support of artists who paint Canadian themes. Ted Xaras' train series for Christian Bell, *Age of Steam*, is among the most popular current series. James Keirstead's scenes of Canadian landscapes and mills, and Nori Peter's depictions of Eskimo life in her *Arctic Spring* series for Anna-Perenna, also have attracted loyal audiences. Artists whose work is popular on both sides of the border include Sandra Kuck, Donald Zolan, Kevin Daniel and William Chambers.

The 1984 Canadian Plate of the Year, annually awarded by The Bradford Exchange for best performance in the market, was "Spring Innocence" by Donald Zolan, second issue in Pemberton & Oakes *Wonder of Childhood* series. The New Edition of the Year, recognizing performance by a plate issued in 1984, was "Abby and Lisa" by Edna Hibel, first in the Knowles *Hibel Mother's Day* series.

Dealer Network: A Boon to Collectors

Collectors in Canada enjoy access to approximately 1,000 plate dealers, of which 550 are authorized Bradford dealers. The Canadian Association of Limited Edition Dealers (CALED), founded in 1981, now has 70 members. Similar to the National Association of Limited Edition Dealers (NALED) in the U.S., CALED has adopted a code of ethics that unifies these dealers in their support of the collecting industry.

Canadian Producers Join the Ranks of Successful Platemakers

Another sign of the support Canadians are giving the industry is the number of companies that now produce plates in Canada, to the specific tastes of the Canadian market. Home-grown platemakers include Christian Bell, Canadian Collector Plates, Goldcrown Ceramics, Samaco Trading Limited, Keirstead Gallery and the Sorrina Group.

Other companies that are based elsewhere operate in Canada through Canadian branches. Among these producers are Goebel, Kaiser, Hutschenreuther and Rosenthal of West Germany; Wedgwood and Royal Doulton of Great Britain; and Anna-Perenna and Viletta of the United States.

Posing problems to all producers whose plates are sold in Canada is the softness of the national currency against the American dollar. This situation, combined with customs fees on plates imported from the U.S., often requires companies to price their plates in Canada at 50 percent higher than the U.S. issue prices.

By year-end, however, there were signs of an improving Canadian economy: interest and mortgage rates began to drop, raising hopes of a revitalized Canadian dollar. A stronger dollar would positively affect the plate market in Canada, putting many issues from the U.S. more within the reach of Canadian collectors.

Reaching an Untapped Resource

Another long-recognized problem has found an effective, though expensive, solution. The province of Que-

"Spring Innocence" by Donald Zolan
1984 Canadian Plate of the Year

bec has traditionally been an untapped market for collector's plates. Because French is the official language of Quebec province, plate brochures printed in English went unread.

Now, Canadian companies such as Christian Bell print brochures with color photos only, leaving areas for text blank. Henry and Bev Musty at the Homestead, a dealership in Lennoxville, Quebec, translate the plate brochure information into French and send the French text and color brochures to a second printer, who puts them together for the Quebecois. Though the process is expensive, apparently it is worth the effort: the Mustys have found the French Canadians to be an appreciative and enthusiastic new audience for collecting.

Native Artists Poised to Enter Market

For more good news, observers look to the introduction of first series by well-known native artists. Peter Fromme-Douglas' *Eyes of the Child* series for Wedgwood won over Canadians instantly—the first issue, "Little Lady Love," won Plate of the Show recognition at the 1984 Toronto Plate Fair. Kevin Danby began his *Reflections of Youth* series for Samaco Trading Limited with "The Swimmers" and "The Daydreamer."

More Canadian artists will soon issue their first plates, and many more plates with Canadian themes will be produced in the year ahead. This development, combined with the growth of collectors' clubs, plate convention attendance and an improving economy, indicate that plate collecting has found a permanent home in Canada.

Not only that, but the Canadian influence is being felt strongly by the U.S. market, which has already tagged Christian Bell's *Symphony in Steam* as a market winner. Soon, the work of Canadian artists will be highly-valued—and traded—all over the collecting world. This can be a continuing source of pride for collectors and producers alike.

"The Baked Potato Man," first issue in
Wedgwood's *Street Sellers of London* series, by John Finnie.

PLATE COLLECTING IN THE UNITED KINGDOM

The United Kingdom, with its population of about 56 million, has an estimated 500,000 plate collectors. A 1984 survey defines the strongest concentration of collectors as occurring in the south and the southeast of England, but numbers outside these areas are increasing as well.

British Market Shows Healthy Growth

The Bradford Exchange U.K. headquarters, in a suburb of London, shows an increase of 12 per cent in primary and secondary market activity from its own clients in 1984 alone. This percentage demonstrates increased interest and a healthy growth potential for the British plate market.

Much of the interest of collectors is encouraged by British dealers. Although those who specialize in collector's plates are few at this time, they influence market trends. In 1985, a group of leading dealers began discussing the creation of the first collectibles dealers' organization in the country.

Since late in 1980, British collectors have been able to follow the market with the United Kingdom edition of the *Current Quotations*, published bi-monthly. In the 18-month period from January 1, 1984 to June 30, 1985, the Market Bradex in Britain moved from 283 to 271;

new collector attention to improved means of secondary market trading was also indicated. Twelve new plate series were Bradex-listed in 1984 and 1985, bringing the total number of issues listed in the United Kingdom to 761.

For the first time, collectors in the U.K. were getting more support from media as well. *Collector's World*, a monthly magazine that covers the antique and collectibles market in Britain, is planning expanded coverage of plate collecting in the near future. In the meantime, it provides subscribers with a reprint of the complete U.K. Bradex listings.

Collectors Enjoy "Plate Evenings"

Club activities in the United Kingdom are still somewhat limited, although a few enterprising dealers now sponsor them. Rather than joining clubs, British collectors sometimes meet at "plate evenings," when they visit the home of a local dealer to see displays of the newest plates—bringing real meaning to the term "open house."

As yet, there is no national or local convention for collectors, as in the U.S. But the largest trade show of the year, the Birmingham Spring Fair, has become the showcase for more and more limited-edition plates in

U.K. dealers respond to collector interest.

recent years. This shows that collecting is attracting the serious interest of both manufacturers and dealers in the U.K.

Artwork "With a Heart" Does Well

British collectors like plate art with simple, uncluttered lines. And they prefer emotionally captivating scenes, rich with human interest. Animals in their natural environments are also appealing to the British collector. And, although they are loyal to plate issues produced in the U.K. itself, they are also able to look outward to identify a "winner."

Thus it is that plates from other countries are the biggest primary market sellers here: *Josephine and Napoleon*, from D'Arceau-Limoges, *Sulamith's Love Song* from Königszelt Bayern, the *Heritage* series from the Rockwell Society (particularly the 1985 issue, "The Gourmet"), the *McClelland's Mother Goose* series from Reco International, and *The King and I* series from Knowles.

As the British plate market reaches a certain level of expertise, there has been a noticeable trend toward collecting British subjects, with perhaps a little nostalgia for the Edwardian and Victorian eras. This nationalistic appeal favors such manufacturers as Wedgwood, Royal Doulton, Royal Worcester, Davenport Pottery, Spode Longton Crown Pottery. Native artist John Finnie's first series, entitled *Street Sellers of London*, for Wedgwood, is fast becoming a bestseller. Other favorite native British artists include Kevin Platt (the *Wildlife in Winter* series by Crown Staffordshire) and Mary Vickers.

Unique Media Are Well Accepted in Britain

Three series, in vastly different media and art styles, also are doing well. The first is the ivory alabaster *Ghiberti Doors* series by Studio Dante di Volteradici; the second is the blue cameo stone of the *Voyage of Ulysses*, by Incolay; the third—again, a reflection on local pride—is the *Toby Plate Collection* by Davenport Pottery (based on the designs of the celebrated Toby mugs). However, it is not surprising that, once they depart from the "unique media" idea, Britons favor plates on fine bone china—the translucent yet durable ceramic that claims its origin in Britain itself.

British Warm to American Subjects

Collectors in the United Kingdom are more willing to accept American subjects than in any other European country, and Norman Rockwell's artwork is well-known and widely appreciated here. Other popular American artists include Donald Zolan and John McClelland, who toured the entire U.K. in 1982 on behalf of his *Mother Goose* series and won friends from coast to coast.

U.K. Collectors Want to Know Series Length

British plate producers and dealers have learned over time that British collectors want to know, in advance, the total number of plates that will be produced in a series. Collectors in general like to purchase three or four plates a year, carefully planning their acquisitions in a predictable, quality market. And, just as in the U.S., they put a premium value on a plate that has been signed by the artist—and will go well out of their way to get a favorite autograph.

Challenges of a Youthful Marketplace

"The overall market in the United Kingdom is still in its 'infancy,'" says Gijsbert J. Rijkeboer, General Manager of The Bradford Exchange in the United Kingdom. "And it needs a lot of education. As an example, there is little organized secondary-market activity outside of The Bradford Exchange."

Rijkeboer also notes a British affinity for commemorative plates. This taste is being met by plate producers making special-edition single issues, and could have a depressing effect on the secondary market. But overall, the trends in both manufacture and collector awareness are very encouraging. British plate producers are responding quickly to increased demands from local collectors. This augurs well for the future of plate collecting in such a traditional marketplace.

"The Recital," 1985 issue in Wedgwood's *My Memories* series by Mary Vickers.

"Bauernhaus in Fronhausen," first issue in
Königszelt Bayern's *German Half-Timbered Houses* series.

PLATE COLLECTING IN GERMANY

Thousands of new plate collectors entered the market in Germany in 1984, bringing the total number of collectors in that country to approximately 250,000, out of a total population of 65 million people.

German plate collectors have strong collector preferences. This makes them perhaps the most distinctive among other collectors in Europe or North America. Germans grow up surrounded by art and are taught to appreciate it from childhood; therefore, they have definite ideas of what they like well before they enter the collectors' market. This is reflected in the way the plate market has developed in Germany.

German Tastes Are Rooted in Tradition

The German plate collector is attracted to art that depicts flowers, animals and reproductions of old masters' works, according to Rainer Dembach, Bradford's head of operations in Germany. "In general," says Dembach, "the artwork of the 18th and 19th centuries still is considered the standard of excellence by most Germans." Klaus Vogt, president of Anna-Perenna, adds: "For Americans, it's Norman Rockwell. But Germans like art that shows their own traditions and architecture."

Those comments are reflected in the styles of the best-selling primary-market plate series in Germany in 1984: *Deutsches Fachwerk* (*German Half-Timbered Houses*) (Königszelt Bayern), *Sulamith's Love Song* (Königszelt

Bayern), *Josephine and Napoleon* (D'Arceau-Limoges), *Russian Fairy Tales* (Heinrich/Villeroy & Boch) and *Heritage* (Rockwell Society).

Dealers Support Secondary Market

Much of the activity on the German secondary market is generated by dealers, who maintain their own secondary-market price lists and trade both among themselves and with collectors. On the German secondary market, the Exchanges's most actively-traded series in 1984 included the Studio Dante di Volteradici *Living Madonnas* series, the Rockwell Society *Heritage* series and the D'Arceau-Limoges *Women of the Century* series.

In addition, there was significant price appreciation of the first issue in the Edwin M. Knowles *Biblical Mothers* series, which reminds Germans of the much-admired artwork of Gustav Klimt, although it is the work of American artist Eve Licea. Also trading well are the Königszelt Bayern *Sulamith's Love Song* series, and Heinrich/Villeroy & Boch *Russian Fairy Tales* series.

German Heritage for Quality Is Strong

Although the plate market is still in its infancy in Germany, Exchange analysts have called it a "sleeping market." For hundreds of years Germans have loved and respected porcelain. The traditions, innovations and quality craftsmanship achieved by such porcelain houses as Meissen, Rosenthal, Hutschenreuther and

Heinrich/Villeroy & Boch, are the pride of many Germans. Ever since a German alchemist recreated the Oriental secret of hard-paste porcelain in 1708, German producers have continued to set high standards for porcelain-making that have been followed around the world. In Great Britain and Scandinavia the plate market may be more organized, but in Germany the potential is significant.

One way to look at the growing importance of the German market is to count the number of names that share this common heritage. There is Barthmann Cristall, Goebel, Königszelt Bayern, Royal Bayreuth, Schumann, Berlin Design, Bareuther, Glaskunst/Schott-Zwiesel, Kaiser, Hutschenreuther, Rosenthal, Heinrich/Villeroy & Boch, Tirschenreuth, KPM and Furstenberg, among others. Many of these names are familiar to collectors in the U.S. for the exceptional quality of their plate issues.

In Germany, although most of these companies are best known for their dinnerware, their collector's plates share the tradition of quality craftsmanship. Three of the largest firms—Rosenthal, Hutschenreuther and the bone china factory of Heinrich/Villeroy & Boch—are located in eastern West Germany around Selb, often called Germany's "City of Porcelain." It is a rural region in northern Bavaria known for its rich supply of minerals, which contributes to its reputation for excellence in ceramics.

No Real "Collectibles" Dealers

Despite the high regard for porcelain in Germany and the strong traditions it represents, there are few specialized collector's plate shops, no plate clubs and no plate shows there—at least, not as we know them in North America. In Germany, porcelain dinnerware is bought in small porcelain shops, rather than in department stores, and it is in these shops that collector's plates can be found.

But most porcelain dealers do not yet understand the plate market, nor are they fully aware of its potential. With time and education, however, German dealers should become more receptive to developing their plate business, says one German producer, if they believe it will improve their appeal to customers. As German collectors become more comfortable with the idea of collecting and trading, their preferences will be made known to leading porcelain dealers. Eventually, this should lead to the widespread availability of all issues at the dealer level—just as in the U.S., Canada and the United Kingdom.

Activity Through the Exchange Is Brisk

The purchase of limited editions directly from The Bradford Exchange, however, is a common practice among German collectors, just as in the United States.

The future of plate collecting in this country is promising, as more and more Germans are exposed to the plate market and as more products designed to appeal to their tastes are produced.

A German porcelain shop, with its display of limited-edition plates.

Frankfurt Office Provides Complete Service

To serve this growing market, Bradford's German office was established in Frankfurt about eight years ago. This office now provides a full range of services to collectors who, over the years, have developed tastes for plates not widely available in the United States, but actively traded in Germany. Some of these plates are innovative, high priced and produced in very small edition sizes by U.S. standards (several hundred), particularly series from Rosenthal, Barthmann Cristall or Glaskunst/Schott-Zwiesel, among others.

Since 1979, a German Bradex has been published; subscribers receive it bi-monthly. As of June 30, 1985, it reported trading on 919 active issues.

Steps to Market Growth

Exchange analysts look to these future developments to facilitate a stronger, more organized German plate market, and to increase the level of services to collectors.

First, *collector education*: The Bradford Exchange currently sends information packets that include news and photographs of new issues to active plate buyers and potential new clients. This will help Germans get a better idea of the complete benefits of collecting, and their place in the worldwide market.

Second, *dealer co-operation*: German dealers might follow the example of plate dealers in the U.S., who earn their customers' respect by offering a full range of limited-edition products and information, so that the customer develops confidence in the dealer and gives him repeat business.

Third, *awareness of producers*: German producers could consider the importance of showing market support with regard to collector's plates, so that new collectors can buy with confidence. And they could produce products that appeal to German tastes in art.

"We've had some good successes here," says Rainer Dembach. "We've started to educate the collectors and we've had press coverage. A good proportion of the Bradex subscribers are active plate buyers; they are beginning to feel that they are a part of the worldwide market. With the right new issues being made available to the German market, I am very optimistic about the future."

"Home Is Best," first issue in Bing & Grøndahl's
Moments of Truth series, by Kurt Ard.

NEW MARKETS FOR PLATE COLLECTING

Although most of the world's approximately eight million plate collectors live in the United States, Canada, the United Kingdom and Germany, in recent years the hobby of plate collecting has also become noticeably popular in several different markets, such as Denmark, Switzerland and Australia.

These markets are developing quickly as more and more collectors buy plates produced for the "modern" market. Also, a smaller but much more rapidly-growing segment of collectors in these countries is beginning to buy and sell back-issue plates, creating the roots of a true secondary market.

Bradford Offices Herald Market Growth

In response to this growth in market activity, The Bradford Exchange has opened offices in Copenhagen, Denmark, and in Zug, Switzerland, and has begun publishing *Current Quotations* for both of these locales. In three other countries—Sweden, Australia and Japan—there is a beginning interest in plate collecting which could eventually lead to the development of a true trading market.

Denmark

Oldest of the "New" Markets

It seems strange to think of Denmark as a "new" market for plate collecting. Plate collecting as we know it today was launched there when Bing & Grøndahl cre-

ated "Behind the Frozen Window," the first limited edition collector's plate, in 1895. And over the decades, acquiring plates has become a national pastime.

Today there are an estimated 300,000 plate collectors in Denmark, a country with a population of 5 million, according to estimates by Jorgen Sannung, the managing director of The Bradford Exchange in Copenhagen.

Many of these Danish collectors, going back several generations in their preferences, order the Bing & Grøndahl and Royal Copenhagen Christmas plates well in advance of the release date. At some retail shops, the local residents line up on the first day the plates go on sale so they can be sure to get one for themselves and one or two to send to relatives in the United States. Although there are more than 400 retailers in Denmark who offer the traditional Danish blue-and-white plates to their customers, the bulk of the business is handled by 80 retail dealers. Most of these dealers are adopting modern marketing methods, and many mail plate information to their Scandinavian customers.

Breaking the Tradition of the Blue-and-Whites

By far, the great majority of plates collected in Denmark are the familiar blue-and-white variety. But in 1984, a full-color plate issue by Bing & Grøndahl was the first of its kind from that maker to be listed on the U.S. Bradex. The artwork was created by Kurt Ard, a highly respected realist painter and a native of Denmark. The series is based on the day-to-day incidents in a child's

life that teach him important things about growing up, and is entitled *Moments of Truth*.

In order to promote the first plate, called "Home Is Best," Ard visited with collectors in five Danish cities, where he was also interviewed by the local newspapers. Promotional tours by artists are almost unheard of in Europe, where collectors choose plates by manufacturer rather than by artist. But Ard was extremely well received wherever he appeared.

And, despite its break with what collectors had come to expect from Bing & Grøndahl, the new plate was very popular in Denmark, Europe, the United States and Canada.

Organized Collecting Is Something New

Even though there are many Danish owners of collector's plates, Denmark is considered a new market because *organized* plate collecting is in its infancy there. There are very few collectors' clubs, and there have not been any major exhibits or conventions for collectors. And, even though there is the ever-present buying and selling of back issue plates, the first Danish Bradex was not published until 1983. Today, it lists 410 active issues—the great majority of them "blue-and-whites."

In the past two years there has been considerable progress in the market. The Bradford Exchange has begun organizing the secondary market, and is now helping collectors and dealers buy and sell in an orderly fashion. A non-blue-and-white plate was successfully introduced into worldwide trading; a Danish artist completed a successful tour, and Royal Copenhagen published the first issue of its magazine for collectors. If you're looking for a safe bet, you could wager a Krone or two that the Danish market will continue to grow in the near future.

Australia

New Frontier for Collecting

If Danish plate collecting is in its infancy, the Australian market could be described as pre-natal. This does not mean there aren't plenty of collectors "Down Under." In fact, there are tens of thousands of Aussie collectors and many retail shops to serve them.

As far back as 1972, Australian consumers could purchase well-known European-made collector's plates in retail stores in Sydney, Brisbane, Melbourne, Perth, Canberra, Port Moresby, Darwin and Adelaide. In addition to plates by Wedgwood, Bing & Grøndahl, Royal Copenhagen, Spode and Hummel, Australian collectors have available a line of collector's plates produced by a Melbourne company, Westminster China. Also, many daily newspapers, such as the Queensland Courier Mail, carry classified ads for back issue plates by Royal Doulton and other producers.

Plate Exhibit Draws Thousands

In 1982, collector-turned-retailer Sandra Chamberlain installed an exhibit of more than 50 collector's plates in the Redcliffe Community Center in Clontarf. She esti-

Artisan at Royal Copenhagen applies color before glazing and firing.

mated that during its six-week run, more than 10,000 people saw the exhibit. In response to this growing interest, The Bradford Exchange established operations in Sydney, and began offering collector's plates to interested Australians.

Sharing the Collecting Tradition

Although plate collecting is a new concept in Australia and there is little secondary market trading, market analysts expect rapid growth. Because Australia's consumers emulate the habits of the British, Canadians and Americans, observers believe it won't be long before the Australian market takes off like the Canadian market did, less than five years ago.

Japan

Curiosity in the Worldwide Phenomenon

Although seven Bradex-listed plate series have been *produced* in Japan, the hobby of plate collecting itself is just beginning to catch on there. Japanese homes are very small by Western standards, and it is not customary to hang objects on the walls. Nonetheless, in the past two years there has been unusual interest by the Japanese in learning more about the worldwide collecting phenomenon.

The Japanese Take a Good, Close Look

Recently, Japanese TV crews came to The Bradford Exchange in Chicago to do video feature stories on plate collecting, and a delegation of 20 to 30 Japanese businessmen visited the Exchange. Early in 1985, the *Japan Economic Journal* reported that "Recently in Japan, an increasing number of people are collecting decorative plates such as Christmas plates offered by European plate makers."

It's too early to tell if this level of interest will lead to increased demand for collector's plates in Japan. Market experts at the Exchange, however, do not expect to see any appreciable gains in the immediate future.

New series based on ancient tradition:
Beauties of the Red Mansion from Ching-te Chen.

THE FUTURE OF PLATE COLLECTING

From Ching-te Chen in the People's Republic of China—the city that gave birth to porcelain in the 7th century A.D.—comes news of a landmark issue. Called "Beauties of the Red Mansion," this series will be the very first modern limited-edition collector's issue ever to be produced in this time-honored city of porcelain artisans. Its appearance in the market brings the idea of collector's plates full circle, and illustrates how genuinely international in scope the market has become.

Closer to home, artist news generated considerable excitement, signalling great things to come in the future. Kevin Daniel, known for his award-winning wildlife art, created a new series, *Birds of Your Garden* for Knowles, which earned the unprecedented sponsorship of the *Encyclopaedia Britannica*. Also new among Knowles artists is Mort Künstler, creator of the *Oklahoma!* series based on the Rodgers and Hammerstein musical. In 1985, Artists of the World announced the beginning of a new DeGrazia series, giving satisfaction to the many collectors who had feared that the artist's death in 1982 meant that access to his work would gradually end. The series is titled *Children at Play.*

Two other popular artists—with vastly different art styles—introduced annual Christmas series in 1985. Many collectors were surprised to learn that "The Angels' Message," from Knowles, is Edna Hibel's first Christmas issue ever, despite a long and noteworthy career (see ARTIST PROFILES). From Sulamith Wülfing, creator of the *Sulamith's Love Song* series, came "The Angels' Vigil," which immediately created a stir among collectors not only in the U.S. but in Europe, where Wülfing has an enormous following.

In fact, the plate markets in Canada and overseas continue to exert remarkable pressure on the availability of certain plates for collectors in the U.S. The best example of this is a new issue from Tirschenreuth of Germany, entitled *Band's Songbirds of Europe*. At first, the producers of this series thought it had little chance of success in the U.S., where the artist, Ursula Band, is unknown and the birds depicted on the plates are unfamiliar. But sponsorship by the prestigious World Wildlife Fund, as well as the inherent appeal of Frau Band's distinctive style, has won support for the series on both sides of the Atlantic.

Finally, the future of a vast segment of collectors worldwide was affected by an announcement in the early summer of 1985.

The Norman Rockwell Family Trust, represented by Norman's son Thomas Rockwell, agreed to review and to affix its seal of authenticity to all limited-edition plates made by Knowles and sponsored by the Rockwell Society of America. The Family also agreed to grant Knowles access to some works of Rockwell art to which the family now holds the rights, which had heretofore been unavailable to the public. This endorsement by the family of the artist was granted first to a new Rockwell Society series entitled *Rockwell's American Dream*. It signals an era in which knowledgeable collectors can make more intelligent choices about the authenticity of the art they wish to acquire.

Part of the pleasure of owning plates is displaying them to best advantage.
Here, the second, third and fourth issues in Knowles
Friends I Remember series on a three-plate rail
from Van Hygan & Smythe.

HOW TO ENHANCE YOUR PLATE COLLECTING PLEASURE

Setting Standards for Your Collection

In today's burgeoning plate market, it is increasingly difficult to decide which plates to acquire for your collection. The temptations are great, the decisions are difficult, and the need for guidelines is more important than ever. New collectors in particular may feel they need some recognized standards to help them get on the right collecting track, and stay on it. For if they develop good collecting habits early on, they will always get the greatest pleasure from collecting.

The Bradford Exchange Eight-Point Check List for the evaluation of new issues, first published in 1972, seems even more valid today than it was 13 years ago, when it was developed for the benefit of beginning collectors. Today, it remains the simplest and most complete means of evaluating limited-edition plates. These eight points help to identify potential market strengths and weaknesses, factors that could literally dictate the long-term market performance—and the ultimate value—of a limited edition.

Although this set of standards was developed for plates when they are newly-issued, a collector should keep this check list in mind when considering the purchase of *any* issue, even one that is already trading on the secondary market. After all, what makes a plate a worthy addition to your collection now should make it equally as worthy later.

But keep in mind that not all points covered by this check list apply to *all* plates, and that a plate can be an excellent acquisition even if it meets only five or six of these criteria. On the other hand, if the plate you want falls short on five or more of these points, you might reconsider your purchase.

A single, treasured plate deserves to be the center of attention. "Bathsheba and Solomon" from Knowles is the perfect example.

The Bradford Exchange Eight-Point Check List

1. MAKER:
Is the plate maker known for its insistence on fine workmanship? Is the continuity of its past and present series reliable in regard to adherence to edition limit, delivery schedules and price?

2. ARTISTRY:
Is the plate artwork original, created especially for this plate by a noteworthy artist? Or is the artwork a quality adaptation of a work by a famous artistic personality? Is the subject matter one of broad, but not trite, appeal?

3. EDITION LIMIT:
Is the edition clearly limited, but not too limited to create a true market? If the edition is sold out, is there sufficient evidence to suggest present or future secondary market activity?

4. COLLECTIBILITY:
Is the plate one of a collectible periodic series, or merely a single issue? Does the theme of the series have widespread appeal?

5. TIME OF ACQUISITION:
Is the plate available at issue price (always preferable with new issues), or at a time when the price is still likely to rise on the secondary market?

6. SPONSORSHIP:
Is the plate, or the series, issued in association with a prestigious institution—preferably one which is not, in and of itself, a producer of plates?

7. COMMEMORATIVE IMPORTANCE:
Does the plate or the series commemorate a seasonal or historic event? If so, does it offer new insight into the event?

8. MATERIALS:
If ceramic, is the plate true hard-paste porcelain, bone china or fine china? If of other materials such as metal or crystal, are they of appropriate quality? Is the plate unique in its workmanship? Does it have a special feature that sets it apart from other issues?

In any form of collecting, the true challenge is to make intelligent choices, while choosing something that you like as well. Market potential, after all, won't help you decorate your living room. The collector who learns to use The Bradford Exchange Eight-Point Check List effectively is well on his or her way to making these intelligent choices, and to achieving a much greater satisfaction from collecting as a result.

Periodicals, reference books and special market reports give the collector valuable information.

Publications for the Collector

In addition to the Eight-Point Check List, there are several publications available to help you evaluate additions to your collection. The most comprehensive coverage of both new and back-issue market prices can be found in the *Bradford Exchange Current Quotations*, otherwise known as the "Bradex" or the "quote sheet." (A complimentary one-year subscription is available upon request from The Bradford Exchange).

Every two months the Bradex reports on trading activity and current prices of the 1,200 most actively-traded plates on the market. Also included in the *Current Quotations* is the *Market Bradex*, a kind of "Dow Jones index" of the overall performance of the collector's plate market. It is expressed as a percentage, and is based on the current price/issue price ratio of 12 key-indicator plate series that are chosen to represent market activity overall.

Each quarter, the Exchange also publishes *Bradex New Issues*, a listing of plates that have just been released for sale at issue price. All plates are listed alphabetically by country of origin along with a photograph of each new plate and other pertinent information. Due to the large number of new issues released during each reporting period, the Exchange reports only those that it is recommending to clients.

There are also several collector periodicals that cover the plate market and its artists. *Plate World* magazine, with a readership of over 70,000, is the leading periodical in this field. Published bi-monthly, it is the *only* full-color magazine devoted exclusively to limited-edition collector's plates, and features a variety of articles on artists, producers and collector events and activities. Also available for plate collectors are the *Plate Collector, Collector Editions* and *Collector's Mart* magazines, as well as the *Antique Trader*, a bi-weekly newspaper that covers all forms of collectibles.

Club membership brings exposure to seminars, product previews.

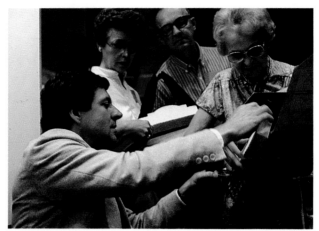
Collectors meet favorite artists at conventions; here Knowles' William Chambers.

Collectors shop back-issues at "buy-and-sell" events.

Local dealers are a source for guidance.

Clubs, Dealers and Conventions

An excellent way to become more knowledgeable about plate collecting is through a local dealer. Throughout the U.S.—and, indeed, throughout the collecting world—there are retail dealers who specialize in the sale and trading of limited-edition collector's plates. Dealers enjoy educating new collectors, while at the same time providing personal service, a wide selection of merchandise, and special in-store events that help the collector gain valuable insight and information.

Another one of the most popular ways to learn about plate collecting is through membership in a collector club. As the hobby continues to grow, more and more such clubs are springing up across the U.S.—105 at last count, in June of 1985. These clubs provide an opportunity to share the experience of collecting with others. Many also publish monthly newsletters, host open houses with artists and offer presentations by industry experts.

Collectors who enjoy sharing their interest and want to learn more about their hobby should seek out the club nearest them by contacting their local dealer or one of the industry publications. And if there's not a club within your area, why not start one up, by making arrangements with a local dealer to post membership information in his store?

Supporters of plate collectors not only offer collector clubs, to stay abreast of trends and new issues—they also host several collector conventions at various locations across the U.S. and Canada. In 1984 and early 1985, events were held in Anaheim, Orlando, Long Island, South Bend and Worcester, Massachusetts.

Again, check with your local dealer or one of the industry publications to find out when and where the next convention will be held in your area. These shows are a wonderful chance to get "sneak previews" on newly-released plate issues, meet favorite artists in person and attend educational seminars.

Plate collecting is an exciting, fulfilling hobby that is enjoyed by many different types of people. In the long run, the limited-edition market can only benefit from a versatile, well-educated public that *thinks* before it buys, and acts on the basis of careful evaluation and sound judgment.

The *Current Quotations*, or "Bradex," tracks the market on active issues.

At 4:00 p.m. in London, England, a Bradford representative calls the U.S. Trading Floor to initiate a trade on "The Toy Maker." Minutes later, at 9:15 a.m. in Chicago, that request affects the price of a plate sold to a collector in Los Angeles. This trading activity, which occurs every day, has significance even for collectors who may have no intention of ever buying or selling plates in the secondary market. For all collectors, there is the satisfaction of knowing that this active trading might increase the value of one's collection over time.

Certainly, other categories of art, antiques and collectibles can—and do—appreciate in value, according to their quality, rarity and age. But because each of these is usually one-of-a-kind, the sale of a valuable object can only identify a possible trend in price.

Activity in Plate Market Is Unique

Collector's plates, of course, are different. Because each plate in the edition is *identical* to all others, a price that is established for one plate, within a certain trading period, should be fairly representative of the market price for all such plates in the same time period. On this concept of organized trading, The Bradford Exchange—the world's largest trading center for limited-edition works of art—was founded.

But the Bradford Exchange Trading Floor is not the *only* place to trade. Collectors who wish to liquidate portions of their collection, or fill in important back-issues, have several other options.

Trade One-on-One with Fellow Collectors

One method is through a local collectors' club, where members frequently exchange buy-and-sell information among themselves, and occasionally actually swap parts of one collection for another. The advantage to trading locally with another collector is that you can examine your purchases *before* you buy, to make sure they are in mint condition.

At The Bradford Exchange, "mint condition" signifies a plate with no visible surface flaws—such as minute cracks, chips, tears or bubbles in the art transfer—and complete with all original documentation, including Certificate of Authenticity, if any. The original box is also required for a plate to be traded through the Exchange; however, many collectors differ on this point, and local standards may vary.

Major convention "buy-and-sell" events are an outstanding option for traders.

Use Classified Advertising

Another useful way to buy and sell plates is through the classified advertising sections of major collectibles publications, such as *The Antique Trader*, a bi-weekly newspaper published in Dubuque, Iowa.

Trading by mail with another collector, however, has certain risks. The first, for the buyer, is whether the plate purchased will be in mint condition. (After all, there may be a reason why the lady in New York is asking $35 less than the "going price" for her "Mary, Mary" plate. Could it be the lack of a certificate, or a tiny chip on the rim?) For the seller, the risk is that the buyer's check might not be good.

Shop the Convention "Buy-and-Sell" Events

One of the best alternatives to buying by mail from another collector is to attend the "buy-and-sell" event at a major collectors' convention. In 1984 and early 1985, these were held at the Orlando and Anaheim shows in early spring, the South Bend show in July and the Worcester (Boston area) show in the fall.

These events give collectors an opportunity to examine and compare prices on hundreds—if not thou-

sands—of plates at one time. Usually, if a collector is interested in a plate that is actively traded, he will find several examples for sale. At some such events, he can negotiate directly with the plate's owner on price. At others, he can hold out to see if the owner will come down in price near the end of the event.

Sometimes, too, the find of a lifetime can be added to a collection, such as the signed "Los Niños," by the late Ted DeGrazia, purchased by a collector for $1,900 at the Anaheim show in April, 1985.

The new Bradford Exchange booth at South Bend in 1985 offers latest market information.

Local dealers can help you acquire back-issues, like these De-Grazia plates.

Look No Further Than Your Local Dealer

Since giant "buy-and-sell" events happen only a few times a year—and for many collectors, not close enough to home—there is still another option that offers professional service on a day-to-day basis: the local collectibles dealer. Most knowledgeable dealers offer at least some level of referral and trading of secondary market plates. Some actually maintain their own "mini-exchanges," with card files of customers' wants that are routinely matched to sellers.

For dealers who are part of The Bradford Exchange Dealer-Member Association, there is the privilege of direct access to The Bradford Exchange Trading Floor. This means the dealer can act as his customer's broker,

A collector shops for sold-out issues in South Bend.

PER CENT INCREASE IN SECONDARY-MARKET ACTIVITY ON U.S. TRADING FLOOR (Since 1981)

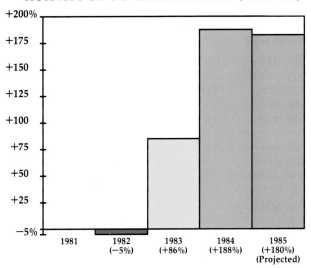

	1981	1982 (−5%)	1983 (+86%)	1984 (+188%)	1985 (+180%) (Projected)

offering the exact service that the Exchange would provide directly. The customer pays no additional premium or fee for this service, other than the commissions that are normally charged by the Exchange.

Choose The Bradford Exchange as Your Market Resource

Of course, if a qualified dealer cannot be found, the collector can always turn directly to The Bradford Exchange Trading Floor itself. Through its staff of knowledgeable brokers, it provides up-to-the-minute information on market prices and trends. And the Exchange guarantees both sides of any transaction that occurs, so that neither buyer nor seller engenders any risk in trading.

With so many choices at hand, it's no wonder that so many collectors are now availing themselves of the options to buy and sell on the secondary market. Through active trading—unique to the art form of limited-edition plates—that market is kept lively as the potential for appreciation spurs collector enthusiasm around the world.

31

The serious collector might wish to visit an artist's studio; here, Kevin Daniel at work.

Collectors Advance to Important Opportunities, Benefits

While thousands of new collectors enter the hobby of plate collecting each year, there are millions more who already own 20, 30, even 50 or more plates, and who proudly and rightfully call themselves "advanced" or "seasoned" collectors.

For these veterans of the collector's plate market, the question is no longer "Should I buy a collector's plate?" Instead, they ask the question "What should I buy, why should I buy it, and when?" To answer this question and at the same time learn to enjoy collecting even more, the advanced collector has many avenues to explore.

Special Club Activities

One of the best avenues—and one with which the advanced collector should already be at least marginally familiar—is the local collectors' club. We have already discussed the benefit of collectors' clubs for the novice collector. For the advanced collector, they offer more.

The collectors' club is a way to learn about new and important trends in collecting, and to learn how to apply these trends to improving one's own collection. Information gathered through a collectors' club can help the advanced collector make decisions about his or her new purchases, as well as back-issue purchases, over the next year.

For example, a casual club get-together with a favorite artist can provide valuable insight on what one already owns. But perhaps more important, the club member usually has the privilege of seeing plates that the artist is *about* to introduce. Also, conversation between artist and collector can reveal how a specific artwork was done and the artist's own personal feelings about it—factors an advanced collector may want to consider when choosing one series over another.

Advanced collectors might also request club programs that deal with home security for collectibles, or with insurance programs for owners of artwork. At still another meeting, collectors who are advanced enough to venture into secondary-market activity might benefit from personal demonstrations by a Bradford Exchange representative—or, in many cases, by trading with fellow club members themselves.

Collectors' club activities, however, need not be limited to club meetings alone. The most ambitious and successful clubs take advantage of outside activities, as well.

For example, advanced collectors often find themselves even more enthusiastic about their hobby after taking a special guided tour of a nearby porcelain manufacturer. Personally viewing the intricate steps in the manufacture of plates gives the collector new respect and insight into what he owns, or hopes to own.

Or, an artist with whom a club has already established a good relationship might invite several members to his studio, to see actual work in progress. And, of course, there are numerous art museums and galleries throughout the country, including The Bradford Musuem of Collector's Plates in Niles, Illinois, where the work of dozens of favorite plate artists can be viewed and enjoyed firsthand. Often, this is the best way for the advanced collector to make decisions about filling in series he owns.

A guided tour of a local platemaker brings new insight; these are the kilns of Pickard.

Conventions bring the chance to discuss your collection with experts, like this Bradford Trading Floor broker.

Collectible Conventions: A Weekend Well-Spent

Perhaps one of the most thoroughly informative experiences for the advanced collector, either as part of a club or with a few friends, is a weekend spent at a collector's convention.

For example, the advanced collector can attend seminars covering topics such as "How to Clean and Protect Your Collectibles" and "The Hottest Collector's Plates on the Market." Or he might seek out several favorite artists or producers and learn what to expect in upcoming plate series.

He might also receive a personal demonstration on how to buy and sell plates on the secondary market, which relates specifically to what he owns. Best of all, he can meet other advanced collectors and share "trade secrets" at any of the social events usually planned for such collectors at the convention.

Above all, advanced collectors say they attend plate conventions because a convention is where the action is—the heart of it all. Conventions are where all the important people in the plate industry meet; they are where major decisions are made. A convention is the one place where the advanced collector can ask direct questions and get direct answers. Not only that, but he may find himself talking to the president of a plate-producing company, who values the advanced collector's opinion.

Displaying a Plate Collection

An increasingly important question from advanced collectors is: "Now that I own several plate series, how can I show them off to best advantage in my home?" Because advanced collectors probably have plates from several different series, representing several different themes, materials or art styles, this is a challenging question.

To learn how to most effectively display his or her collection, the collector might talk to a dealer who carries a good variety of plate stands, frames and rails, all designed to display and protect valuable works of art. If the collector is very serious about displaying his collection to best advantage, he might also contact an interior designer or consultant who has experience in working with collector's plates as a decor option.

At at convention, he should seek out a seminar on decorating with collector's plates—or talk to other advanced collectors to find out how they display plates in their homes—since other collectors often have the simplest, and yet the most creative, ideas!

Finally, he can write to the leading collector magazines, to find out if and when they have recently published a feature on decorating with plates.

The pleasure of ownership is enhanced by proper display. Here, an attractive 12-plate display unit showcases the entire *Rockwell's Rediscovered Women* series, from the Rockwell Society of America. Plate rail courtesy of Van Hygan & Smythe.

A Collector's Best Friend Should Be His Dealer

While other collectors are among the best sources of information for the advanced collector who wants to benefit from the hobby, there is another professional source who makes it his business to help: the local collectibles dealer. To the collector's advantage, the dealer has the additional knowledge of the industry "insider."

The dealer is a wonderful source of information on artists, and the reputability of producers. He can also serve the collector directly by keeping track of the plates the collector already has, and the plates the collector wants in the future. Best of all, he will automatically contact the collector when the next plate in a series becomes available, when a "hot" back issue is the right price, or when a special collectibles event is coming up that he knows his customer won't want to miss.

A local dealer is a valuable resource because he knows collecting inside and out, and is eager to share what he knows with his loyal customers.

Basically, then, the seasoned collector would do well to go directly to his or her best sources for in-depth information: the fellow collector, the dealer and the plate-producing company. Each of these resources will certainly shed new light on the fun of collecting. All will help the long-time collector to enjoy what he owns, in ways he might not have thought possible.

AN INTRODUCTION TO INFORMATION IN THE GALLERY SECTION

The following Gallery section of *The Bradford Book of Collector's Plates* offers complete information on all major issues regularly traded in the market. The plates are arranged in an order exactly corresponding to The Bradford Exchange *Current Quotations:* first, by *country* of the plate's origin, in alphabetical order; second, by *plate maker* within each country, also in alphabetical order; third, by *series* of each maker, in chronological order beginning with the maker's first series; and fourth, by *plate position* in each series, also in chronological order beginning with the first plate.

To speed identification, each plate is listed by its Bradex number, a codified form of the information above. *These numbers are in sequence but not necessarily consecutive.* The number on the upper left-hand corner of each page indicates the first plate listed on that page.

HOW TO READ THE BRADEX NUMBER

(The number used as an example here is that of the 1904 Bing & Grøndahl *Christmas* plate)

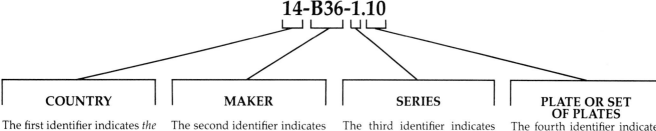

14-B36-1.10

COUNTRY	MAKER	SERIES	PLATE OR SET OF PLATES
The first identifier indicates *the country of origin;* in this case the number *14* is for Denmark.	The second identifier indicates the *plate maker.* The alpha-numeric combination of *B36* represents Bing & Grøndahl. This number is assigned according to a system similar to that used in libraries for the classification of authors' works.	The third identifier indicates the maker's *series,* listed in the chronological order in which it was produced. Thus the number *1* represents Bing & Grøndahl's first series, the *Christmas* series.	The fourth identifier indicates the individual plate (or set of plates) within each series, listed in chronological order. The number *10* is for the tenth plate in the Bing & Grøndahl *Christmas* series, *View of Copenhagen from Frederiksberg Hill,* the 1904 issue. Plates issued in sets use an additional successive digit to indicate their position within a set (example: 22-A3-3.1-1).

For your convenience in determining the location of a listing in this book, you will find individual plates indexed by *country,* by *maker* and *sponsor,* by *type* (or theme) of series, by *plate title* and by *plate artist* in the Indices and Appendices at the back of this book. Please consult the Table of Contents for the correct page number of these items.

HOW TO LOCATE ADDITIONAL PLATE INFORMATION

Maker's listings: contain information on history and trademarks.

Series listings: contain information on artist, medium, edition limits, numbering, plate diameter and hanging provisions.

Individual plate listings: provide the Bradex number, plate title, artist, issue price and market price ranges for the trading period beginning *January 1, 1984* and ending *June 30, 1985.*

HOW TO DETERMINE EDITION LIMITS

Edition limited to 10,000 means that the maker established 10,000 plates as the maximum to be produced in the edition.

Edition size undisclosed; limited by period of issue means that the edition was limited to the number of plates produced during an announced time period. This could be the period preceding a commemorative date, as with Christmas or Mother's Day issues, or it could be the period of manufacture, often expressed as "firing days," the days the kilns are in operation to produce the series.

Edition size undisclosed, limited by year of issue means the edition was limited to the number of plates produced during the year of issue.

CANADA
CHRISTIAN BELL
Mount Forest, Ontario

Founded in 1979, Christian Bell Porcelain Ltd. traces its name to founder Horst S. Muller's great-grandfather, Christian Bell, a prominent figure in the white-ware industry of Siebenbürgen in pre-World War I Austria-Hungary.

The firm's first collector's plate series, *Preserving a Way of Life*, (not U.S. Bradex-listed) began in 1980. Their *Age of Steam* series began in 1981 and celebrates the vital role of the railroads in Canada's national heritage. Their second Bradex-listed series is *Yesterday's Memories*.

Theodore "Ted" Xaras is the artist for both series.

Age of Steam Series

Artist: Theodore Xaras. Artist's signature appears on front

Hard-paste porcelain

Diameter: 24.1 centimeters (9½ inches)

No hanger

Edition size limited to 15,000

Numbered, without certificate through 1982, with certificate thereafter

8-C30-1.1
1981 *Symphony in Steam*
Issue $65.00; High $330.00; Low $100.00;
Close $330.00; Up $230.00

8-C30-1.2
1982 *Brief Encounter*
Issue $65.00; High $105.00; Low $65.00;
Close $80.00; Up $15.00

8-C30-1.3
1983 *No Contest*
Issue $65.00; High $175.00; Low $65.00;
Close $150.00; Up $85.00

8-C30-1.4
1984 *Timber Country*
Issue $65.00; High $145.00; Low $65.00;
Close $115.00; Up $50.00

8-C30-1.5
1985 *White Pass, Gateway to the Yukon*
Issue price: $65.00

Yesterday's Memories Series

Artist: Theodore Xaras. Artist's signature appears on front

Hard-paste porcelain banded in 22k gold

Diameter: 21 centimeters (8¼ inches)

No hanger

Edition size undisclosed, limited by announced period of issue

Not numbered, without certificate

8-C30-8.1
1984 *Ice*
Issue price: $45.00

DENMARK
BING & GRØNDAHL
Copenhagen

KONGELIG HOFLEVERANDØR

Bing & Grøndahl, Denmark's second oldest existing porcelain maker (after Royal Copenhagen), was established in 1853 by Frederick Vilhelm Grøndahl and Meyer and Jacob Bing. Grøndahl, a young sculptor previously employed by Royal Copenhagen, supplied the artistic talent while the Bing brothers provided financial backing. Although Grøndahl died before the manufactory's third year of operation, his name was retained in honor of his contribution. Bing & Grøndahl has continued under the leadership of the Bing family for five generations.

The world's first collector's plate, "Behind the Frozen Window," was issued by Bing & Grøndahl in 1895. This began its *Christmas* series which has been produced each year without interruption despite wars and economic crises. Plates in this series are now the most widely collected of all plates in the market. In 1969 Bing & Grøndahl issued the first Mother's Day plate, "Dog and Puppies." Their *Moments of Truth* series started in 1984.

Besides limited-edition collector's plates, Bing & Grøndahl makes a variety of porcelain articles, including figurines and tableware. Many of their porcelain works can be found in museums around the world, and they have achieved the distinction of appointment to the royal courts of Denmark, Sweden, and Great Britain. This distinction is symbolized by the crown which is part of their trademark.

The artist for the very first collector's plate was Frans August Hallin, a Swede who moved to Copenhagen in 1885. After Harald Bing named him chief designer in 1895, Hallin created a distinctive item for the maker's Christmas giftware line—"Behind the Frozen Window." Its success assured his niche in history. He also designed the Christmas plates for 1896 and 1897. From 1897 until 1929 he served as manager of Bing & Grøndahl's exhibitions abroad, and in 1924 rose to the position of Assisting Director of the maker's artware line. Hallin retired in 1934 and died in Copenhagen in 1947.

Artist Henry Thelander's association with Bing & Grøndahl is unparalleled on the collector's plate market. The 1985 issue marks his twenty-third consecutive design for the *Christmas* series. He also has designed every Bing & Grøndahl *Mother's Day* issue—seventeen in all.

Christmas Series

Artist: as indicated

True underglaze-decorated porcelain hand-painted in Copenhagen blue on bas-relief

Diameter: 17.8 centimeters (7 inches)

Pierced foot rim

Edition size undisclosed, limited by year of issue

Not numbered, without certificate; individually initialed on back by each painter

14-B36-1.1
1895 *Behind the Frozen Window*
Artist: Frans August Hallin
Issue $.50; High $4000.00 Low $3500.00;
Close $3500.00; Down $500.00

14-B36-1.2
1896 *New Moon over Snow-covered Trees*
Artist: Frans August Hallin
Issue $.50; High $2000.00; Low $1500.00;
Close $1500.00; Down $500.00

14-B36-1.3
1897 *Christmas Meal of the Sparrows*
Artist: Frans August Hallin
Issue $.75; High $1270.00; Low $910.00;
Close $910.00; Down $360.00

14-B36-1.4
1898 *Christmas Roses and Christmas Star*
Artist: Fanny Garde
Issue $.75; High $700.00; Low $500.00;
Close $500.00; Down $150.00

14-B36-1.5
1899 *The Crows Enjoying Christmas*
Artist: Dahl Jensen
Issue $.75; High $1440.00; Low $800.00;
Close $800.00; Down $640.00

14-B36-1.6
1900 *Church Bells Chiming in Christmas*
Artist: Dahl Jensen
Issue $.75; High $780.00; Low $690.00;
Close $690.00; Down $90.00

14-B36-1.7
1901 *The Three Wise Men from the East*
Artist: S. Sabra
Issue $1.00; High $400.00; Low $300.00;
Close $300.00; Down $100.00

14-B36-1.8
1902 *Interior of a Gothic Church*
Artist: Dahl Jensen
Issue $1.00; High $350.00; Low $265.00;
Close $265.00; Down $85.00

14-B36-1.9
1903 *Happy Expectation of Children*
Artist: Margrethe Hyldahl
Issue $1.00; High $200.00; Low $140.00;
Close $140.00; Down $60.00

14-B36-1.10
1904 *View of Copenhagen from
Frederiksberg Hill*
Artist: Cathinka Olsen
Issue $1.00; High $124.00; Low $120.00;
Close $120.00; Down $4.00

14-B36-1.11
1905 *Anxiety of the Coming
Christmas Night*
Artist: Dahl Jensen
Issue $1.00; High $150.00; Low $120.00;
Close $130.00; No Change

14-B36-1.12
1906 *Sleighing to Church on
Christmas Eve*
Artist: Dahl Jensen
Issue $1.00; High $105.00; Low $67.00;
Close $67.00; Down $38.00

14-B36-1.13
1907 *The Little Match Girl*
Artist: E. Plockross
Issue $1.00; High $120.00; Low $100.00;
Close $110.00; Down $10.00

14-B36-1.14
1908 *St. Petri Church of Copenhagen*
Artist: Povl Jorgensen
Issue $1.00; High $83.00; Low $50.00;
Close $50.00; Down $33.00

14-B36-1.15
1909 *Happiness over the Yule Tree*
Artist: Aarestrup
Issue $1.50; High $95.00; Low $60.00;
Close $60.00; Down $35.00

14-B36-1.16
1910 *The Old Organist*
Artist: C. Ersgaard
Issue $1.50; High $95.00; Low $70.00;
Close $70.00; Down $25.00

14-B36-1.17
1911 *First It Was Sung by Angels to
Shepherds in the Fields*
Artist: H. Moltke
Issue $1.50; High $85.00; Low $80.00;
Close $80.00; Down $5.00

14-B36-1.18
1912 *Going to Church on Christmas Eve*
Artist: Einar Hansen
Issue $1.50; High $90.00; Low $65.00;
Close $65.00; Down $25.00

14-B36-1.19
1913 *Bringing Home the Yule Tree*
Artist: Th. Larsen
Issue $1.50; High $98.00; Low $55.00;
Close $55.00; Down $43.00

14-B36-1.20
1914 *Royal Castle of Amalienborg,
Copenhagen*
Artist: Th. Larsen
Issue $1.50; High $75.00; Low $59.00;
Close $59.00; Down $16.00

14-B36-1.21
1915 *Chained Dog Getting Double Meal
on Christmas Eve*
Artist: Dahl Jensen
Issue $1.50; High $123.00; Low $100.00;
Close $100.00; Down $23.00

14-B36-1.22
1916 *Christmas Prayer of the Sparrows*
Artist: J. Bloch Jorgensen
Issue $1.50; High $95.00; Low $90.00;
Close $90.00; Down $5.00

14-B36-1.23
1917 *Arrival of the Christmas Boat*
Artist: Achton Friis
Issue $1.50; High $75.00; Low $58.00;
Close $58.00; Down $4.00

14-B36-1.24
1918 *Fishing Boat Returning Home
for Christmas*
Artist: Achton Friis
Issue $1.50; High $85.00; Low $65.00;
Close $65.00; Down $20.00

14-B36-1.25
1919 *Outside the Lighted Window*
Artist: Achton Friis
Issue $2.00; High $86.00; Low $60.00;
Close $60.00; Down $26.00

14-B36-1.26
1920 *Hare in the Snow*
Artist: Achton Friis
Issue $2.00; High $70.00; Low $45.00;
Close $55.00; Down $10.00

14-B36-1.27
1921 *Pigeons in the Castle Court*
Artist: Achton Friis
Issue $2.00; High $60.00; Low $40.00;
Close $42.00; Down $18.00

14-B36-1.28
1922 *Star of Bethlehem*
Artist: Achton Friis
Issue $2.00; High $60.00; Low $45.00;
Close $50.00; Down $10.00

14-B36-1.29
1923 *Royal Hunting Castle, the Ermitage*
Artist: Achton Friis
Issue $2.00; High $50.00; Low $45.00;
Close $48.00; Down $2.00

14-B36-1.30
1924 *Lighthouse in Danish Waters*
Artist: Achton Friis
Issue $2.50; High $65.00; Low $50.00;
Close $50.00; Down $15.00

14-B36-1.31
1925 *The Child's Christmas*
Artist: Achton Friis
Issue $2.50; High $80.00; Low $45.00;
Close $50.00; Down $30.00

14-B36-1.32
1926 *Churchgoers on Christmas Day*
Artist: Achton Friis
Issue $2.50; High $66.00; Low $50.00;
Close $60.00; Down $6.00

14-B36-1.33
1927 *Skating Couple*
Artist: Achton Friis
Issue $2.50; High $112.00; Low $95.00;
Close $95.00; Down $17.00

14-B36-1.34
1928 *Eskimo Looking at Village Church
in Greenland*
Artist: Achton Friis
Issue $2.50; High $50.00; Low $50.00;
Close $50.00; No Change

14-B36-1.35
1929 *Fox Outside Farm on Christmas Eve*
Artist: Achton Friis
Issue $2.50; High $75.00; Low $60.00;
Close $70.00; No Change

14-B36-1.36
1930 *Yule Tree in Town Hall Square
of Copenhagen*
Artist: H. Flugenring
Issue $2.50; High $100.00; Low $80.00;
Close $80.00; Down $20.00

14-B36-1.37
1931 *Arrival of the Christmas Train*
Artist: Achton Friis
Issue $2.50; High $95.00; Low $70.00;
Close $70.00; Down $5.00

14-B36-1.38
1932 *Lifeboat at Work*
Artist: H. Flugenring
Issue $2.50; High $92.00; Low $80.00;
Close $80.00; Down $12.00

14-B36-1.39
1933 *The Korsor-Nyborg Ferry*
Artist: H. Flugenring
Issue $3.00; High $72.00; Low $60.00;
Close $60.00; Down $12.00

14-B36-1.40
1934 *Church Bell in Tower*
Artist: Immanuel Tjerne
Issue $3.00; High $73.00; Low $50.00;
Close $60.00; Down $13.00

14-B36-1.41
1935 *Lillebelt Bridge Connecting Funen
with Jutland*
Artist: Ove Larsen
Issue $3.00; High $64.00; Low $64.00;
Close $64.00; No Change

14-B36-1.42
1936 *Royal Guard Outside Amalienborg
Castle in Copenhagen*
Artist: Ove Larsen
Issue $3.00; High $78.00; Low $65.00;
Close $75.00; Down $3.00

14-B36-1.43
1937 *Arrival of Christmas Guests*
Artist: Ove Larsen
Issue $3.00; High $73.00; Low $65.00;
Close $65.00; Down $5.00

14-B36-1.44
1938 *Lighting the Candles*
Artist: Immanuel Tjerne
Issue $3.00; High $110.00; Low $100.00;
Close $100.00; No Change

14-B36-1.45
1939 *Ole Lock-Eye, the Sandman*
Artist: Immanuel Tjerne
Issue $3.00; High $165.00; Low $155.00;
Close $155.00; Down $10.00

14-B36-1.46
1940 *Delivering Christmas Letters*
Artist: Ove Larsen
Issue $4.00; High $170.00; Low $155.00;
Close $155.00; Down $15.00

14-B36-1.47
1941 *Horses Enjoying Christmas Meal
in Stable*
Artist: Ove Larsen
Issue $4.00; High $345.00; Low $320.00;
Close $320.00; Down $25.00

14-B36-1.48
1942 *Danish Farm on Christmas Night*
Artist: Ove Larsen
Issue $4.00; High $150.00; Low $110.00;
Close $110.00; Down $40.00

14-B36-1.49
1943 *The Ribe Cathedral*
Artist: Ove Larsen
Issue $5.00; High $155.00; Low $130.00;
Close $130.00; Down $20.00

14-B36-1.50
1944 *Sorgenfri Castle*
Artist: Ove Larsen
Issue $5.00; High $110.00; Low $80.00;
Close $100.00; Down $10.00

14-B36-1.51
1945 *The Old Water Mill*
Artist: Ove Larsen
Issue $5.00; High $135.00; Low $100.00;
Close $100.00; Down $35.00

14-B36-1.52
1946 *Commemoration Cross in Honor of
Danish Sailors Who Lost Their Lives in
World War II*
Artist: Margrethe Hyldahl
Issue $5.00; High $90.00; Low $70.00;
Close $70.00; Down $20.00

14-B36-1.53
1947 *Dybbol Mill*
Artist: Margrethe Hyldahl
Issue $5.00; High $76.00; Low $65.00;
Close $70.00; Down $6.00

14-B36-1.54
1948 *Watchman, Sculpture of Town Hall, Copenhagen*
Artist: Margrethe Hyldahl
Issue $5.50; High $80.00; Low $50.00;
Close $50.00; Down $30.00

14-B36-1.55
1949 *Landsoldaten, 19th Century Danish Soldier*
Artist: Margrethe Hyldahl
Issue $5.50; High $76.00; Low $55.00;
Close $55.00; Down $21.00

14-B36-1.56
1950 *Kronborg Castle at Elsinore*
Artist: Margrethe Hyldahl
Issue $5.50; High $145.00; Low $140.00;
Close $140.00; Down $5.00

14-B36-1.57
1951 *Jens Bang, New Passenger Boat Running Between Copenhagen and Aalborg*
Artist: Margrethe Hyldahl
Issue $6.00; High $111.00; Low $89.00;
Close $90.00; Down $21.00

14-B36-1.58
1952 *Old Copenhagen Canals at Wintertime with Thorvaldsen Museum in Background*
Artist: Borge Pramvig
Issue $6.00; High $84.00; Low $80.00;
Close $80.00; Down $4.00

14-B36-1.59
1953 *Royal Boat in Greenland Waters*
Artist: Kjeld Bonfils
Issue $7.00; High $100.00; Low $86.00;
Close $86.00; Down $14.00

14-B36-1.60
1954 *Birthplace of Hans Christian Andersen, with Snowman*
Artist: Borge Pramvig
Issue $7.50; High $130.00; Low $100.00;
Close $100.00; Down $10.00

14-B36-1.61
1955 *Kalundborg Church*
Artist: Kjeld Bonfils
Issue $8.00; High $105.00; Low $90.00;
Close $105.00; No Change

14-B36-1.62
1956 *Christmas in Copenhagen*
Artist: Kjeld Bonfils
Issue $8.50; High $144.00; Low $100.00;
Close $100.00; Down $44.00

14-B36-1.63
1957 *Christmas Candles*
Artist: Kjeld Bonfils
Issue $9.00; High $155.00; Low $110.00;
Close $110.00; Down $45.00

14-B36-1.64
1958 *Santa Claus*
Artist: Kjeld Bonfils
Issue $9.50; High $105.00; Low $90.00;
Close $90.00; Down $15.00

14-B36-1.65
1959 *Christmas Eve*
Artist: Kjeld Bonfils
Issue $10.00; High $130.00; Low $110.00;
Close $110.00; Down $10.00

14-B36-1.66
1960 *Danish Village Church*
Artist: Kjeld Bonfils
Issue $10.00; High $184.00; Low $135.00;
Close $135.00; Down $49.00

14-B36-1.67
1961 *Winter Harmony*
Artist: Kjeld Bonfils
Issue $10.50; High $110.00; Low $90.00;
Close $95.00; Down $9.00

14-B36-1.68
1962 *Winter Night*
Artist: Kjeld Bonfils
Issue $11.00; High $90.00; Low $70.00;
Close $85.00; Up $3.00

14-B36-1.69
1963 *The Christmas Elf*
Artist: Henry Thelander
Issue $11.00; High $120.00; Low $95.00;
Close $100.00; Down $20.00

14-B36-1.70
1964 *The Fir Tree and Hare*
Artist: Henry Thelander
Issue $11.50; High $50.00; Low $44.00;
Close $50.00; Up $6.00

14-B36-1.71
1965 *Bringing Home the Christmas Tree*
Artist: Henry Thelander
Issue $12.00; High $60.00; Low $55.00;
Close $60.00; Up $5.00

14-B36-1.72
1966 Home for Christmas
Artist: Henry Thelander
Issue $12.00; High $50.00; Low $35.00;
Close $35.00; Down $15.00

14-B36-1.73
1967 Sharing the Joy of Christmas
Artist: Henry Thelander
Issue $13.00; High $45.00; Low $45.00;
Close $50.00; Up $5.00

14-B36-1.74
1968 Christmas in Church
Artist: Henry Thelander
Issue $14.00; High $45.00; Low $35.00;
Close $35.00; Down $9.00

14-B36-1.75
1969 Arrival of Christmas Guests
Artist: Henry Thelander
Issue $14.00; High $30.00; Low $17.00;
Close $17.00; Down $13.00

14-B36-1.76
1970 Pheasants in the Snow at Christmas
Artist: Henry Thelander
Issue $14.50; High $25.00; Low $20.00;
Close $20.00; No Change

14-B36-1.77
1971 Christmas at Home
Artist: Henry Thelander
Issue $15.00; High $20.00; Low $15.00;
Close $20.00; No Change

14-B36-1.78
1972 Christmas in Greenland
Artist: Henry Thelander
Issue $16.50; High $16.00; Low $10.00;
Close $12.00; Down $4.00

14-B36-1.79
1973 Country Christmas
Artist: Henry Thelander
Issue $19.50; High $25.00; Low $18.00;
Close $22.00; Down $3.00

14-B36-1.80
1974 Christmas in the Village
Artist: Henry Thelander
Issue $22.00; High $25.00; Low $13.00;
Close $13.00; Down $9.00

14-B36-1.81
1975 *The Old Water Mill*
Artist: Henry Thelander
Issue $27.50; High $28.00; Low $18.00;
Close $18.00; Down $6.00

14-B36-1.82
1976 *Christmas Welcome*
Artist: Henry Thelander
Issue $27.50; High $28.00; Low $17.00;
Close $17.00; Down $7.00

14-B36-1.83
1977 *Copenhagen Christmas*
Artist: Henry Thelander
Issue $29.50; High $26.00; Low $17.00;
Close $17.00; Down $9.00

14-B36-1.84
1978 *A Christmas Tale*
Artist: Henry Thelander
Issue $32.00; High $37.00; Low $27.00;
Close $27.00; Down $3.00

14-B36-1.85
1979 *White Christmas*
Artist: Henry Thelander
Issue $36.50; High $35.00; Low $26.00;
Close $26.00; Down $3.00

14-B36-1.86
1980 *Christmas in the Woods*
Artist: Henry Thelander
Issue $42.50; High $40.00; Low $38.00;
Close $40.00; No Change

14-B36-1.87
1981 *Christmas Peace*
Artist: Henry Thelander
Issue $49.50; High $42.00; Low $25.00;
Close $25.00; Down $17.00

14-B36-1.88
1982 *The Christmas Tree*
Artist: Henry Thelander
Issue $54.50; High $55.00; Low $33.00;
Close $33.00; Down $21.50

14-B36-1.89
1983 *Christmas in the Old Town*
Artist: Henry Thelander
Issue $54.50; High $55.00; Low $40.00;
Close $40.00; Down $14.50

14-B36-1.90
1984 *The Christmas Letter*
Artist: Henry Thelander
Issue $54.50; High $55.00; Low $54.50;
Close $55.00; Up $.50

14-B36-1.91
1985 *Christmas Eve at the Farmhouse*
Artist: Edvard Jensen
Issue price: $54.50

Mother's Day Series

Artist: Henry Thelander

True underglaze-decorated porcelain hand-painted in Copenhagen blue on bas-relief

Diameter: 15.2 centimeters (6 inches)

Pierced foot rim

Edition size undisclosed, limited by year of issue

Not numbered, without certificate; individually initialed on back by each painter

14-B36-3.1
1969 *Dog and Puppies*
Issue $9.75; High $475.00; Low $425.00;
Close $425.00; Down $20.00

14-B36-3.2
1970 *Bird and Chicks*
Issue $10.00; High $40.00; Low $30.00;
Close $30.00; Down $10.00

14-B36-3.3
1971 *Cat and Kitten*
Issue $11.00; High $17.00; Low $10.00;
Close $15.00; Down $2.00

14-B36-3.4
1972 *Mare and Foal*
Issue $12.00; High $20.00; Low $12.00;
Close $15.00; Down $4.00

14-B36-3.5
1973 *Duck and Ducklings*
Issue $13.00; High $22.00; Low $13.00;
Close $13.00; Down $9.00

14-B36-3.6
1974 *Bear and Cubs*
Issue $16.50; High $22.00; Low $15.00;
Close $20.00; Down $2.00

14-B36-3.7
1975 *Doe and Fawns*
Issue $19.50; High $22.00; Low $16.00;
Close $16.00; Down $6.00

14-B36-3.8
1976 *Swan Family*
Issue $22.50; High $25.00; Low $19.00;
Close $20.00; Down $5.00

14-B36-3.9
1977 *Squirrel and Young*
Issue $23.50; High $30.00; Low $24.00;
Close $24.00; Down $1.00

14-B36-3.10
1978 *Heron*
Issue $24.50; High $25.00; Low $22.00;
Close $23.00; Down $1.00

14-B36-3.11
1979 *Fox and Cubs*
Issue $27.50; High $35.00; Low $24.00;
Close $24.00; Down $4.00

14-B36-3.12
1980 *Woodpecker and Young*
Issue $29.50; High $40.00; Low $24.00;
Close $24.00; Down $6.00

14-B36-3.13
1981 *Hare and Young*
Issue $36.50; High $40.00; Low $30.00;
Close $30.00; Down $10.00

14-B36-3.14
1982 *Lioness and Cubs*
Issue $39.50; High $45.00; Low $36.00;
Close $39.00; Down $6.00

14-B36-3.15
1983 *Raccoon and Young*
Issue $39.50; High $45.00; Low $40.00;
Close $40.00; Down $5.00

14-B36-3.16
1984 *Stork and Nestlings*
Issue: $39.50; High $49.00; Low $39.50;
Close $40.00; Up $.50

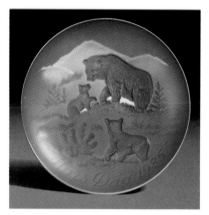

14-B36-3.17
1985 *Bear with Cubs*
Issue price: $39.50

Moments of Truth Series

Artist: Kurt Ard. Artist's signature appears on front

Porcelain

Diameter: 21.1 centimeters
(8⁵⁄₁₆ inches)

Pierced foot rim

Edition size undisclosed, limited by period of issue

Numbered with certificate

14-B36-7.1
1984 *Home Is Best*
Issue $29.50; High $35.00; Low $29.50;
Close $35.00; Up $5.50

14-B36-7.2
1984 *The Road to Virtuosity*
Issue $29.50; High $29.50; Low $29.50;
Close $29.50; No Change

14-B36-7.3
1985 *First Things First*
Issue price: $29.50

Children's Day Series

Artist: Carole Roller

True underglaze-decorated porcelain hand-painted in Copenhagen blue on bas-relief

Diameter: 13 centimeters (5¹⁄₈ inches)

Pierced foot rim

Edition size undisclosed, limited by year of issue

Not numbered, without certificate; individually initialed on back by each painter

14-B36-13.1
1985 *The Magical Tea Party*
Issue price: $24.50

14-G65-1.9 *"Little Mermaid Near Kronborg"*
1983 Grande Copenhagen *Christmas*
Detail from true underglaze-decorated porcelain hand-painted in Copenhagen blue on bas-relief.

DENMARK
GRANDE COPENHAGEN
Copenhagen

Grande Copenhagen plates are produced at the Eslau porcelain factory near Copenhagen. Grande Copenhagen began its *Christmas* series of plates depicting Danish winter scenes in 1975. The series ended in 1984.

Artists for Grande Copenhagen *Christmas* plates prior to 1980 are undisclosed. The artist for the 1980, 1981, 1982, and 1983 issues is Frode Bahnsen of Aarhus, Jutland, Denmark.

Christmas Series

Artist: as indicated

True underglaze-decorated porcelain hand-painted in Copenhagen blue on bas-relief

Diameter: 18.4 centimeters (7¼ inches)

Pierced foot rim

Edition size undisclosed, limited by year of issue

Not numbered, without certificate through 1979; numbered with certificate thereafter

14-G65-1.1
1975 *Alone Together*
Artist: Undisclosed
Issue $24.50; High $35.00; Low $25.00;
Close $25.00; Down $5.00

14-G65-1.2
1976 *Christmas Wreath*
Artist: Undisclosed
Issue $24.50; High $27.00; Low $25.00;
Close $25.00; Down $2.00

14-G65-1.3
1977 *Fishwives at Gammelstrand*
Artist: Undisclosed
Issue $26.50; High $30.00; Low $27.00;
Close $27.00; Down $1.00

14-G65-1.4
1978 *Hans Christian Andersen*
Artist: Undisclosed
Issue $32.50; High $60.00; Low $33.00;
Close $60.00; Up $27.00

14-G65-1.5
1979 *Pheasants in the Snow*
Artist: Undisclosed
Issue $34.50; High $35.00; Low $35.00;
Close $35.00; No Change

14-G65-1.6
1980 *The Snow Queen in the Tivoli*
Artist: Frode Bahnsen
Issue $39.50; High $45.00; Low $40.00;
Close $45.00; No Change

14-G65-1.7
1981 *Little Match Girl in Nyhavn*
Artist: Frode Bahnsen
Issue $42.50; High $45.00; Low $43.00;
Close $45.00; Up $2.00

14-G65-1.8
1982 *The Shepherdess and the
Chimney Sweep*
Artist: Frode Bahnsen
Issue $45.00; High $60.00; Low $52.00;
Close $60.00; Up $8.00

14-G65-1.9
1983 *The Little Mermaid Near Kronborg*
Artist: Frode Bahnsen
Issue $45.00; High $170.00; Low $45.00;
Close $170.00; Up $125.00

14-G65-1.10
1984 *The Sandman at Amalienborg*
Artist: Frode Bahnsen
Issue $45.00; High $90.00; Low $45.00;
Close $70.00; Up $25.00

DENMARK
ROYAL COPENHAGEN
Copenhagen

The Royal Copenhagen Porcelain Manufactory, Denmark's oldest existing porcelain maker, was established by Franz Henrich Muller with the support of Denmark's queen dowager, Juliane Marie, in January 1775. Since the 1760s, members of the Danish royal family had been interested in the white hard-paste porcelain made in China, but it was not until 1772 that Muller, a Danish pharmacist and chemist, was able to duplicate the fine porcelain. In 1779 "The Danish Porcelain Factory," as Royal Copenhagen was then called, came under royal control.

The Danish Court controlled the firm from 1779 to 1867, a period in its history that is still symbolized by the crown in its trademark. The three wavy lines under the crown, part of the factory trademark since 1775, pay tribute to Denmark's tradition as a seafaring nation and represent Denmark's three ancient waterways: the Sound, the Great Belt, and the Little Belt. In 1867 the factory was sold and has continued under private ownership. It is still a supplier to the royal court in Denmark.

The first Royal Copenhagen *Christmas* plate was issued in 1908, and the series has continued every year since then. From the beginning, the motif for each year's *Christmas* plate has been selected from suggestions submitted by employees of the Royal Copenhagen factory. Until 1941, small quantities of plates in the *Christmas* series were created with the word "Christmas" translated into other languages to meet the demand from non-Danish collectors. The Royal Copenhagen *Mother's Day* series, started in 1971, ended in 1982.

In 1982, their *Motherhood* series started with artwork by Sven Vestergaard.

Christian Thomsen, designer of the first Royal Copenhagen collector's plate, served an apprenticeship as a woodcarver before joining the firm in 1898. His porcelain creations won a silver medal in a Milan exhibit in 1908 and a gold medal in a Brussels exhibit in 1910. His work now hangs in the Museum of Decorative Arts in Copenhagen. Arnold Krog innovated the famed cobalt-blue underglaze design technique which has become a tradition in Danish plate making. He worked for Royal Copenhagen from 1884 to 1916, rising to art director and taking the Grand Prix for decorative art in Paris in 1900. Krog's most famous creation is his fountain located in The Hague, The Netherlands. Artist Kai Lange has been with Royal Copenhagen since the age of seventeen and, after more than half a century with the firm, is regarded as one of the most knowledgeable artists working in the porcelain medium today. The first Kai Lange design selected for the annual *Christmas* plate was for the 1940 issue, and since 1963 every plate, except the 1976 issue, has been a Kai Lange creation. Kamma Svenson, artist for the first two *Mother's Day* issues, has gained a world following for her illustrations of Danish literary scenes. Since 1950 she has worked as an illustrator for *Politiken,* one of the two largest Copenhagen newspapers. Her work, "Russian Dolls," was reproduced as a UNICEF Christmas card. The Royal Academy of Fine Arts has sponsored numerous exhibitions of her work. Ib Spang Olsen, artist for the *Mother's Day* series, is a recipient of the Danish Children's Book Prize.

Christmas Series

Artist: as indicated. Artist's name appears on back since 1955

True underglaze-decorated porcelain hand-painted in Copenhagen blue on bas-relief

Diameter: 15.2 centimeters (6 inches) for 1908 through 1910; 17.8 centimeters (7 inches) thereafter

Pierced foot rim

Edition size undisclosed, limited by year of issue

Not numbered, without certificate; individually initialed on back by each painter

14-R59-1.1
1908 *Madonna and Child*
Artist: Christian Thomsen
Issue $1.00; High $1800.00; Low $1700.00;
Close $1700.00; Down $100.00

14-R59-1.2
1909 *Danish Landscape*
Artist: St. Ussing
Issue $1.00; High $170.00; Low $150.00;
Close $160.00; Down $10.00

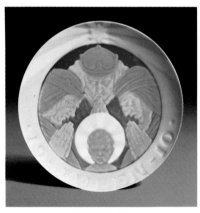

14-R59-1.3
1910 *The Magi*
Artist: Christian Thomsen
Issue $1.00; High $140.00; Low $130.00;
Close $130.00; Down $10.00

14-R59-1.4
1911 *Danish Landscape*
Artist: Oluf Jensen
Issue $1.00; High $120.00; Low $112.00;
Close $120.00; No Change

14-R59-1.5
1912 *Elderly Couple by Christmas Tree*
Artist: Christian Thomsen
Issue $1.00; High $138.00; Low $128.00;
Close $128.00; Down $10.00

14-R59-1.6
1913 *Spire of Frederik's Church,*
Copenhagen
Artist: A. Boesen
Issue $1.50; High $135.00; Low $110.00;
Close $110.00; Down $25.00

14-R59-1.7
1914 *Sparrows in Tree at Church of the*
Holy Spirit, Copenhagen
Artist: A. Boesen
Issue $1.50; High $120.00; Low $100.00;
Close $120.00; Up $5.00

14-R59-1.8
1915 *Danish Landscape*
Artist: Arnold Krog
Issue $1.50; High $206.00; Low $176.00;
Close $196.00; Down $10.00

14-R59-1.9
1916 *Shepherd in the Field on
Christmas Night*
Artist: Ricard Böcher
Issue $1.50; High $95.00; Low $75.00;
Close $75.00; Down $20.00

14-R59-1.10
1917 *Tower of Our Savior's Church,
Copenhagen*
Artist: Oluf Jensen
Issue $2.00; High $82.00; Low $70.00;
Close $75.00; Up $5.00

14-R59-1.11
1918 *Sheep and Shepherds*
Artist: Oluf Jensen
Issue $2.00; High $85.00; Low $78.00;
Close $80.00; Down $5.00

14-R59-1.12
1919 *In the Park*
Artist: Oluf Jensen
Issue $2.00; High $83.00; Low $56.00;
Close $56.00; Down $27.00

14-R59-1.13
1920 *Mary with the Child Jesus*
Artist: G. Rode
Issue $2.00; High $80.00; Low $70.00;
Close $70.00; Down $10.00

14-R59-1.14
1921 *Aabenraa Marketplace*
Artist: Oluf Jensen
Issue $2.00; High $75.00; Low $73.00;
Close $73.00; Down $2.00

14-R59-1.15
1922 *Three Singing Angels*
Artist: Ellinor Selschau
Issue $2.00; High $75.00; Low $54.00;
Close $54.00; Down $21.00

14-R59-1.16
1923 *Danish Landscape*
Artist: Oluf Jensen
Issue $2.00; High $80.00; Low $60.00;
Close $80.00; Up $5.00

14-R59-1.17
1924 *Christmas Star over the Sea and
Sailing Ship*
Artist: Benjamin Olsen
Issue $2.00; High $105.00; Low $80.00;
Close $80.00; Down $25.00

14-R59-1.18
1925 *Street Scene from Christianshavn,*
Copenhagen
Artist: Oluf Jensen
Issue $2.00; High $88.00; Low $80.00;
Close $80.00; Down $8.00

14-R59-1.19
1926 *View of Christianshavn Canal,*
Copenhagen
Artist: Ricard Böcher
Issue $2.00; High $80.00; Low $70.00;
Close $70.00; Down $2.00

14-R59-1.20
1927 *Ship's Boy at the Tiller on*
Christmas Night
Artist: Benjamin Olsen
Issue $2.00; High $152.00; Low $135.00;
Close $135.00; Down $17.00

14-R59-1.21
1928 *Vicar's Family on Way to Church*
Artist: G. Rode
Issue $2.00; High $75.00; Low $70.00;
Close $70.00; Down $5.00

14-R59-1.22
1929 *Grundtvig Church, Copenhagen*
Artist: Oluf Jensen
Issue $2.00; High $120.00; Low $80.00;
Close $100.00; Up $20.00

14-R59-1.23
1930 *Fishing Boats on the Way*
to the Harbor
Artist: Benjamin Olsen
Issue $2.50; High $80.00; Low $75.00;
Close $80.00; No Change

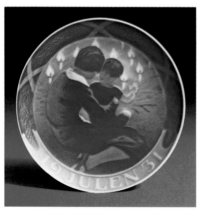

14-R59-1.24
1931 *Mother and Child*
Artist: G. Rode
Issue $2.50; High $90.00; Low $65.00;
Close $65.00; Down $10.00

14-R59-1.25
1932 *Frederiksberg Gardens with Statue*
of Frederik VI
Artist: Oluf Jensen
Issue $2.50; High $85.00; Low $80.00;
Close $85.00; Up $5.00

14-R59-1.26
1933 *The Great Belt Ferry*
Artist: Benjamin Olsen
Issue $2.50; High $117.00; Low $100.00;
Close $110.00; No Change

14-R59-1.27
1934 *The Hermitage Castle*
Artist: Oluf Jensen
Issue $2.50; High $122.00; Low $100.00;
Close $116.00; Down $6.00

14-R59-1.28
1935 *Fishing Boat off Kronborg Castle*
Artist: Benjamin Olsen
Issue $2.50; High $144.00; Low $140.00;
Close $140.00; Down $4.00

14-R59-1.29
1936 *Roskilde Cathedral*
Artist: Ricard Böcher
Issue $2.50; High $135.00; Low $120.00;
Close $120.00; Down $15.00

14-R59-1.30
1937 *Christmas Scene in Main Street,
Copenhagen*
Artist: Nils Thorsson
Issue $2.50; High $135.00; Low $130.00;
Close $130.00; Down $5.00

14-R59-1.31
1938 *Round Church in Osterlars on
Bornholm*
Artist: Herne Nielsen
Issue $3.00; High $200.00; Low $194.00;
Close $194.00; Down $6.00

14-R59-1.32
1939 *Expeditionary Ship in the Pack-Ice
of Greenland*
Artist: Sv. Nic. Nielsen
Issue $3.00; High $200.00; Low $135.00;
Close $135.00; Down $65.00

14-R59-1.33
1940 *The Good Shepherd*
Artist: Kai Lange
Issue $3.00; High $300.00; Low $260.00;
Close $260.00; Down $40.00

14-R59-1.34
1941 *Danish Village Church*
Artist: Th. Kjolner
Issue $3.00; High $312.00; Low $238.00;
Close $238.00; Down $74.00

14-R59-1.35
1942 *Bell Tower of Old Church in Jutland*
Artist: Nils Thorsson
Issue $4.00; High $350.00; Low $255.00;
Close $255.00; Down $95.00

14-R59-1.36
1943 *Flight of Holy Family into Egypt*
Artist: Nils Thorsson
Issue $4.00; High $450.00; Low $410.00;
Close $410.00; Down $40.00

14-R59-1.37
1944 *Typical Danish Winter Scene*
Artist: Viggo Olsen
Issue $4.00; High $170.00; Low $95.00;
Close $95.00; Down $75.00

14-R59-1.38
1945 *A Peaceful Motif*
Artist: Ricard Böcher
Issue $4.00; High $360.00; Low $325.00;
Close $325.00; Down $35.00

14-R59-1.39
1946 *Zealand Village Church*
Artist: Nils Thorsson
Issue $4.00; High $155.00; Low $150.00;
Close $150.00; Down $5.00

14-R59-1.40
1947 *The Good Shepherd*
Artist: Kai Lange
Issue $4.50; High $200.00; Low $198.00;
Close $198.00; Down $2.00

14-R59-1.41
1948 *Nodebo Church at Christmastime*
Artist: Th. Kjolner
Issue $4.50; High $170.00; Low $150.00;
Close $150.00; Down $20.00

14-R59-1.42
1949 *Our Lady's Cathedral, Copenhagen*
Artist: Hans H. Hansen
Issue $5.00; High $165.00; Low $145.00;
Close $145.00; Down $20.00

14-R59-1.43
1950 *Boeslunde Church, Zealand*
Artist: Viggo Olsen
Issue $5.00; High $185.00; Low $165.00;
Close $165.00; Down $20.00

14-R59-1.44
1951 *Christmas Angel*
Artist: Ricard Böcher
Issue $5.00; High $300.00; Low $255.00;
Close $255.00; Down $45.00

14-R59-1.45
1952 Christmas in the Forest
Artist: Kai Lange
Issue $5.00; High $120.00; Low $90.00;
Close $90.00; Down $30.00

14-R59-1.46
1953 Frederiksberg Castle
Artist: Th. Kjolner
Issue $6.00; High $120.00; Low $95.00;
Close $95.00; Down $25.00

14-R59-1.47
1954 Amalienborg Palace, Copenhagen
Artist: Kai Lange
Issue $6.00; High $145.00; Low $130.00;
Close $130.00; Down $15.00

14-R59-1.48
1955 Fano Girl
Artist: Kai Lange
Issue $7.00; High $230.00; Low $193.00;
Close $195.00; Up $2.00

14-R59-1.49
1956 Rosenborg Castle, Copenhagen
Artist: Kai Lange
Issue $7.00; High $160.00; Low $130.00;
Close $130.00; Down $30.00

14-R59-1.50
1957 The Good Shepherd
Artist: Hans H. Hansen
Issue $8.00; High $117.00; Low $60.00;
Close $60.00; Down $57.00

14-R59-1.51
1958 Sunshine over Greenland
Artist: Hans H. Hansen
Issue $9.00; High $135.00; Low $95.00;
Close $95.00; Down $40.00

14-R59-1.52
1959 Christmas Night
Artist: Hans H. Hansen
Issue $9.00; High $140.00; Low $95.00;
Close $95.00; Down $25.00

14-R59-1.53
1960 The Stag
Artist: Hans H. Hansen
Issue $10.00; High $155.00; Low $100.00;
Close $110.00; Down $45.00

14-R59-1.54
1961 *Training Ship Danmark*
Artist: Kai Lange
Issue $10.00; High $160.00; Low $130.00;
Close $130.00; Down $22.00

14-R59-1.55
1962 *The Little Mermaid at Wintertime*
Artist: Undisclosed
Issue $11.00; High $200.00; Low $150.00;
Close $160.00; Down $40.00

14-R59-1.56
1963 *Hojsager Mill*
Artist: Kai Lange
Issue $11.00; High $85.00; Low $55.00;
Close $55.00; Down $30.00

14-R59-1.57
1964 *Fetching the Christmas Tree*
Artist: Kai Lange
Issue $11.00; High $75.00; Low $49.00;
Close $49.00; Down $26.00

14-R59-1.58
1965 *Little Skaters*
Artist: Kai Lange
Issue $12.00; High $60.00; Low $45.00;
Close $50.00; Down $10.00

14-R59-1.59
1966 *Blackbird at Christmastime*
Artist: Kai Lange
Issue $12.00; High $52.00; Low $39.00;
Close $45.00; Down $7.00

14-R59-1.60
1967 *The Royal Oak*
Artist: Kai Lange
Issue $13.00; High $45.00; Low $29.00;
Close $29.00; Down $16.00

14-R59-1.61
1968 *The Last Umiak*
Artist: Kai Lange
Issue $13.00; High $36.00; Low $24.00;
Close $24.00; Down $12.00

14-R59-1.62
1969 *The Old Farmyard*
Artist: Kai Lange
Issue $14.00; High $34.00; Low $28.00;
Close $28.00; Down $6.00

14-R59-1.63
1970 *Christmas Rose and Cat*
Artist: Kai Lange
Issue $14.00; High $45.00; Low $28.00;
Close $28.00; Down $12.00

14-R59-1.64
1971 *Hare in Winter*
Artist: Kai Lange
Issue $15.00; High $27.00; Low $24.00;
Close $24.00; Down $3.00

14-R59-1.65
1972 *In the Desert*
Artist: Kai Lange
Issue $16.00; High $22.00; Low $19.00;
Close $19.00; Down $1.00

14-R59-1.66
1973 *Train Homeward Bound for
Christmas*
Artist: Kai Lange
Issue $22.00; High $27.00; Low $27.00;
Close $27.00; No Change

14-R59-1.67
1974 *Winter Twilight*
Artist: Kai Lange
Issue $22.00; High $28.00; Low $22.00;
Close $22.00; Down $3.00

14-R59-1.68
1975 *Queen's Palace*
Artist: Kai Lange
Issue $27.50; High $23.00; Low $19.00;
Close $20.00; Down $3.00

14-R59-1.69
1976 *Danish Watermill*
Artist: Sven Vestergaard
Issue $27.50; High $38.00; Low $30.00;
Close $38.00; Up $8.00

14-R59-1.70
1977 *Immervad Bridge*
Artist: Kai Lange
Issue $32.00; High $35.00; Low $20.00;
Close $20.00; Down $10.00

14-R59-1.71
1978 *Greenland Scenery*
Artist: Kai Lange
Issue $35.00; High $40.00; Low $26.00;
Close $26.00; Down $10.00

14-R59-1.72
1979 *Choosing the Christmas Tree*
Artist: Kai Lange
Issue $42.50; High $65.00; Low $45.00;
Close $45.00; Down $15.00

14-R59-1.73
1980 *Bringing Home the Christmas Tree*
Artist: Kai Lange
Issue $49.50; High $55.00; Low $35.00;
Close $35.00; Down $10.00

14-R59-1.74
1981 *Admiring the Christmas Tree*
Artist: Kai Lange
Issue $52.50; High $50.00; Low $40.00;
Close $40.00; Down $10.00

14-R59-1.75
1982 *Waiting for Christmas*
Artist: Kai Lange
Issue $54.50; High $63.00; Low $45.00;
Close $55.00; Down $8.00

14-R59-1.76
1983 *Merry Christmas*
Artist: Kai Lange
Issue $54.50; High $55.00; Low $45.00;
Close $45.00; Down $9.50

14-R59-1.77
1984 *Jingle Bells*
Artist: Kai Lange
Issue $54.50; High $60.00; Low $54.00;
Close $54.00; Down $.50

14-R59-1.78
1985 *The Snowman*
Artist: Kai Lange
Issue price: $54.50

Mother's Day Series

Artist: as indicated

True underglaze-decorated porcelain hand-painted in Copenhagen blue on bas-relief

Diameter: 15.9 centimeters (6¼ inches)

Pierced foot rim

Edition size undisclosed, limited by year of issue

Not numbered, without certificate; individually initialed on back by each painter

14-R59-2.1
1971 *American Mother*
Artist: Kamma Svensson
Issue $12.50; High $13.00; Low $7.00;
Close $8.00; Down $5.00

14-R59-2.2
1972 *Oriental Mother*
Artist: Kamma Svensson
Issue $14.00; High $8.00; Low $6.00;
Close $7.00; Down $1.00

14-R59-2.3
1973 *Danish Mother*
Artist: Arne Ungermann
Issue $16.00; High $13.00; Low $12.00;
Close $12.00; No Change

14-R59-2.4
1974 *Greenland Mother*
Artist: Arne Ungermann
Issue $16.50; High $17.00; Low $8.00;
Close $9.00; Down $6.00

14-R59-2.5
1975 *Bird in Nest*
Artist: Arne Ungermann
Issue $20.00; High $20.00; Low $18.00;
Close $18.00; Down $1.00

14-R59-2.6
1976 *Mermaids*
Artist: Arne Ungermann
Issue $20.00; High $20.00; Low $14.00;
Close $18.00; Down $2.00

14-R59-2.7
1977 *The Twins*
Artist: Arne Ungermann
Issue $24.00; High $20.00; Low $17.00;
Close $20.00; No Change

14-R59-2.8
1978 *Mother and Child*
Artist: Ib Spang Olsen
Issue $26.00; High $25.00; Low $15.00;
Close $20.00; Down $5.00

14-R59-2.9
1979 A Loving Mother
Artist: Ib Spang Olsen
Issue $29.50; High $26.00; Low $18.00;
Close $18.00; Down $7.00

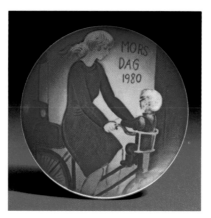

14-R59-2.10
1980 An Outing with Mother
Artist: Ib Spang Olsen
Issue $37.50; High $35.00; Low $20.00;
Close $20.00; Down $10.00

14-R59-2.11
1981 Reunion
Artist: Ib Spang Olsen
Issue $39.00; High $37.00; Low $30.00;
Close $30.00; Down $5.00

14-R59-2.12
1982 The Children's Hour
Artist: Ib Spang Olsen
Issue $39.50; High $50.00; Low $42.00;
Close $42.00; Down $3.00
Series Closed

Motherhood Series

Artist: Sven Vestergaard

True underglaze-decorated porcelain hand-painted in Copenhagen blue on bas-relief

Diameter: 15.2 centimeters (6 inches)

Pierced foot rim

Edition size undisclosed, limited by year of issue

Not numbered, without certificate

14-R59-4.1
1982 Mother Robin and Her Young Ones
Issue $29.50; High $40.00; Low $29.50;
Close $30.00; Up $.50

14-R59-4.2
1983 Mother Cat and Kitten
Issue $29.50; High $32.00; Low $26.00;
Close $30.00; Up $.50

14-R59-4.3
1984 Mare with Foal
Issue $29.50; High $34.00; Low $30.00;
Close $30.00; Up $.50

14-R59-4.4
1985 Mother Rabbit with Bunny
Issue price: $32.50

ARABIA
FINLAND

In 1873 Arabia was founded as a subsidiary of the Swedish firm Rörstrand (see Sweden, RÖRSTRAND). The factory was located on the outskirts of Helsinki, a site chosen in hopes of supplying the growing markets for ceramics in Finland and the Russian Empire. Early products included dinner services, pitchers, and mugs, almost all based on Rörstrand designs.

In 1884 Arabia was reorganized as a Finnish company, Arabia Aktiefabrik, and developed its own designs from that time on. The company won a gold medal at the Paris World Exhibition in 1900, and is the only pottery producing both household and art ceramics in Finland today.

To celebrate the one-hundredth anniversary of the firm in 1873, Arabia produced a limited-edition anniversary plate. Its success, in turn, led to the introduction in 1976 of an annual limited-edition series based on the Finnish national epic, the *Kalevala*, by artist Raija Uosikkinen.

Kalevala Series

Artist: Raija Uosikkinen

Stoneware

Diameter: 19 centimeters square (7½ inches square)

Pierced foot rim

Edition size undisclosed

Not numbered, without certificate

16-A69-1.1
1976 Vainamoinen's Sowing
Issue $30.00; High $250.00; Low $225.00;
Close $240.00; Down $10.00

16-A69-1.2
1977 Aino's Fate
Issue $30.00; High $50.00; Low $40.00;
Close $40.00; Down $10.00

16-A69-1.3
1978 *Lemminkainen's Chase*
Issue $39.00; High $50.00; Low $40.00;
Close $40.00; Down $10.00

16-A69-1.4
1979 *Kullervo's Revenge*
Issue $39.50; High $45.00; Low $34.00;
Close $35.00; Down $5.00

16-A69-1.5
1980 *Vainamoinen's Rescue*
Issue $45.00; High $70.00; Low $55.00;
Close $55.00; Down $15.00

16-A69-1.6
1981 *Vainamoinen's Magic*
Issue $49.50; High $57.00; Low $45.00;
Close $45.00; Down $12.00

16-A69-1.7
1982 *Joukahainen Shoots the Horse*
Issue $55.50; High $80.00; Low $60.00;
Close $65.00; Up $5.00

16-A69-1.8
1983 *Lemminkainen's Escape*
Issue $60.00; High $86.00; Low $60.00;
Close $80.00; Up $20.00

16-A69-1.9
1984 *Lemminkainen's Magic Feathers*
Issue $60.00; High $84.00; Low $60.00;
Close $84.00; Up $24.00

FRANCE
PORCELAINE GEORGES BOYER
Limoges

PORCELAINE

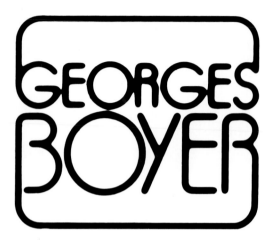

LIMOGES

Porcelaine Georges Boyer of Limoges, France was founded in 1933 by Georges Boyer; his is the second generation of Boyers to work in porcelain. His father, Jean Boyer, originally worked for the house of Haviland before forming his own company, in which Georges worked as technical director. Today, the firm is managed by Gerard Boyer, son of Georges, thus continuing the family tradition.

Porcelaine Georges Boyer is the third-ranking company in the renowned porcelain center of Li-moges, producing porcelain dinnerware as well as limited-edition collector's plates. The firm numbers among its efforts the production of extremely small limited-edition plate series based upon the works of Pierre Auguste Renoir and Maurice Utrillo. In 1982, Porcelaine Georges Boyer introduced its first collector's series for the United States market under its own name—the *Alice in Wonderland* series by British artist Sandy Nightingale.

Alice in Wonderland Series

Artist: Sandy Nightingale

Overglaze-decorated porcelain banded in 24k gold

Diameter: 21.6 centimeters (8½ inches)

Attached back hanger

Edition size undisclosed, limited by announced period of issue

Numbered with certificate

18-B61-1.1
1982 *Alice and the White Rabbit*
Issue $36.96; High $75.00; Low $37.00;
Close $37.00; Down $38.00

18-B61-1.2
1983 *Alice and the Caterpillar*
Issue $36.96; High $60.00; Low $36.96;
Close $42.00; Up $5.04

18-B61-1.3
1983 *Alice and the Cheshire Cat*
Issue $36.96; High $57.00; Low $36.96;
Close $50.00; Up $13.04

18-B61-1.4
1983 *Alice and the Mad Hatter*
Issue $36.96; High $70.00; Low $36.96;
Close $58.00; Up $21.04

18-B61-1.5
1984 *Painting the Roses*
Issue $36.96; High $65.00; Low $36.96;
Close $60.00; Up $23.04

18-B61-1.6
1984 *Alice and the Croquet Game*
Issue $36.96; High $60.00; Low $36.96;
Close $60.00; Up $23.04

18-B61-1.7
1984 *The Gryphon and Mock Turtle*
Issue $36.96; High $36.96; Low $36.96;
Close $36.96; No Change

18-B61-1.8
1984 *The Knave of Hearts*
Issue $36.96; High $36.96; Low $36.96;
Close $36.96; No Change
Series Closed

The hallmark of Henri d'Arceau L. & Fils is one of the most prestigious in the famous porcelain center of Limoges. The firm, which claims to adhere to the original "Grellet Standard" of 1768 for handcraftsmanship, is today directed by Gerard Boyer, a descendant of the founder.

The firm was commissioned by L'Association l'Esprit de Lafayette to produce the six-plate bicentennial series *Collection Le Patrimoine de Lafayette (Lafayette Legacy Collection)*, 1973-1975, which chronicles the role of the Marquis de Lafayette in America's War of Independence. The D'Arceau-Limoges *Christmas* series, *Noël Vitrail*, begun in 1975, was inspired by the stained-glass windows of the cathedral at Chartres. It ended in 1982. *Les Femmes du Siècle (Women of the Century)*, a twelve-plate series commissioned by the Chambre Syndicale de la Couture Parisienne, began in 1976 and ended in 1979. This series, recognized by the United Nations, depicts Western women's fashions from 1865 to 1965. Introduced in 1978 was *Les Jeunes Filles des Saisons (Girls of the Seasons)*, which ended in 1981, and in 1979 *Les Très Riches Heures (The Very Rich Hours)*, which adapts its artwork from an early fifteenth-century illuminated manuscript. In 1980, the firm, in collaboration with La Société de Paris et Son Histoire, issued Louis Dali's *Les Douze Sites Parisiens de Louis Dali (The Twelve Parisian Places of Louis Dali)* series, a collection of the artist's unique impressions of the famous city. In 1984 *Joséphine et Napoléon* was introduced with artwork by Claude Boulmé. Their *Cambier Mother's Day* series began in 1983 with artwork by French classicist Guy Cambier. In early 1985, they introduced their first series relating to a classic motion picture, *Gigi*, by Jean-Claude Guidou.

Among the artists who have designed works for D'Arceau-Limoges are the late André Restieau, world authority on the techniques of re-creating medieval stained glass coloration in porcelain; neo-Classicist Guy Cambier, and the late François Ganeau, resident consultant to the Theatre Comedie Française, as well as Louis Dali.

Collection Le Patrimoine de Lafayette

(The Lafayette Legacy Collection)

Artist: André Restieau. Artist's signature appears on front, initials on back

Overglaze-decorated porcelain

Diameter: 21.6 centimeters (8½ inches)

Attached back hanger

Edition size undisclosed, limited by announced period of issue

Numbered with certificate

18-D15-1.1
1973 *The Secret Contract*
Issue $14.82; High $36.00; Low $15.00;
Close $15.00; Down $21.00

18-D15-1.2
1973 *The Landing at North Island*
Issue $19.82; High $51.00; Low $20.00;
Close $20.00; Down $31.00

18-D15-1.3
1974 *The Meeting at City Tavern*
Issue $19.82; High $42.00; Low $20.00;
Close $20.00; Down $22.00

18-D15-1.4
1974 *The Battle of Brandywine*
Issue $19.82; High $48.00; Low $20.00;
Close $20.00; Down $28.00

18-D15-1.5
1975 *The Messages to Franklin*
Issue $19.82; High $54.00; Low $22.00;
Close $22.00; Down $32.00

18-D15-1.6
1975 *The Siege at Yorktown*
Issue $19.82; High $47.00; Low $20.00;
Close $20.00; Down $27.00
Series Closed

Noël Vitrail

(Stained-glass Christmas)

Artist: André Restieau. Artist's signature appears on front, initials on back

Overglaze-decorated porcelain

Diameter: 21.6 centimeters (8½ inches)

Attached back hanger

Edition size undisclosed, limited by announced period of issue

Numbered with certificate

18-D15-2.1
1975 *La Fuite en Egypte*
(Flight into Egypt)
Issue $24.32; High $95.00; Low $37.00;
Close $37.00; Down $58.00

18-D15-2.2
1976 *Dans la Crêche*
(In the Manger)
Issue $24.32; High $49.00; Low $34.00;
Close $34.00; Down $5.00

18-D15-2.3
1977 *Le Refus d'Hèbergement*
(No Room at the Inn)
Issue $24.32; High $40.00; Low $35.00;
Close $35.00; Down $5.00

18-D15-2.4
1978 *La Purification*
(The Purification)
Issue $26.81; High $40.00; Low $35.00;
Close $35.00; No Change

18-D15-2.5
1979 *L'Adoration des Rois*
(The Adoration of Kings)
Issue $26.81; High $42.00; Low $36.00;
Close $37.00; Up $1.00

18-D15-2.6
1980 *Joyeuse Nouvelle*
(Tidings of Great Joy)
Issue $28.74; High $47.00; Low $37.00;
Close $37.00; Down $5.00

18-D15-2.7
1981 *Guides par l'Etoile*
(Guided by the Star)
Issue $28.74; High $60.00; Low $38.00;
Close $38.00; Down $22.00

18-D15-2.8
1982 *L'Annunciation*
(The Annunciation)
Issue $30.74; High $64.00; Low $44.00;
Close $44.00; Down $11.00
Series Closed

Les Femmes du Siècle

(The Women of the Century)

Artist: François Ganeau. Artist's signature appears on front, initials on back

Overglaze-decorated porcelain

Diameter: 21.6 centimeters (8½ inches)

Attached back hanger

Edition size undisclosed, limited by announced period of issue

Numbered with certificate

18-D15-3.1
1976 *Scarlet en Crinoline*
Issue $17.67; High $25.00; Low $20.00;
Close $20.00; Down $5.00

18-D15-3.2
1976 *Sarah en Tournure*
Issue $22.74; High $30.00; Low $24.00;
Close $24.00; Down $6.00

18-D15-3.3
1976 *Colette, la Femme Sportive*
Issue $22.74; High $26.00; Low $25.00;
Close $25.00; No Change

18-D15-3.4
1976 *Léa, la Femme Fleur*
Issue $22.74; High $26.00; Low $25.00;
Close $25.00; Down $1.00

18-D15-3.5
1977 *Albertine, la Femme Liane*
Issue $22.74; High $26.00; Low $25.00;
Close $25.00; Down $1.00

18-D15-3.6
1977 *Edith, la Femme Pratique*
Issue $22.74; High $28.00; Low $25.00;
Close $25.00; Down $2.00

18-D15-3.7
1977 *Daisy, la Garçonne*
Issue $22.74; High $27.00; Low $25.00;
Close $25.00; Down $2.00

18-D15-3.8
1977 *Marlène, la Vamp*
Issue $22.74; High $25.00; Low $24.00;
Close $24.00; Down $1.00

18-D15-3.9
1978 *Hélène, l'Intrépide*
Issue $22.74; High $30.00; Low $25.00;
Close $25.00; Down $3.00

18-D15-3.10
1978 *Sophie, la Féminité Retrouvée*
Issue $22.74; High $30.00; Low $22.74;
Close $25.00; Down $5.00

18-D15-3.11
1979 *Françoise en Pantalon*
Issue $22.74; High $40.00; Low $22.74;
Close $22.74; Down $7.26

18-D15-3.12
1979 *Brigitte en Mini-jupe*
Issue $22.74; High $34.00; Low $22.74;
Close $22.74; Down $7.26
Series Closed

Les Juenes Filles des Saisons
(The Girls of the Seasons)

Artist: Guy Cambier. Artist's
signature appears on front

Overglaze-decorated porcelain
banded in gold

Diameter: 24.8 centimeters
(9¾ inches)

No hanger

Edition size limited to 15,000

Numbered with certificate

18-D15-4.1
1978 *La Jeune Fille d'Eté*
(Summer Girl)
Issue $105.00; High $120.00; Low $105.00;
Close $105.00; Down $15.00

18-D15-4.2
1979 *La Jeune Fille d'Hiver*
(Winter Girl)
Issue $105.00; High $110.00; Low $105.00;
Close $105.00; Down $5.00

18-D15-4.3
1980 *La Jeune Fille du Printemps*
(Spring Girl)
Issue $105.00; High $115.00; Low $105.00;
Close $105.00; Down $5.00

18-D15-4.4
1981 *La Jeune Fille d'Automne*
(Autumn Girl)
Issue $105.00; High $150.00; Low $110.00;
Close $130.00; Down $15.00
Series Closed

Les Très Riches Heures

(The Very Rich Hours)

Artist: Jean Dutheil. Artist's
signature appears on back

Overglaze-decorated porcelain

Diameter: 24.8 centimeters
(9¾ inches)

Attached back hanger

Edition size unannounced

Numbered with certificate

18-D15-5.1
1979 *Janvier (January)*
Issue $75.48; High $76.00; Low $76.00;
Close $76.00; No Change

18-D15-5.2
1980 *Avril (April)*
Issue $75.48; High $85.00; Low $78.00;
Close $80.00; No Change

18-D15-5.3
1981 *Août (August)*
Issue $75.48; High $120.00; Low $90.00;
Close $95.00; Up $5.00

18-D15-5.4
1982 *Juin (June)*
Issue $75.48; High $150.00; Low $75.48;
Close $140.00; Up $64.52

18-D15-5.5
1983 *Mai (May)*
Issue $75.48; High $120.00; Low $75.48;
Close $120.00; Up $44.52

18-D15-5.6
1984 *Octobre (October)*
Issue $75.48; High $75.48; Low $75.48;
Close $75.48; No Change
Series Closed

Les Douze Sites Parisiens de Louis Dali (The Twelve Parisian Places of Louis Dali)

Artist: Louis Dali. Artist's signature appears on front

Overglaze-decorated porcelain

Diameter: 21.6 centimeters (8½ inches)

Attached back hanger

Edition size undisclosed, limited by announced period of issue

Numbered with certificate

18-D15-6.1
1980 *L'Arc de Triomphe*
(The Arch of Triumph)
Issue $22.94; High $35.00; Low $24.00;
Close $30.00; Up $6.00

18-D15-6.2
1981 *La Cathedrale Notre-Dame*
(Notre Dame Cathedral)
Issue $24.94; High $25.00; Low $25.00;
Close $25.00; No Change

18-D15-6.3
1981 *La Place de la Concorde*
(Concord Place)
Issue $24.94; High $48.00; Low $25.00;
Close $34.00; Up $9.00

18-D15-6.4
1981 *L'Église Saint-Pierre et le Sacré-*
Coeur de Montmartre
(St. Peter's Church and Sacred Heart
Basilica)
Issue $26.83; High $28.00; Low $27.00;
Close $28.00; Up $1.00

18-D15-6.5
1982 *Le Marché aux Fleurs et la*
Conciergerie
(The Flower Market and the Conciergerie)
Issue $26.83; High $27.00; Low $26.83;
Close $26.83; Down $.17

18-D15-6.6
1982 *La Pointe du Vert Galant et le Pont Neuf (Vert Galant Point and the New Bridge)*
Issue $26.83; High $30.00; Low $26.83; Close $26.83; Down $3.17

18-D15-6.7
1983 *Le Jardin des Tuileries (The Garden of the Tuileries)*
Issue $26.83; High $26.83; Low $26.83; Close $26.83; No Change

18-D15-6.8
1983 *Le Moulin Rouge (The Moulin Rouge)*
Issue $26.83; High $26.83; Low $26.83; Close $26.83; No Change

18-D15-6.9
1983 *Le Pont Alexandre III (The Alexander III Bridge)*
Issue $26.83; High $26.83; Low $26.83; Close $26.83; No Change

18-D15-6.10
1983 *L'Opéra (The Opera)*
Issue $26.83; High $26.83; Low $26.83; Close $26.83; No Change

18-D15-6.11
1983 *La Tour Eiffel (The Eiffel Tower)*
Issue $26.83; High $26.83; Low $26.83; Close $26.83; No Change

18-D15-6.12
1983 *L'Hôtel de Ville de Paris (The Hotel de Ville de Paris)*
Issue $26.83; High $26.83; Low $26.83; Close $26.83; No Change
Series Closed

Joséphine et Napoléon
(Josephine and Napoleon)

Artist: Claude Boulmé. Artist's signature appears on front

Overglaze-decorated porcelain

Diameter: 21.6 centimeters (8½ inches)

Edition size undisclosed, limited by announced period of issue

Numbered with certificate

18-D15-7.1
1984 *L'Imperatrice Josephine*
(The Empress Josephine)
Issue $29.32; High $65.00; Low $29.32;
Close $45.00; Up $15.68

18-D15-7.2
1984 *Bonaparte traversant les Alpes*
(Bonaparte Crossing the Alps)
Issue $29.32; High $40.00; Low $29.32;
Close $40.00; Up $10.68

18-D15-7.3
1984 *La Rencontre*
(The Meeting)
Issue $29.32; High $29.32; Low $29.32;
Close $29.32; No Change

18-D15-7.4
1985 *Sacre de Napoléon*
(The Coronation)
Issue price: $29.32

Cambier Mother's Day Series

Artist: Guy Cambier. Artist's signature appears on front

Overglaze-decorated porcelain

Diameter: 21.6 centimeters (8½ inches)

No hanger

Edition size undisclosed, limited by year of issue

Numbered with certificate

18-D15-8.1
1983 *Michèle et Sylvie*
Issue $32.84; High $70.00; Low $40.00;
Close $40.00; Down $20.00

18-D15-8.2
1984 *Marie et Jacqueline*
Issue $32.84; High $45.00; Low $32.84;
Close $40.00; Up $7.16

18-D15-8.3
1985 *Monique et François*
Issue Price: $32.84

Gigi Series

Artist: Jean-Claude Guidou. Artist's signature appears on front

Overglaze-decorated porcelain

Diameter: 21.6 centimeters (8½ inches)

No hanger

Edition size undisclosed, limited by announced period of issue

Numbered with certificate

18-D15-9.1
1985 *Gigi*
Issue price: $24.73

In 1839 David Haviland of New York City became the first American importer of Limoges porcelain made from white kaolin clay. When, in 1842, he realized that French factories would not adjust methods to meet the tastes of his American market, Haviland established his own pottery in Limoges.

In 1892 his son, Theodore, left the firm but remained in Limoges to set up Theodore Haviland & Company for production of porcelain dinnerware and decorative pieces. In the 1930s, Theodore Haviland & Company opened an American Haviland factory to produce tableware; the firm also bought the original Haviland & Company established by David Haviland.

All Haviland collector's plates are produced in Limoges, France. *The Twelve Days of Christmas* series, begun in 1970, is based on the carol of the same title. 1979 marked the beginning of the *Mille et Une Nuits* series based on the literary classic *One Thousand One Arabian Nights*.

Adept in a variety of styles, French painter Remy Hétreau is the principal artist for Haviland collector's plates, with two distinctively different series to his credit. Noted watercolorist Liliane Tellier is the creator of the *Mille et Une Nuits* series.

The Twelve Days of Christmas Series

Artist: Remy Hétreau. Artist's signature appears on back

Overglaze-decorated porcelain

Diameter: 21.3 centimeters (8³/₈ inches)

No hanger

Edition size limited to announced quantity of 30,000

Not numbered, without certificate

18-H6-1.1
1970 *A Partridge in a Pear Tree*
Issue $25.00; High $160.00; Low $80.00;
Close $80.00; Down $80.00

18-H6-1.2
1971 *Two Turtle Doves*
Issue $25.00; High $53.00; Low $30.00;
Close $30.00; Down $23.00

18-H6-1.3
1972 *Three French Hens*
Issue $27.50; High $20.00; Low $12.00;
Close $12.00; Down $8.00

18-H6-1.4
1973 *Four Colly Birds*
Issue $28.50; High $22.00; Low $12.00;
Close $12.00; Down $10.00

18-H6-1.5
1974 *Five Golden Rings*
Issue $30.00; High $28.00; Low $15.00;
Close $15.00; Down $13.00

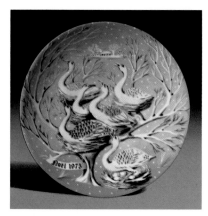

18-H6-1.6
1975 *Six Geese A'Laying*
Issue $32.50; High $25.00; Low $15.00;
Close $15.00; Down $10.00

18-H6-1.7
1976 *Seven Swans A'Swimming*
Issue $38.00; High $36.00; Low $18.00;
Close $18.00; Down $18.00

18-H6-1.8
1977 *Eight Maids A'Milking*
Issue $40.00; High $45.00; Low $40.00;
Close $40.00; No Change

18-H6-1.9
1978 *Nine Ladies Dancing*
Issue $45.00; High $50.00; Low $34.00;
Close $40.00; Up $6.00

18-H6-1.10
1979 *Ten Lords A'Leaping*
Issue $50.00; High $45.00; Low $30.00;
Close $30.00; Down $15.00

18-H6-1.11
1980 *Eleven Pipers Piping*
Issue $55.00; High $52.00; Low $35.00;
Close $45.00; Down $7.00

18-H6-1.12
1981 *Twelve Drummers Drumming*
Issue $60.00; High $60.00; Low $40.00;
Close $60.00; Up $4.00
Series Closed

Mille et Une Nuits

(1001 Arabian Nights)

Artist: Liliane Tellier. Artist's
signature appears on front

Porcelain banded in gold

Diameter: 24.1 centimeters
(9½ inches)

No hanger

Edition size undisclosed, limited
by period of issue

Numbered with certificate

18-H6-4.1
1979 *Le Cheval Magique*
(The Magic Horse)
Issue $54.50; High $65.00; Low $55.00;
Close $55.00; No Change

18-H6-4.2
1980 *Aladin et la Lampe Merveilleuse*
(Aladin and the Wonderful Lamp)
Issue $54.50; High $100.00; Low $75.00;
Close $75.00; Down $10.00

18-H6-4.3
1981 *Scheherazade*
Issue $54.50; High $110.00; Low $54.50;
Close $100.00; Up $45.50

18-H6-4.4
1982 *Sinbad the Sailor*
Issue $54.50; High $75.00; Low $54.50;
Close $70.00; Up $15.50
Series Closed

18-H8-1.1 "Unicorn in Captivity"
1971 Haviland & Parlon *Tapestry*
This series captures the delightful mythical quality and great detail of "The Hunt of the Unicorn," a series of French medieval tapestries now hanging in The Cloisters of New York's Metropolitan Museum of Art.

FRANCE
HAVILAND & PARLON
Limoges

Haviland & Parlon is a chapter in the intricate Haviland porcelain story. In 1853 Robert Haviland left New York City to work for his brother David Haviland in Limoges (see France, HAVILAND). In 1870 Robert's son Charles Field Haviland also established a porcelain factory in Limoges and used "Ch. Field Haviland" as his trade name. After he retired in 1881, the firm was known by several different names until 1942, when Robert Haviland (Robert's great-grandson) purchased it. The firm is now known as Robert Haviland & C. Parlon but retains the "Ch. Field Haviland" trademark.

The *Tapestry* series, begun in 1971, reproduced six scenes from the French medieval tapestries, "The Hunt of the Unicorn," now hanging in the Cloisters of New York's Metropolitan Museum of Art. The *Christmas* series of famous Renaissance Madonnas began in 1972 and ended in 1979; a second *Tapestry* series of six plates began in 1977, reproducing scenes from "The Lady and the Unicorn" tapestries hanging in the Cluny Museum in Paris.

Designs for the *Christmas* series are taken from works by the great masters as indicated.

Tapestry Series

Artist: Unknown. Reproduced from French medieval tapestries

Overglaze-decorated porcelain banded in gold

Diameter: 25.4 centimeters (10 inches)

No hanger

Edition size limited to announced quantity of 10,000

Not numbered, without certificate

18-H8-1.1
1971 *The Unicorn in Captivity*
Issue $35.00; High $158.00; Low $115.00;
Close $120.00; Down $38.00

18-H8-1.2
1972 *Start of the Hunt*
Issue $35.00; High $70.00; Low $35.00;
Close $35.00; Down $35.00

18-H8-1.3
1973 *Chase of the Unicorn*
Issue $35.00; High $130.00; Low $85.00;
Close $100.00; Down $20.00

18-H8-1.4
1974 *End of the Hunt*
Issue $37.50; High $140.00; Low $60.00;
Close $60.00; Down $60.00

18-H8-1.5
1975 *The Unicorn Surrounded*
Issue $40.00; High $78.00; Low $30.00;
Close $40.00; Down $38.00

18-H8-1.6
1976 *The Unicorn Is Brought
to the Castle*
Issue $42.50; High $58.00; Low $35.00;
Close $35.00; Down $23.00
Series Closed

Christmas Series

Artist: as indicated

Overglaze-decorated porcelain banded in gold

Diameter: 25.4 centimeters (10 inches)

No hanger

Edition size: as indicated

Numbered without certificate

18-H8-2.1
1972 Madonna and Child
Artist: Raphael/Edition: 5,000
Issue $35.00; High $100.00; Low $85.00;
Close $90.00; Down $10.00

18-H8-2.2
1973 Madonnina
Artist: Feruzzi/Edition: 5,000
Issue $40.00; High $90.00; Low $78.00;
Close $80.00; Down $10.00

18-H8-2.3
1974 Cowper Madonna and Child
Artist: Raphael/Edition: 5,000
Issue $42.50; High $65.00; Low $35.00;
Close $40.00; Down $25.00

18-H8-2.4
1975 Madonna and Child
Artist: Murillo/Edition: 7,500
Issue $42.50; High $56.00; Low $35.00;
Close $35.00; Down $10.00

18-H8-2.5
1976 Madonna and Child
Artist: Botticelli/Edition: 7,000
Issue $45.00; High $50.00; Low $35.00;
Close $35.00; Down $15.00

18-H8-2.6
1977 Madonna and Child
Artist: Bellini/Edition: 7,500
Issue $48.00; High $40.00; Low $25.00;
Close $38.00; Down $2.00

18-H8-2.7
1978 Madonna and Child
Artist: Fra Filippo Lippi/
Edition: 7,500
Issue $48.00; High $65.00; Low $65.00;
Close $65.00; No Change

18-H8-2.8
1979 Madonna of the Eucharist
Artist: Botticelli/Edition: 7,500
Issue $49.50; High $150.00; Low $105.00;
Close $105.00; Down $45.00
Series Closed

The Lady and the Unicorn Series

Artist: Unknown. Reproduced from French medieval tapestries

Overglaze-decorated porcelain banded in gold

Diameter: 25.4 centimeters (10 inches)

No hanger

Edition size: as indicated

Not numbered, without certificate

18-H8-4.1
1977 To My Only Desire
Edition: 20,000
Issue $45.00; High $60.00; Low $45.00;
Close $50.00; Down $10.00

18-H8-4.2
1978 Sight
Edition: 20,000
Issue $45.00; High $43.00; Low $25.00;
Close $30.00; Down $11.00

18-H8-4.3
1979 Sound
Edition: 20,000
Issue $47.50; High $60.00; Low $40.00;
Close $40.00; Down $11.00

18-H8-4.4
1980 Touch
Edition: 15,000
Issue $52.50; High $110.00; Low $70.00;
Close $70.00; Down $33.00

18-H8-4.5
1981 Scent
Edition: 10,000
Issue $59.00; High $70.00; Low $58.00;
Close $58.00; Down $7.00

18-H8-4.6
1982 Taste
Edition: 10,000
Issue $59.00; High $90.00; Low $65.00;
Close $65.00; Down $15.00
Series Closed

Réné Lalique, founder of the firm that bears his name, began his career as a goldsmith and jeweler in the late nineteenth century. His clients included such notables as Sarah Bernhardt and the dealers Cartier and Boucheron.

In 1902 his interests turned to glassmaking and he acquired a small glassworks at Clairfontaine, France. In 1909 he opened a glass factory near Paris where he produced bottles for the leading Parisian *parfumeurs*, and in 1918 he opened the present Lalique factory in Alsace. Here he began to produce glass items in the Art Deco style. His designs, usually created in pressed glass, are noted for the frosted and satin effects of the glass. Until his death in 1945, Lalique produced numerous commercial glass objects such as perfume bottles, vases and figurines.

Upon Réné's death in 1945, his son Marc—himself a noted artist—inherited the firm and served as its president until his death in 1977. The firm is currently headed by Marc's daughter, Marie-Claude. As Lalique's chief designer she created the *Annual* series of Lalique crystal collector's plates which began in 1965 and ended in 1976.

Annual Series

Artist: Marie-Claude Lalique

Full lead crystal with incised designs

Diameter: 21.6 centimeters (8½ inches)

No hanger

Edition size: as indicated. Announced between 5,000 and 8,000 from 1967 through 1976

Not numbered, without certificate; engraved "Lalique-France" on back

18-L3-1.1
1965 *Deux Oiseaux (Two Birds)*
Edition: 2,000
Issue $25.00; High $1600.00; Low $700.00;
Close $700.00; Down $775.00

18-L3-1.2
1966 *Rose de Songerie (Dream Rose)*
Edition: 5,000
Issue $25.00; High $300.00; Low $200.00;
Close $200.00; Down $100.00

18-L3-1.3
1967 *Ballet de Poisson (Fish Ballet)*
Issue $25.00; High $200.00; Low $140.00;
Close $140.00; Down $60.00

18-L3-1.4
1968 *Gazelle Fantaisie (Gazelle Fantasy)*
Issue $25.00; High $100.00; Low $65.00;
Close $65.00; Down $35.00

18-L3-1.5
1969 *Papillon (Butterfly)*
Issue $30.00; High $100.00; Low $75.00;
Close $75.00; Down $25.00

18-L3-1.6
1970 *Paon (Peacock)*
Issue $30.00; High $105.00; Low $45.00;
Close $55.00; Down $50.00

18-L3-1.7
1971 *Hibou (Owl)*
Issue $35.00; High $80.00; Low $65.00;
Close $65.00; Down $15.00

18-L3-1.8
1972 *Coquillage (Shell)*
Issue $40.00; High $75.00; Low $45.00;
Close $70.00; Down $5.00

18-L3-1.9
197? *Petit Geai (Jayling)*
Issue $42.50; High $60.00; Low $55.00;
Close $50.00; Down $10.00

18-L3-1.10
1974 *Sous d'Argent (Silver Pennies)*
Issue $47.50; High $70.00; Low $55.00;
Close $70.00; No Change

18-L3-1.11
1975 *Duo de Poisson (Fish Duet)*
Issue $50.00; High $85.00; Low $78.00;
Close $80.00; No Change

18-L3-1.12
1976 *Aigle (Eagle)*
Issue $60.00; High $110.00; Low $85.00;
Close $85.00; Down $25.00
Series Closed

18-L52-2.1 "Cinderella"
1983 Limoges-Turgot *Quellier's Morals of Perrault*
Many of today's most beloved children's tales began as serious examples of morality for adults. Such was true of "Cinderella," a tale with origins in 17th century France, here interpreted in the graceful style of that period by André Quellier.

1773 Aut. *L'Intendant*

Porcelaines Limoges-Turgot

The porcelain house of Limoges-Turgot draws upon a tradition of porcelain making which began with A.-R.-J. Turgot, Baron de l'Aulne, Louis XVI's administrator for the Limousin province of which Limoges was the capital. When kaolin clay, the key ingredient in true hard-fire porcelain, was discovered in 1768 at the nearby town of Saint-Yrieix, it was largely due to Turgot's efforts that the Limoges porcelain industry was established and achieved world renown.

Les Enfants de Durand, (Durand's Children Collection), by Paul Durand, began in 1978 and is the first proprietary series by Limoges-Turgot. The series ended in 1980. *Quellier's Morals of Perrault* series, by André Quellier, began in 1983. Their third series, entitled *Children of the Turn of the Century*, was created by Bernard Peltriaux.

Les Enfants de Durand
(Durand's Children)

Artist: Paul Durand. Artist's signature appears on front

Overglaze-decorated porcelain

Diameter: 20.3 centimeters (8 inches)

Attached back hanger

Edition size undisclosed, limited by year of issue

Numbered with certificate

18-L52-1.1
1978 *Marie-Ange*
Issue $36.40; High $38.00; Low $37.00;
Close $37.00; Down $1.00

18-L52-1.2
1979 *Emilie et Philippe*
Issue $36.40; High $40.00; Low $37.00;
Close $37.00; Down $3.00

18-L52-1.3
1980 *Christiane et Fifi*
Issue $36.40; High $45.00; Low $37.00;
Close $37.00; Down $8.00

18-L52-1.4
1980 *Cecile et Raoul*
Issue $36.40; High $65.00; Low $37.00;
Close $37.00; Down $28.00
Series Closed

Quellier's Morals of Perrault Series

Artist: André Quellier. Artist's signature appears on front

Overglaze-decorated porcelain

Diameter: 21.6 centimeters (8½ inches)

No hanger

Edition size undisclosed, limited by announced period of issue

Numbered with certificate

18-L52-2.1
1983 *Cinderella*
Issue $28.67; High $85.00; Low $28.67;
Close $47.00; Up $18.33

18-L52-2.2
1984 *Little Tom Thumb*
Issue $28.67; High $55.00; Low $28.67;
Close $42.00; Up $13.33

18-L52-2.3
1984 *Little Red Riding Hood*
Issue $28.67; High $28.67; Low $28.67;
Close $28.67; No Change

18-L52-2.4
1985 *Sleeping Beauty*
Issue price: $28.67
Series Closed

Les Enfants de la Fin du Siècle de Peltriaux

(Peltriaux's Children of the Turn of the Century)

Artist: Bernard Peltriaux. Artist's signature appears on front

Overglaze-decorated porcelain

Diameter: 21.6 centimeters (8½ inches)

Attached back hanger

Edition size undisclosed, limited by announced period of issue

Numbered with certificate

18-L52-3.1
1985 *Patinage au Trocadéro*
(Skating at the Trocadéro)
Issue price: $24.82

18-L52-3.2
1985 *Petits Voiliers au Bassin des Tuileries (Setting Sail at the Tuileries)*
Issue price: $29.82

22-A3-3.1-1 "Gabriel"
1979 Anna-Perenna *Triptych*
This issue is one of a three-plate set entitled "The Byzantine Triptych." A modern
interpretation of the three-paneled altar-
pieces of the 14th century, called triptychs,
it is the work of husband-and-wife artist
team Frank Russell and Gertrude Barrer.

Named for Anna Perenna, the Roman goddess associated with health, abundance, and the rebirth of spring, Anna-Perenna, Inc. was founded in 1977 by its president, Klaus D. Vogt, exclusively to produce high-quality limited-edition plates in hard-paste porcelain.

Two *Triptych* sets, inspired by the portable altar-pieces of the Middle Ages, were issued in 1979 and 1980. Each three-plate set reinterprets ancient Byzantine religious motifs. In 1979, Anna-Perenna introduced *Romantic Loves*, a four-plate series celebrating great romantic loves of history. Their four-plate series, *Uncle Tad's Cats*, began in 1979 and ended in 1981.

Frank Russell and Gertrude Barrer, the creators of the *Triptych* and the *Romantic Loves* series, are husband-and-wife co-workers who have blended their talents to become a successful art-producing team. Thaddeus Krumeich ("Uncle Tad") is the artist for the *Uncle Tad's Cats* series.

The Triptych Series

Artist: Frank Russell and Gertrude Barrer. Artists' signatures appear on front

Hard-paste porcelain with hinged frame

Diameter: plates one and three, 21.6 cm. (8½ in.); plate two, 24.8 cm (9¾ in.); overall triptych, 88.9 cm. x 45.7 cm. (35 in. x 18 in.) for 1979 set; 83.8 cm. x 38.1 cm. (33 in. x 15 in.) for 1980 set

Attached back hanger

Edition size: 5,000 sets

Individually hand-numbered with certificate

A triptych is a set of three panels hinged side by side, bearing paintings or carvings usually on a religious theme and often used as a portable altarpiece.

22-A3-3.1-1
1979 Gabriel
Issue $325.00; High $130.00; Low $75.00;
Close $75.00; Down $50.00

22-A3-3.1-2
1979 Madonna and Child
The Byzantine Triptych

22-A3-3.1-3
1979 Michael

22-A3-3.2-1
1980 Saul
Issue $350.00; High $350.00; Low $150.00;
Close $150.00; Down $200.00
Series Closed

22-A3-3.2-2
1980 David
The Jerusalem Triptych

22-A3-3.2-3
1980 Solomon

Romantic Loves Series

Artist: Frank Russell and Gertrude Barrer. Artists' signatures appear on front

Hard-paste porcelain banded in gold

Diameter: 25 centimeters (9⅞ inches)

Attached back hanger

Editions size limited to 7,500

Individually hand-numbered with certificate

22-A3-4.1
1979 Romeo and Juliet
Issue $95.00; High $75.00; Low $40.00;
Close $40.00; Down $35.00

22-A3-4.2
1980 Lancelot and Guinevere
Issue $95.00; High $95.00; Low $60.00;
Close $60.00; Down $35.00

22-A3-4.3
1981 Helen and Paris
Issue $95.00; High $95.00; Low $60.00;
Close $60.00; Down $35.00

22-A3-4.4
1982 Lovers of the Taj Mahal
Issue $95.00; High $110.00; Low $80.00;
Close $80.00; Down $15.00
Series Closed

Uncle Tad's Cats Series

Artist: Thaddeus Krumeich.
Artist's signature appears on front

Hard-paste porcelain

Diameter: 24.8 centimeters
(9¾ inches)

Attached back hanger

Edition size limited to 5,000

Individually hand-numbered with
certificate

22-A3-5.1
1979 Oliver's Birthday
Issue $75.00; High $250.00; Low $180.00;
Close $225.00; Up $35.00

22-A3-5.2
1980 Peaches and Cream
Issue $75.00; High $110.00; Low $79.00;
Close $90.00; Up $5.00

22-A3-5.3
1981 Princess Aurora, Queen of the Night
Issue $80.00; High $92.00; Low $60.00;
Close $70.00; Down $7.00

22-A3-5.4
1981 Walter's Window
Issue $85.00; High $100.00; Low $75.00;
Close $100.00; Up $20.00
Series Closed

GERMANY
BAREUTHER
Waldsassen

The Bareuther & Company porcelain factory began to produce dinnerware, vases, and giftware in 1867. The small shop was established with a porcelain kiln and an annular brick kiln by sculptor Johann Matthaeus Ries. In 1884 Ries's son sold the shop to Oskar Bareuther who continued to produce fine tableware.

To observe the one-hundredth anniversary of the factory in 1967, Bareuther began a series of limited-edition *Christmas* plates. A *Father's Day* series, depicting the great castles of Germany, was started in 1969.

Hans Mueller is the principal artist for all Bareuther series.

Christmas Series

Artist: Hans Mueller, except 1971

Porcelain decorated in cobalt blue underglaze

Diameter: 20.3 centimeters
(8 inches)

Pierced foot rim

Edition size limited to announced quantity of 10,000

Not numbered, without certificate

22-B7-1.1
1967 *Stiftskirche*
Issue $12.00; High $125.00; Low $95.00;
Close $120.00; Down $5.00

22-B7-1.2
1968 *Kappl*
Issue $12.00; High $50.00; Low $35.00;
Close $49.00; Up $9.00

22-B7-1.3
1969 *Christkindlesmarkt*
Issue $12.00; High $18.00; Low $10.00;
Close $15.00; Down $3.00

22-B7-1.4
1970 *Chapel in Oberndorf*
Issue $12.50; High $15.00; Low $10.00;
Close $14.00; Down $1.00

22-B7-1.5
1971 *Toys for Sale*
From drawing by Ludwig Richter
Issue $12.75; High $28.00; Low $13.00;
Close $13.00; Down $8.00

22-B7-1.6
1972 *Christmas in Munich*
Issue $14.50; High $40.00; Low $30.00;
Close $40.00; No Change

22-B7-1.7
1973 *Christmas Sleigh Ride*
Issue $15.00; High $30.00; Low $28.00;
Close $30.00; Up $2.00

22-B7-1.8
1974 *Church in the Black Forest*
Issue $19.00; High $30.00; Low $21.00;
Close $25.00; Up $1.00

22-B7-1.9
1975 *Snowman*
Issue $21.50; High $30.00; Low $20.00;
Close $25.00; Down $2.00

22-B7-1.10
1976 *Chapel in the Hills*
Issue $23.50; High $29.00; Low $21.00;
Close $25.00; No Change

22-B7-1.11
1977 *Story Time*
Issue $24.50; High $35.00; Low $30.00;
Close $35.00; No Change

22-B7-1.12
1978 *Mittenwald*
Issue $27.50; High $36.00; Low $30.00;
Close $30.00; Down $6.00

22-B7-1.13
1979 *Winter Day*
Issue $35.00; High $40.00; Low $30.00;
Close $30.00; Down $10.00

22-B7-1.14
1980 *Miltenberg*
Issue $37.50; High $43.00; Low $35.00;
Close $40.00; Down $3.00

22-B7-1.15
1981 *Walk in the Forest*
Issue $39.50; High $40.00; Low $33.00;
Close $33.00; Down $7.00

22-B7-1.16
1982 *Bad Wimpfen*
Issue $39.50; High $45.00; Low $35.00;
Close $35.00; Down $5.00

22-B7-1.17
1983 *The Night Before Christmas*
Issue $39.50; High $48.00; Low $39.50;
Close $42.00; Up $2.50

22-B7-1.18
1984 *Zeil on the River Main*
Issue $42.50; High $43.00; Low $42.50;
Close $43.00; Up $.50

22-B7-1.19
1985 *Winter Wonderland*
Issue price: $42.50

Father's Day Series

Artist: Hans Mueller

Porcelain decorated in cobalt blue underglaze

Diameter: 20.3 centimeters (8 inches)

Pierced foot rim

Edition size limited to announced quantity of 2,500

Not numbered, without certificate

22-B7-2.1
1969 *Castle Neuschwanstein*
Issue $10.50 ; High $50.00; Low $35.00;
Close $45.00; No Change

22-B7-2.2
1970 *Castle Pfalz*
Issue $12.50; High $18.00; Low $11.00;
Close $11.00; Down $7.00

22-B7-2.3
1971 *Castle Heidelberg*
Issue $12.75; High $28.00; Low $20.00;
Close $20.00; Down $8.00

22-B7-2.4
1972 *Castle Hohenschwangau*
Issue $14.50; High $50.00; Low $23.00;
Close $50.00; Up $27.00

22-B7-2.5
1973 *Castle Katz*
Issue $15.00; High $30.00; Low $25.00;
Close $25.00; Down $5.00

22-B7-2.6
1974 *Wurzburg Castle*
Issue $19.00; High $60.00; Low $46.00;
Close $50.00; No Change

22-B7-2.7
1975 *Castle Lichtenstein*
Issue $21.50; High $33.00; Low $27.00;
Close $27.00; Down $6.00

22-B7-2.8
1976 *Castle Hohenzollern*
Issue $23.50; High $30.00; Low $28.00;
Close $28.00; No Change

22-B7-2.9
1977 *Castle Eltz*
Issue $24.50; High $40.00; Low $28.00;
Close $40.00; Up $12.00

22-B7-2.10
1978 *Castle Falkenstein*
Issue $27.50; High $30.00; Low $26.00;
Close $26.00; Down $4.00

22-B7-2.11
1979 *Castle Rheinstein*
Issue $35.00; High $30.00; Low $25.00;
Close $25.00; Down $5.00

22-B7-2.12
1980 *Castle Cochem*
Issue $37.50; High $35.00; Low $31.00;
Close $31.00; Down $4.00

22-B7-2.13
1981 *Castle Gutenfels*
Issue $39.50; High $40.00; Low $40.00;
Close $40.00; No Change

22-B7-2.14
1982 *Castle Zwingenberg*
Issue $39.50; High $40.00; Low $30.00;
Close $30.00; Down $10.00

22-B7-2.15
1983 *Castle Lauenstein*
Issue $39.50; High $40.00; Low $40.00;
Close $40.00; No Change

22-B7-2.16
1984 *Castle Neuenstein*
Issue $42.50; High $44.00; Low $42.50;
Close $43.00; Up $.50

22-B7-2.17
1985 *Castle Wartburg Near Eisenach*
Issue price: $42.50

GERMANY
BERLIN DESIGN
Staffelstein

Berlin Design's limited-edition plates, mugs, and other collectibles are manufactured by the Kaiser Porcelain Company (see Germany, KAISER), and are identified by the distinctive bear-and-crown symbol of the city of Berlin.

The *Christmas* series, introduced in 1970, depicts Yule festivities in German towns. Artists for Berlin Design *Christmas* plates are not disclosed.

Their *Holiday Week of the Family Kappelmann* series began in 1984. It is by artist Detlev Nitschke.

Christmas Series

Artist: Undisclosed

Porcelain decorated in cobalt blue underglaze

Diameter: 19.7 centimeters (7¾ inches)

Pierced foot rim

Edition size: limited to 4,000 in 1970; 20,000 thereafter

Not numbered, without certificate

22-B20-1.1
1970 *Christmas in Bernkastel*
Issue $14.50; High $180.00; Low $110.00;
Close $110.00; Down $70.00

22-B20-1.2
1971 *Christmas in Rothenburg on Tauber*
Issue $14.50; High $40.00; Low $25.00;
Close $40.00; Up $10.00

22-B20-1.3
1972 *Christmas in Michelstadt*
Issue $15.00; High $40.00; Low $35.00;
Close $40.00; Up $5.00

22-B20-1.4
1973 *Christmas in Wendelstein*
Issue $20.00; High $44.00; Low $25.00;
Close $25.00; Down $19.00

22-B20-1.5
1974 *Christmas in Bremen*
Issue $25.00; High $30.00; Low $20.00;
Close $20.00; Down $10.00

22-B20-1.6
1975 *Christmas in Dortland*
Issue $30.00; High $28.00; Low $22.00;
Close $24.00; Down $4.00

22-B20-1.7
1976 *Christmas Eve in Augsburg*
Issue $32.00; High $42.00; Low $20.00;
Close $20.00; Down $15.00

22-B20-1.8
1977 *Christmas Eve in Hamburg*
Issue $32.00; High $40.00; Low $33.00;
Close $35.00; Up $2.00

22-B20-1.9
1978 *Christmas Market at the Dome of Berlin*
Issue $36.00; High $38.00; Low $20.00;
Close $20.00; Down $18.00

22-B20-1.10
1979 *Christmas Eve in Greetsiel*
Issue $47.50; High $52.00; Low $52.00;
Close $52.00; No Change

22-B20-1.11
1980 *Christmas Eve in Miltenberg*
Issue $55.00; High $61.00; Low $60.00;
Close $60.00; Down $1.00

22-B20-1.12
1981 *Christmas Eve in Hahnenklee*
Issue $55.00; High $56.00; Low $50.00;
Close $50.00; Down $6.00

22-B20-1.13
1982 *Christmas Eve in Wasserburg*
Issue $55.00; High $65.00; Low $55.00;
Close $60.00; Up $5.00

22-B20-1.14
1983 *The Chapel in Oberndorf*
Issue $55.00; High $75.00; Low $55.00;
Close $60.00; Up $5.00

22-B20-1.15
1984 *Christmas Eve in Ramsau*
Issue $55.00; High $55.00; Low $55.00;
Close $55.00; No Change

22-B20-1.16
1985 *Christmas Eve in Bad Wimpfen*
Issue price: $55.00

Holiday Week of the Family Kappelmann Series

Artist: Detlev Nitschke. Artist's signature appears on front

Porcelain decorated in cobalt blue underglaze

Diameter: 19 centimeters (7½ inches)

Pierced foot rim

Edition size undisclosed, limited by period of issue

Numbered with certificate

22-B20-4.1
1984 *Monday*
Issue $33.00; High $50.00; Low $33.00;
Close $35.00; Up $2.00

22-B20-4.2
1984 *Tuesday*
Issue $33.00; High $33.00; Low $33.00;
Close $33.00; No Change

22-B20-4.3
1985 *Wednesday*
Issue price: $33.00

22-B20-4.4
1985 *Thursday*
Issue price: $33.00

Goebel

W. Goebel Porzellanfabrik was established in 1871 in Oeslau by Franz-Detleff Goebel and his son William. Headed by Wilhelm Goebel, who represents the fifth generation of the founding family, Goebel produces handcrafted figurines, plates, dinnerware, and gift items.

In 1935 Goebel introduced the famous M. I. Hummel figurines based on sketches by the Franciscan nun. In 1971, to celebrate the one-hundredth anniversary of the firm, Goebel inaugurated an *Annual* series of limited-edition plates with the M. I. Hummel designs.

The Hummel *Anniversary* series began in 1975, with a new plate to be issued every five years.

Hummel Annual Series

Artist: Sister M. I. Hummel.
Artist's signature appears on front

Stoneware with hand-painted bas-relief

Diameter: 19 centimeters
(7½ inches)

Pierced foot rim

Edition size undisclosed, limited by year of issue

Not numbered, without certificate

22-G54-1.1
1971 *Heavenly Angel*
Issue $25.00; High $850.00; Low $700.00;
Close $700.00; Down $75.00

22-G54-1.2
1972 *Hear Ye, Hear Ye*
Issue $30.00; High $75.00; Low $55.00;
Close $55.00; Down $20.00

22-G54-1.3
1973 *Globe Trotter*
Issue $32.50; High $160.00; Low $120.00;
Close $120.00; Down $30.00

22-G54-1.4
1974 *Goose Girl*
Issue $40.00; High $110.00; Low $70.00;
Close $80.00; Down $20.00

22-G54-1.5
1975 *Ride into Christmas*
Issue $50.00; High $90.00; Low $70.00;
Close $70.00; Down $20.00

22-G54-1.6
1976 *Apple Tree Girl*
Issue $50.00; High $92.00; Low $79.00;
Close $80.00; Down $12.00

22-G54-1.7
1977 *Apple Tree Boy*
Issue $50.00; High $108.00; Low $85.00;
Close $90.00; Down $18.00

22-G54-1.8
1978 *Happy Pastime*
Issue $65.00; High $90.00; Low $60.00;
Close $60.00; Down $30.00

22-G54-1.9
1979 *Singing Lesson*
Issue $90.00; High $65.00; Low $50.00;
Close $50.00; Down $15.00

22-G54-1.10
1980 *School Girl*
Issue $100.00; High $80.00; Low $59.00;
Close $59.00; Down $21.00

22-G54-1.11
1981 *Umbrella Boy*
Issue $100.00; High $90.00; Low $60.00;
Close $70.00; Down $20.00

22-G54-1.12
1982 *Umbrella Girl*
Issue $100.00; High $140.00; Low $100.00;
Close $130.00; Up $30.00

22-G54-1.13
1983 *The Postman*
Issue $108.00; High $160.00; Low $108.00;
Close $135.00; Up $27.00

22-G54-1.14
1984 *Little Helper*
Issue $108.00; High $125.00; Low $95.00;
Close $95.00; Down $13.00

22-G54-1.15
1985 *Chick Girl*
Issue price: $110.00

Hummel Anniversary Series

Artist: Sister M. I. Hummel. Artist's signature appears on front

Stoneware with hand-painted bas-relief

Diameter: 25.4 centimeters (10 inches)

Pierced foot rim

Edition size undisclosed, limited by year of issue

Not numbered, without certificate

22-G54-3.1
1975 *Stormy Weather*
Issue $100.00; High $175.00; Low $150.00;
Close $175.00; Up $5.00

22-G54-3.2
1980 *Spring Dance*
Issue $225.00; High $135.00; Low $100.00;
Close $100.00; Down $35.00

22-G54-3.3
1985 *Auf Wiedersehen*
Issue price: $225.00
Series Closed

The history of Heinrich Porzellan dates from the opening by Franz Heinrich of a porcelain-painting studio in 1896 in Selb, Bavaria, near the Czechoslovakian border. In 1901, Heinrich established his own porcelain factory, Heinrich & Co., which produced fine table- and giftware. The firm remained under the control of the Heinrich family until 1976, when it was purchased by Villeroy & Boch. Heinrich creations are now distributed worldwide through Villeroy & Boch's marketing channels.

From 1980 thru 1983, Heinrich issued a twelve-plate series of porcelain plates entitled *Russian Fairy Tales*, adapted from the artwork of famous Russian illustrator Boris Zvorykin. The *Fairies of the Fields and Flowers* series began in 1982, with artwork by Cicely Mary Barker. The *Once Upon a Rhyme* series began in 1984, featuring for the first time the work of an American artist, Renee Faure.

Russian Fairy Tales Series

Artist: Boris Zvorykin

Hard-paste porcelain banded in gold

Diameter: 21 centimeters (8¼ inches)

No hanger

Edition size limited to 27,500

Not numbered, with certificate

22-H18-1.1
1980 *The Snow Maiden*
Issue $70.00; High $160.00; Low $130.00;
Close $160.00; Up $30.00

22-H18-1.2
1980 *The Snow Maiden at the Court of Tsar Berendei*
Issue $70.00; High $95.00; Low $70.00;
Close $75.00; Down $15.00

22-H18-1.3
1980 *The Snow Maiden and Lel the Shepherd Boy*
Issue $70.00; High $90.00; Low $79.00;
Close $79.00; Down $11.00

22-H18-1.4
1981 *The Red Knight*
Issue $70.00; High $85.00; Low $65.00;
Close $70.00; Down $8.00

22-H18-1.5
1981 *Vassilissa and Her Stepsisters*
Issue $70.00; High $87.00; Low $75.00;
Close $78.00; Up $3.00

22-H18-1.6
1981 *Vassilissa Is Presented to the Tsar*
Issue $70.00; High $85.00; Low $65.00;
Close $65.00; Down $10.00

22-H18-1.7
1982 *In Search of the Firebird*
Issue $70.00; High $100.00; Low $72.00;
Close $72.00; Down $28.00

22-H18-1.8
1982 *Ivan and Tsarevna on the Grey Wolf*
Issue $70.00; High $100.00; Low $70.00;
Close $70.00; Down $30.00

22-H18-1.9
1982 *The Wedding of Tsarevna Elena the Fair*
Issue $70.00; High $85.00; Low $75.00; Close $80.00; Down $5.00

22-H18-1.10
1983 *Maria Morevna and Tsarevich Ivan*
Issue $70.00; High $75.00; Low $70.00; Close $72.00; Up $2.00

22-H18-1.11
1983 *Koshchey Carries off Maria Morevna*
Issue $70.00; High $75.00; Low $70.00; Close $75.00; Up $5.00

22-H18-1.12
1983 *Tsarevich Ivan and the Beautiful Castle*
Issue $70.00; High $85.00; Low $70.00; Close $75.00; Up $5.00
Series Closed

Fairies of the Fields and Flowers Series

Artist: Cicely Mary Barker

Bone china banded in 24k gold

Diameter: 21.6 centimeters (8½ inches)

Attached back hanger

Edition size undisclosed, limited by announced period of issue

Numbered with certificate

22-H18-3.1
1982 *Ragged Robin*
Issue $49.00; High $55.00; Low $40.00;
Close $50.00; Down $5.00

22-H18-3.2
1983 *Willow*
Issue $49.00; High $50.00; Low $45.00;
Close $50.00; Up $1.00

22-H18-3.3
1984 *Elderberry*
Issue $49.00; High $49.00; Low $40.00;
Close $40.00; Down $9.00

22-H18-3.4
1984 *Vetch*
Issue $49.00; High $52.00; Low $45.00;
Close $50.00; Up $1.00

22-H18-3.5
1984 *Narcissus*
Issue $49.00; High $55.00; Low $49.00;
Close $55.00; Up $6.00

22-H18-3.6
1985 *Nasturtium*
Issue price: $49.00

22-H18-3.7
1985 *Phlox*
Issue price: $49.00

22-H18-3.8
1985 *Gorse*
Issue price: $49.00
Series Closed

Once Upon a Rhyme Series

Artist: Renée Faure. Artist's signature appears on front

Overglaze-decorated porcelain

Diameter: 19.7 centimeters (7¾ inches)

Attached back hanger

Edition size undisclosed, limited by announced period of issue

Numbered with certificate

22-H18-4.1
1984 *Roses Are Red*
Issue $35.00; High $35.00; Low $35.00;
Close $35.00; No Change

22-H18-4.2
1985 *A Tisket, a Tasket*
Issue price: $35.00

22-H31-1.2 ''David, Bathsheba and Solomon''
1980 Hibel Studio *David*
A magnificent example of Edna Hibel's celebrated gift for portraiture, this plate is unusual among Hibel works, so few of which feature male subjects. It also demonstrates the beauty of the lavish gold overlay which is so characteristic of her work.

GERMANY
HIBEL STUDIO
Staffelstein

Hibel Studio was founded in 1976. Headquartered in Riviera Beach, Florida, the studio specializes in original stone lithographs, lithographs on porcelain, and limited-edition collector's plates. All artwork is approved by Edna Hibel, and plates are made by Kaiser Porcelain and Rosenthal China (see Germany, KAISER, ROSENTHAL).

Hibel Studio began its first series of collector's plates, the *David* series, in 1979. The four-plate series, with artwork by Edna Hibel, is based on the biblical story of King David.

David Series

Artist: Edna Hibel. Artist's signature appears on front

Porcelain highlighted and banded in gold

Diameter: 25.7 centimeters (10⅛ inches)

Pierced foot rim

Edition size limited to 5,000

Numbered with certificate

22-H31-1.1
1979 *The Wedding of David and Bathsheba*
Issue $250.00; High $300.00; Low $200.00;
Close $300.00; Up $100.00

22-H31-1.2
1980 *David, Bathsheba and Solomon*
Issue $275.00; High $275.00; Low $225.00;
Close $225.00; Down $50.00

22-H31-1.3
1982 *David the King*
Issue $275.00; High $300.00; Low $250.00;
Close $300.00; Up $25.00

22-H31-1.4
1983 *Bathsheba*
Issue $275.00; High $275.00; Low $275.00;
Close $275.00; No Change
Series Closed

Hutschenreuther has produced limited-edition collector's plates since 1973, when they introduced their *Canada Christmas* series (not U.S. Bradex-listed). The *Love for All Seasons* series was issued in 1982 and 1983 and depicts six scenes of medieval romance as portrayed by the artist team of Charlotte and William Hallett.

Love for All Seasons Series

Artist: Charlotte and William Hallett. Artists' signatures appear on back

Hard-paste porcelain with gold design on border

Diameter: 20.3 centimeters (8 inches)

Attached back hanger

Edition size limited to 10,000

Not numbered, without certificate

22-H82-6.1
1982 *The Minstrel Song*
Issue $125.00; High $125.00; Low $120.00;
Close $120.00; Down $5.00

22-H82-6.2
1982 *Affection*
Issue $125.00; High $149.00; Low $125.00;
Close $125.00; No Change

22-H82-6.3
1982 *The Tournament*
Issue $125.00; High $127.00; Low $125.00;
Close $125.00; No Change

22-H82-6.4
1983 *The Falcon Hunt*
Issue $125.00; High $180.00; Low $125.00;
Close $125.00; No Change

22-H82-6.5
1983 *Winter Romance*
Issue $125.00; High $150.00; Low $125.00;
Close $125.00; No Change

22-H82-6.6
1983 *The Ride Out*
Issue $125.00; High $145.00; Low $125.00;
Close $135.00; Up $10.00
Series Closed

GERMANY
KAISER
Staffelstein

Kaiser porcelain dates to 1872 when porcelain painter August Alboth set up his own workshop in Coburg. When he retired in 1899, his son Ernst moved the pottery to Bavaria. Marriage united the Alboth and Kaiser families in 1922, resulting in the ALKA trademark—a combination of the first two letters of both names.

In 1938 the firm purchased the old Bavarian pottery of Silbermann Brothers, which had been awarded a royal diploma in 1882 for its "magnificent" cobalt blue underglaze. The company opened its modern factory in Staffelstein in 1953 and in 1970 the trademark was changed to Kaiser Porcelain.

Long a producer of porcelain coffee sets, dinnerware, and figurines, Kaiser introduced its first series of limited-edition plates, the *Christmas* series, in 1970. The series ended in 1982. The *Mother's Day* series began in 1971 and ended in 1983. These series feature the artwork of Toni Schoener and Nori Peter. The *Classic Fairy Tales Collection* began in 1982, with artwork by Gerda Neubacher.

Christmas Series

Artist: as indicated

Porcelain decorated in cobalt blue underglaze

Diameter: 19 centimeters (7½ inches)

Pierced foot rim

Edition size undisclosed, limited by year of issue except 1974

Not numbered, without certificate

22-K4-1.1
1970 *Waiting for Santa Claus*
Artist: Toni Schoener
Issue $12.50; High $35.00; Low $23.00;
Close $30.00; Down $4.00

22-K4-1.2
1971 *Silent Night*
Artist: Kurt Bauer
Issue $13.50; High $25.00; Low $13.00;
Close $13.00; Down $12.00

22-K4-1.3
1972 *Welcome Home*
Artist: Kurt Bauer
Issue $16.50; High $16.00; Low $14.00;
Close $14.00; Down $2.00

22-K4-1.4
1973 *Holy Night*
Artist: Toni Schoener
Issue $18.00; High $43.00; Low $35.00;
Close $40.00; Down $3.00

22-K4-1.5
1974 *Christmas Carolers*
Artist: Kurt Bauer/Edition: 8,000
Issue $25.00; High $34.00; Low $28.00;
Close $29.00; Down $5.00

22-K4-1.6
1975 *Bringing Home the Christmas Tree*
Artist: Joann Northcott
Issue $25.00; High $25.00; Low $18.00;
Close $18.00; Down $7.00

22-K4-1.7
1976 *Christ the Saviour Is Born*
Artist: Carlo Maratti
Issue $25.00; High $20.00; Low $17.00;
Close $17.00; Down $3.00

22-K4-1.8
1977 *The Three Kings*
Artist: Toni Schoener
Issue $25.00; High $20.00; Low $15.00;
Close $20.00; Up $4.00

22-K4-1.9
1978 *Shepherds in the Field*
Artist: Toni Schoener
Issue $30.00; High $23.00; Low $14.00;
Close $14.00; Down $6.00

22-K4-1.10
1979 *Christmas Eve*
Artist: Hannelore Blum
Issue $32.00; High $24.00; Low $17.00;
Close $18.00; Down $6.00

22-K4-1.11
1980 *Joys of Winter*
Artist: Hannelore Blum
Issue $40.00; High $40.00; Low $25.00;
Close $25.00; Down $8.00

22-K4-1.12
1981 *Most Holy Night*
Artist: Kurt Bauer
Issue $40.00; High $43.00; Low $43.00;
Close $43.00; No Change

22-K4-1.13
1982 *Bringing Home the Christmas Tree*
Artist: Kurt Bauer
Issue $40.00; High $40.00; Low $35.00;
Close $35.00; No Change
Series Closed

Mother's Day Series

Artist: as indicated

Porcelain decorated in cobalt blue underglaze

Diameter: 19 centimeters
(7½ inches)

Pierced foot rim

Edition size undisclosed, limited by year of issue except 1974

Not numbered, without certificate

22-K4-2.1
1971 *Mare and Foal*
Artist: Toni Schoener
Issue $13.00; High $35.00; Low $20.00;
Close $25.00; Down $10.00

22-K4-2.2
1972 *Flowers for Mother*
Artist: Toni Schoener
Issue $16.50; High $20.00; Low $15.00;
Close $15.00; Down $5.00

22-K4-2.3
1973 *Cats*
Artist: Toni Schoener
Issue $17.00; High $40.00; Low $26.00;
Close $35.00; Up $9.00

22-K4-2.4
1974 *Fox*
Artist: Toni Schoener/Edition: 7,000
Issue $22.00; High $44.00; Low $16.00;
Close $44.00; Up $28.00

22-K4-2.5
1975 *German Shepherd*
Artist: Toni Schoener
Issue $25.00; High $51.00; Low $50.00;
Close $50.00; No Change

22-K4-2.6
1976 *Swan and Cygnets*
Artist: Toni Schoener
Issue $25.00; High $15.00; Low $12.00;
Close $12.00; Down $3.00

22-K4-2.7
1977 *Mother Rabbit and Young*
Artist: Toni Schoener
Issue $25.00; High $35.00; Low $15.00;
Close $35.00; Up $20.00

22-K4-2.8
1978 *Hen and Chicks*
Artist: Toni Schoener
Issue $30.00; High $25.00; Low $15.00;
Close $15.00; No Change

22-K4-2.9
1979 *A Mother's Devotion*
Artist: Nori Peter
Issue $32.00; High $24.00; Low $21.00;
Close $21.00; Down $3.00

22-K4-2.10
1980 *Raccoon Family*
Artist: Joann Northcott
Issue $40.00; High $40.00; Low $35.00;
Close $35.00; Down $3.00

22-K4-2.11
1981 *Safe Near Mother*
Artist: Hannelore Blum
Issue $40.00; High $36.00; Low $35.00;
Close $35.00; Down $1.00

22-K4-2.12
1982 *Pheasant Family*
Artist: Kurt Bauer
Issue $40.00; High $40.00; Low $40.00;
Close $40.00; No Change

22-K4-2.13
1983 *Tender Care*
Artist: Kurt Bauer
Issue $40.00; High $40.00; Low $40.00;
Close $40.00; No Change
Series Closed

Classic Fairy Tales Collection

Artist: Gerda Neubacher. Artist's signature appears on front

Porcelain banded in 24k gold

Diameter: 19.7 centimeters (7¾ inches)

Pierced foot rim

Edition size undisclosed, limited by announced period of issue

Numbered without certificate

22-K4-5.1
1982 *The Frog King*
Issue $39.50; High $50.00; Low $40.00;
Close $40.00; Down $10.00

22-K4-5.2
1983 *Puss in Boots*
Issue $39.50; High $50.00; Low $39.50;
Close $40.00; Up $.50

22-K4-5.3
1983 *Little Red Riding Hood*
Issue $39.50; High $42.00; Low $39.50;
Close $40.00; Up $.50

22-K4-5.4
1983 *Hansel and Gretel*
Issue $39.50; High $39.50; Low $39.50;
Close $39.50; No Change

22-K4-5.5
1984 *Cinderella*
Issue $39.50; High $39.50; Low $39.50;
Close $39.50; No Change

22-K4-5.6
1984 *Sleeping Beauty*
Issue $39.50; High $39.50; Low $39.50;
Close $39.50; No Change
Series Closed

22-K46-1.1 "The Adoration"
1979 Königszelt Bayern *Hedi Keller*
Christmas
A dramatic, semi-primitive style highlights
all of Hedi Keller's work. Here, she draws
on forms from nature to create her own
retelling of episodes from the life of
Christ.

GERMANY
KÖNIGSZELT BAYERN
Waldsassen

Königszelt Bayern entered the collector's plate market in 1979 with the first issue in its *Hedi Keller Christmas* series, more than a century after the creation of the first porcelain bearing the hallmark of Königszelt of Silesia. The likeness of Wilhelm I (1797-1888), king of Prussia and first sovereign of a united Germany, is incorporated in the hallmark of Königszelt Bayern—a tribute to his early patronage under which Bavarian porcelain began its rise to prominence among the porcelain creations of the world. In 1981 the *Grimm's Fairy Tales* series began in commemoration of the two-hundredth anniversary of the Grimm brothers' birth, with art by Charles Gehm. *Sulamith's Love Song* series, created by Sulamith Wülfing, began in 1982. Her *Christmas* series made its debut in 1985. The *German Half-Timbered Houses* series, by Karl Bedal, was introduced in 1984.

GERMANY
KÖNIGSZELT BAYERN

Hedi Keller Christmas Series

Artist: Hedi Keller. Artist's signature appears on front

Overglaze-decorated porcelain

Diameter: 24 centimeters (9½ inches)

Pierced foot rim

Edition size unannounced

Numbered with certificate

22-K46-1.1
1979 *The Adoration*
Issue $29.50; High $100.00; Low $45.00;
Close $45.00; Down $30.00

22-K46-1.2
1980 *Flight into Egypt*
Issue $29.50; High $65.00; Low $45.00;
Close $45.00; Down $15.00

22-K46-1.3
1981 *Return into Galilee*
Issue $29.50; High $45.00; Low $40.00;
Close $40.00; No Change

22-K46-1.4
1982 *Following the Star*
Issue $29.50; High $50.00; Low $45.00;
Close $45.00; Down $5.00

22-K46-1.5
1983 *Rest on the Flight*
Issue $29.50; High $42.00; Low $29.50;
Close $40.00; Up $10.50

22-K46-1.6
1984 *The Nativity*
Issue $29.50; High $60.00; Low $29.50;
Close $50.00; Up $20.50

22-K46-1.7
1985 *Gift of the Magi*
Issue price: $34.50

Grimm's Fairy Tale Series

Artist: Charles Gehm. Artist's signature appears on front

Overglaze-decorated porcelain

Diameter: 19 centimeters (7½ inches)

Pierced foot rim

Edition size undisclosed, limited by period of issue

Numbered with certificate

22-K46-2.1
1981 *Rumpelstilzchen*
Issue $23.00; High $30.00; Low $24.00;
Close $24.00; Down $1.00

22-K46-2.2
1982 *Rapunzel*
Issue $25.00; High $40.00; Low $29.00;
Close $35.00; No Change

22-K46-2.3
1982 *Hänsel and Gretel*
Issue $25.00; High $70.00; Low $25.00;
Close $45.00; Up $20.00

22-K46-2.4
1983 *The Shoemaker and the Elves*
Issue $25.00; High $49.00; Low $25.00;
Close $35.00; Up $10.00

22-K46-2.5
1984 *The Golden Goose*
Issue $29.00; High $29.00; Low $29.00;
Close $29.00; No Change

Sulamith's Love Song Series

Artist: Sulamith Wülfing. Artist's signature appears on front

Overglaze-decorated porcelain

Diameter: 19 centimeters (7½ inches)

Pierced foot rim

Edition size undisclosed, limited by announced period of issue

Numbered with certificate

22-K46-3.1
1982 *The Music*
Issue $29.00; High $60.00; Low $35.00;
Close $35.00; Down $15.00

22-K46-3.2
1983 *The Pledge*
Issue $29.00; High $60.00; Low $29.00;
Close $43.00; Up $14.00

22-K46-3.3
1983 *The Vision*
Issue $29.00; High $40.00; Low $29.00;
Close $40.00; Up $11.00

22-K46-3.4
1983 *The Gift*
Issue $29.00; High $42.00; Low $29.00;
Close $42.00; Up $13.00

22-K46-3.5
1984 *The Circle*
Issue $29.00; High $29.00; Low $29.00;
Close $29.00; No Change

22-K46-3.6
1984 *The Centre*
Issue $29.00; High $29.00; Low $29.00;
Close $29.00; No Change

22-K46-3.7
1984 *The Journey*
Issue $29.00; High $29.00; Low $29.00;
Close $29.00; No Change

22-K46-3.8
1984 *The Completion*
Issue $29.00; High $29.00; Low $29.00;
Close $29.00; No Change
Series Closed

Deutsches Fachwerk
(German Half-Timbered Houses)

Artist: Karl Bedal. Artist's signature appears on front

Overglaze-decorated porcelain

Diameter: 19 centimeters (7½ inches)

Pierced foot rim

Edition size undisclosed, limited by announced period of issue

Numbered with certificate

22-K46-4.1
1984 *Bauernhaus in Fronhausen*
Issue $24.00; High $44.00; Low $24.00;
Close $40.00; Up $16.00

22-K46-4.2
1984 *Niedersachsenhaus bei Thedinghausen*
Issue $24.00; High $24.00; Low $24.00;
Close $24.00; No Change

22-K46-4.3
1985 *Moselhaus in Rißbach*
Issue price: $27.00

Sulamith's Christmas Series

Artist: Sulamith Wülfing. Artist's signature appears on front

Overglaze-decorated porcelain double-banded in 24k gold

Diameter: 24.1 centimeters (9½ inches)

No hanger

Edition size undisclosed, limited by year of issue

Numbered with certificate

22-K46-5.1
1985 *The Angels' Vigil*
Issue price: $35.00

22-R55-1.1 "Winter Peace"
1910 Rosenthal *Christmas*
Although Rosenthal had produced some Christmas issues prior to 1910, this plate was the first plate of the first series to bear the Rosenthal name exclusively. In its subtle introduction of a second color—yellow—to the familiar blue-and-white underglaze style, it creates a unique look which has survived to the present day.

GERMANY
ROSENTHAL

Selb, Rothbühl, Kronach, Amberg, Bad Soden,
Landstuhl, Thomas Kulm, Waldershofen

Philipp Rosenthal, Sr. began his business in 1879 in the town of Selb in Bavaria. He initially purchased "white ware" from various porcelain manufacturers in Selb (including Hutschenreuther) and painted it with his own designs.

In 1895 he established his own factory in Kronach where he produced fine porcelain signed *Rosenthal* on the back, making him one of the first porcelain makers to use his name rather than a symbol. Philipp died in 1937 and the business was taken over by his son, Philipp, Jr., who still heads the firm.

Rosenthal's *Traditional Classic Rose Christmas* series began in 1910 and continues through 1984. In 1974, Rosenthal changed its backstamp to reflect their Classic Rose Collection. From 1969 to 1971 some of the earlier plates were reissued in small quantities (no more than 500 per reissue). Reissued plates, regardless of the year de-picted, have a post-1957 backstamp and their foot rims are not pierced. After 1971, the firm discontinued the practice of reissuing plates from previous years, and each Rosenthal collector's plate is now produced only during its current year. The *Traditional Classic Rose Christmas* plates now qualify as limited editions.

In 1971 Rosenthal began the first of its Studio-Linie collections with the *Wiinblad Christmas* series, by noted designer Bjorn Wiinblad. These plates carry intricate modern designs partially hand-painted in as many as eighteen colors and are embellished with platinum and 18k gold. The *Nobility of Children* series and the *Oriental Gold* series also began in 1976 and carried Rosenthal's Classic Rose Collection backstamp. Both series ended in 1979. They featured the artwork of Edna Hibel.

*Traditional Classic Rose
Christmas Series*

Artist: as indicated. Artist's name
appears on back

Overglaze-decorated porcelain,
many in series have gold inner rim
and lettering

Diameter: 21.6 centimeters
(8½ inches)

Pierced foot rim until 1971,
attached back hanger thereafter

Edition size undisclosed

Not numbered, without certificate

22-R55-1.1
1910 *Winter Peace*
Artist: Jul V. Guldbrandson
Issue price: $1.34

22-R55-1.2
1911 *The Three Wise Men*
Artist: Heinrich Vogoler
Issue price: $1.95

22-R55-1.3
1912 *Shooting Stars*
Artist: Paul Rieth
Issue price: $1.03

22-R55-1.4
1913 *Christmas Lights*
Artist: Julius Dietz
Issue price: $1.47

22-R55-1.5
1914 *Christmas Song*
Artist: Prof. Ludwig von Zumbusch
Issue price: $1.47

22-R55-1.6
1915 *Walking to Church*
Artist: Jul V. Guldbrandson
Issue price: $1.47

22-R55-1.7
1916 *Christmas During War*
Artist: Jul V. Guldbrandson
Issue price: $1.47

22-R55-1.8
1917 *Angel of Peace*
Artist: Prof. Mermagen
Issue price: $1.47

22-R55-1.9
1918 *Peace on Earth*
Artist: K. Pfeiffer
Issue price: $1.47

22-R55-1.10
1919 *St. Christopher with the Christ Child*
Artist: Dr. W. Schertel
Issue price: $5.96

22-R55-1.11
1920 *The Manger in Bethlehem*
Artist: Dr. W. Schertel
Issue price: $5.96

22-R55-1.12
1921 *Christmas in the Mountains*
Artist: Jupp Wiertz
Issue price: $5.96

22-R55-1.13
1922 *Advent Branch*
Artist: Friedrich Nicolai
Issue price: $5.96

22-R55-1.14
1923 *Children in the Winter Wood*
Artist: Ernst Hofer
Issue price: $5.96

22-R55-1.15
1924 *Deer in the Woods*
Artist: Theo Karner
Issue price: $2.98

22-R55-1.16
1925 *The Three Wise Men*
Artist: Otto Tauscheck
Issue price: $2.98

22-R55-1.17
1926 *Christmas in the Mountains*
Artist: Theo Schmutz-Baudiss
Issue price: $2.98

22-R55-1.18
1927 *Station on the Way*
Artist: Theo Schmutz-Baudiss
Issue price: $2.98

22-R55-1.19
1928 *Chalet Christmas*
Artist: Heinrich Fink
Issue price: $2.98

22-R55-1.20
1929 *Christmas in the Alps*
Artist: Heinrich Fink
Issue price: $2.98

22-R55-1.21
1930 *Group of Deer under the Pines*
Artist: Theo Karner
Issue price: $2.98

22-R55-1.22
1931 *Path of the Magi*
Artist: Heinrich Fink
Issue price: $3.09

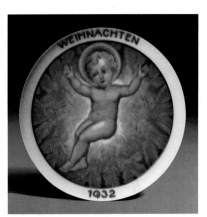

22-R55-1.23
1932 *Christ Child*
Artist: Otto Koch
Issue price: $3.09

22-R55-1.24
1933 *Through the Night to Light*
Artist: Hans Schiffner
Issue price: $3.09

22-R55-1.25
1934 *Christmas Peace*
Artist: Heinrich Fink
Issue price: $3.09

22-R55-1.26
1935 *Christmas by the Sea*
Artist: Heinrich Fink
Issue price: $3.09

22-R55-1.27
1936 *Nurnberg Angel*
Artist: Heinrich Fink
Issue price: $3.09

22-R55-1.28
1937 *Berchtesgaden*
Artist: Heinrich Fink
Issue price: $3.09

22-R55-1.29
1938 *Christmas in the Alps*
Artist: Heinrich Fink
Issue price: $3.09

22-R55-1.30
1939 *Schneekoppe Mountain*
Artist: Heinrich Fink
Issue price: $3.09

22-R55-1.31
1940 *Marien Church in Danzig*
Artist: Walter Mutze
Issue price: $3.09

22-R55-1.32
1941 *Strassburg Cathedral*
Artist: Walter Mutze
Issue price: $3.09

22-R55-1.33
1942 *Marianburg Castle*
Artist: Walter Mutze
Issue price: $3.09

22-R55-1.34
1943 *Winter Idyll*
Artist: Amadeus Dier
Issue price: $3.09

22-R55-1.35
1944 *Wood Scape*
Artist: Willi Hein
Issue price: $3.09

22-R55-1.36
1945 *Christmas Peace*
Artist: Alfred Mundel
Issue price: $3.09

22-R55-1.37
1946 *Christmas in an Alpine Valley*
Artist: Willi Hein
Issue price: $3.09

22-R55-1.38
1947 *The Dillingen Madonna*
Artist: Louis Hagen
Issue price: $6.00

22-R55-1.39
1948 *Message to the Shepherds*
Artist: Richard Hoffman
Issue price: $6.00

22-R55-1.40
1949 *The Holy Family*
Artist: Prof. Karl
Issue price: $6.00

22-R55-1.41
1950 *Christmas in the Forest*
Artist: Willi Hein
Issue price: $5.25

22-R55-1.42
1951 *Star of Bethlehem*
Artist: Anne V. Groote
Issue price: $5.75

22-R55-1.43
1952 *Christmas in the Alps*
Artist: Willi Hein
Issue price: $5.75

22-R55-1.44
1953 *The Holy Light*
Artist: Willi Hein
Issue price: $5.75

22-R55-1.45
1954 *Christmas Eve*
Artist: Willi Hein
Issue price: $6.25

22-R55-1.46
1955 *Christmas in a Village*
Artist: Willi Hein
Issue price: $6.25

22-R55-1.47
1956 *Christmas in the Alps*
Artist: Willi Hein
Issue price: $6.25

22-R55-1.48
1957 *Christmas by the Sea*
Artist: Willi Hein
Issue price: $6.25

22-R55-1.49
1958 *Christmas Eve*
Artist: Willi Hein
Issue price: $6.50

22-R55-1.50
1959 *Midnight Mass*
Artist: Willi Hein
Issue price: $6.75

22-R55-1.51
1960 *Christmas in Small Village*
Artist: Willi Hein
Issue price: $7.25

22-R55-1.52
1961 *Solitary Christmas*
Artist: Willi Hein
Issue price: $7.75

22-R55-1.53
1962 *Christmas Eve*
Artist: Willi Hein
Issue price: $8.75

22-R55-1.54
1963 *Silent Night*
Artist: Willi Hein
Issue price: $8.75

22-R55-1.55
1964 *Christmas Market in Nurnberg*
Artist: Georg Küspert
Issue price: $8.75

22-R55-1.56
1965 *Christmas in Munich*
Artist: Georg Küspert
Issue price: $11.00

22-R55-1.57
1966 *Christmas in Ulm*
Artist: Georg Küspert
Issue price: $11.00

22-R55-1.58
1967 *Christmas in Regensburg*
Artist: Georg Küspert
Issue price: $11.00

22-R55-1.59
1968 *Christmas in Bremen*
Artist: Georg Küspert
Issue price: $11.00

22-R55-1.60
1969 *Christmas in Rothenburg*
Artist: Georg Küspert
Issue price: $15.75

22-R55-1.61
1970 *Christmas in Cologne*
Artist: Georg Küspert
Issue price: $16.00

22-R55-1.62
1971 *Christmas in Garmisch*
Artist: Georg Küspert
Issue $66.00; High $90.00; Low $80.00;
Close $80.00; Down $10.00

22-R55-1.63
1972 *Christmas Celebration in Franconia*
Artist: Georg Küspert
Issue $66.00; High $99.00; Low $75.00;
Close $75.00; Down $24.00

22-R55-1.64
1973 *Christmas in Lübeck-Holstein*
Artist: Georg Küspert
Issue $84.00; High $110.00; Low $105.00;
Close $108.00; Up $3.00

22-R55-1.65
1974 *Christmas in Wurzburg*
Artist: Georg Küspert
Issue $85.00; High $100.00; Low $100.00;
Close $100.00; No Change

22-R55-1.66
1974 *Memorial Church in Berlin*
Artist: Helmut Drexler
Issue $84.00; High $200.00; Low $200.00;
Close $200.00; No Change

22-R55-1.67
1975 *Freiburg Cathedral*
Artist: Helmut Drexler
Issue $75.00; High $100.00; Low $100.00;
Close $100.00; No Change

22-R55-1.68
1976 *The Castle Cochem*
Artist: Helmut Drexler
Issue $95.00; High $80.00; Low $78.00;
Close $78.00; Down $2.00

22-R55-1.69
1977 *Hannover Town Hall*
Artist: Helmut Drexler
Issue $125.00; High $115.00; Low $110.00;
Close $110.00; No Change

22-R55-1.70
1978 *Cathedral at Aachen*
Artist: Helmut Drexler
Issue $150.00; High $140.00; Low $120.00;
Close $120.00; Down $20.00

22-R55-1.71
1979 *Cathedral in Luxemburg*
Artist: Helmut Drexler
Issue $165.00; High $135.00; Low $120.00;
Close $120.00; Down $15.00

22-R55-1.72
1980 *Christmas in Brussels*
Artist: Helmut Drexler
Issue $190.00; High $180.00; Low $175.00;
Close $175.00; No Change

22-R55-1.73
1981 *Christmas in Trier*
Artist: Helmut Drexler
Issue $190.00; High $190.00; Low $70.00;
Close $70.00; Down $120.00

22-R55-1.74
1982 *Milan Cathedral*
Artist: Helmut Drexler
Issue $190.00; High $190.00; Low $190.00;
Close $190.00; No Change

22-R55-1.75
1983 *Church at Castle Wittenberg*
Artist: Helmut Drexler
Issue $195.00; High $195.00; Low $195.00;
Close $195.00; No Change

22-R55-1.76
1984 *City Hall of Stockholm*
Artist: Helmut Drexler
Issue $195.00; High $195.00; Low $195.00;
Close $195.00; No Change

Wiinblad Christmas Series

Artist: Bjørn Wiinblad. Artist's
signature appears on front

Overglaze-decorated porcelain
partially hand-painted in 18 colors
with 18k gold design on border

Diameter: 29.2 centimeters
(11½ inches)

Attached back hanger

Edition size undisclosed

Not numbered, without certificate

22-R55-2.1
1971 *Maria and Child*
Issue $100.00; High $1300.00; Low $1000.00;
Close $1000.00; Down $300.00

22-R55-2.2
1972 *Caspar*
Issue $100.00; High $550.00; Low $300.00;
Close $300.00; Down $250.00

22-R55-2.3
1973 *Melchior*
Issue $125.00; High $500.00; Low $350.00;
Close $500.00; Up $10.00

22-R55-2.4
1974 *Balthazar*
Issue $125.00; High $500.00; Low $390.00;
Close $390.00; Down $110.00

22-R55-2.5
1975 *The Annunciation*
Issue $195.00; High $200.00; Low $159.00;
Close $159.00; Down $41.00

22-R55-2.6
1976 *Angel with Trumpet*
Issue $195.00; High $180.00; Low $120.00;
Close $120.00; Down $60.00

22-R55-2.7
1977 *Adoration of the Shepherds*
Issue $225.00; High $235.00; Low $175.00;
Close $190.00; Down $45.00

22-R55-2.8
1978 *Angel with Harp*
Issue $275.00; High $275.00; Low $250.00;
Close $250.00; Down $25.00

22-R55-2.9
1979 *Exodus from Egypt*
Issue $310.00; High $310.00; Low $310.00;
Close $310.00; No Change

22-R55-2.10
1980 *Angel with a Glockenspiel*
Issue $360.00; High $360.00; Low $360.00;
Close $360.00; No Change

22-R55-2.11
1981 *Christ Child Visits Temple*
Issue $375.00; High $375.00; Low $360.00;
Close $360.00; Down $15.00

22-R55-2.12
1982 *Christening of Christ*
Issue $375.00; High $375.00; Low $360.00;
Close $360.00; Down $15.00
Series Closed

The Nobility of Children Series

Artist: Edna Hibel. Artist's signature appears on front

Overglaze-decorated porcelain banded in gold

Diameter: 25.4 centimeters (10 inches)

Attached back hanger

Edition size limited to 12,750

Numbered with certificate

22-R55-6.1
1976 *La Contessa Isabella*
Issue $120.00; High $165.00; Low $90.00;
Close $90.00; Down $75.00

22-R55-6.2
1977 *Le Marquis Maurice-Pierre*
Issue $120.00; High $110.00; Low $85.00;
Close $85.00; Down $25.00

22-R55-6.3
1978 *Baronesse Johanna-Maryke Van Vollendam Tot Marken*
Issue $130.00; High $135.00; Low $130.00;
Close $130.00; Down $5.00

22-R55-6.4
1979 *Chief Red Feather*
Issue $140.00; High $140.00; Low $130.00;
Close $130.00; Down $10.00
Series Closed

Oriental Gold Series

Artist: Edna Hibel. Artist's signature appears on front

Overglaze-decorated porcelain highlighted in gold

Diameter: 25.4 centimeters (10 inches)

Attached back hanger

Edition size limited to 2,000

Numbered with certificate

22-R55-8.1
1976 *Yasuko*
Issue $275.00; High $1100.00; Low $800.00;
Close $800.00; Down $300.00

22-R55-8.2
1977 *Mr. Obata*
Issue $275.00; High $560.00; Low $520.00;
Close $520.00; Down $40.00

22-R55-8.3
1978 *Sakura*
Issue $295.00; High $450.00; Low $400.00;
Close $400.00; No Change

22-R55-8.4
1979 *Michio*
Issue $325.00; High $450.00; Low $350.00;
Close $350.00; Down $100.00
Series Closed

22-R58-2.7 *"Young Americans VI"*
1979 Royal Bayreuth *Mother's Day*
Luminous eyes and realistic flesh tones characterized the artwork of the late Leo Jansen.

The pottery now known as Royal Bayreuth began in 1794 in the mountain village of Tettau as the Koniglich Privilegierter Porzellanfabrik Tettau, the first porcelain manufacturer in Bavaria. Now a subsidiary of Royal Tettau, Royal Bayreuth began its *Mother's Day* series in 1973 with art by contemporary artists. The series ended in 1982.

Brazilian Ozz Franca, a specialist in the art of children's portraiture, began the *Mother's Day* series in 1973. In 1974 Leo Jansen succeeded him as the series artist.

Mother's Day Series

Artist: as indicated. Artist's signature appears on back until 1975, on front thereafter

Overglaze-decorated porcelain

Diameter: 19.7 centimeters (7¾ inches)

Attached back hanger

Edition size: as indicated

Numbered without certificate

22-R58-2.1
1973 *Consolation*
Artist: Ozz Franca/Edition: 4,000
Issue $16.50; High $44.00; Low $30.00;
Close $30.00; Down $14.00

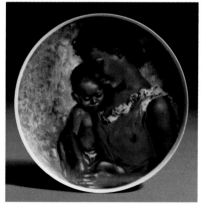

22-R58-2.2
1974 *Young Americans*
Artist: Leo Jansen/Edition: 4,000
Issue $25.00; High $175.00; Low $145.00;
Close $145.00; Down $15.00

22-R58-2.3
1975 *Young Americans II*
Artist: Leo Jansen/Edition: 5,000
Issue $25.00; High $110.00; Low $95.00;
Close $95.00; Down $15.00

22-R58-2.4
1976 *Young Americans III*
Artist: Leo Jansen/Edition: 5,000
Issue $30.00; High $63.00; Low $50.00;
Close $50.00; Down $13.00

22-R58-2.5
1977 *Young Americans IV*
Artist: Leo Jansen/Edition: 5,000
Issue $40.00; High $55.00; Low $45.00;
Close $45.00; Down $10.00

22-R58-2.6
1978 *Young Americans V*
Artist: Leo Jansen/Edition: 5,000
Issue $45.00; High $40.00; Low $28.00;
Close $35.00; Up $7.00

22-R58-2.7
1979 *Young Americans VI*
Artist: Leo Jansen/Edition: 5,000
Issue $60.00; High $75.00; Low $65.00;
Close $70.00; Down $5.00

22-R58-2.8
1980 *Young Americans VII*
Artist: Leo Jansen/Edition: 5,000
Issue $65.00; High $60.00; Low $40.00;
Close $55.00; Up $5.00

22-R58-2.9
1981 *Young Americans VIII*
Artist: Leo Jansen/Edition: 5,000
Issue $65.00; High $50.00; Low $30.00;
Close $30.00; Down $20.00

22-R58-2.10
1982 *Young Americans IX*
Artist: Leo Jansen/Edition: 5,000
Issue $65.00; High $65.00; Low $59.00;
Close $59.00; Down $6.00
Series Closed

Schmid

Schmid was established in Boston in the 1930s. Since then the firm has been a specialized importer of porcelain bells and mugs as well as plates. Schmid limited-edition plates are produced by the Porzellanfabrik Johann Seltmann Vohenstrauss GmbH factory in Germany.

Both the *Christmas* series, which began in 1971, and the *Mother's Day* series, which started the following year, feature art created by the late Berta Hummel. The Hummel plates bear her signature depending on whether Berta Hummel had signed the original artwork.

Both Hummel series feature art created by Berta Hummel before she entered the Franciscan order at Siessen in 1934 and took the name Sister Maria Innocentia Hummel (see Germany, GOEBEL). Prior to taking her vows, she had received extensive training at art academies in Simbach and Munich, where she evolved the distinctive style that instantly identifies her work to collectors worldwide.

Christmas Series

Artist: Berta Hummel. Artist's signature or initials appear on front from 1971 thru 1974, 1976 and 1978 thru 1980

Overglaze-decorated porcelain

Diameter: 19.7 centimeters (7¾ inches)

Attached back hanger

Edition size undisclosed, limited by year of issue

Not numbered, without certificate

22-S12-1.1
1971 *Angel in a Christmas Setting*
Issue $15.00; High $60.00; Low $27.00;
Close $27.00; Down $33.00

22-S12-1.2
1972 *Angel with Flute*
Issue $15.00; High $32.00; Low $23.00;
Close $23.00; Down $9.00

22-S12-1.3
1973 *The Nativity*
Issue $15.00; High $200.00; Low $140.00;
Close $140.00; Down $60.00

22-S12-1.4
1974 *The Guardian Angel*
Issue $18.50; High $35.00; Low $24.00;
Close $24.00; Down $11.00

22-S12-1.5
1975 *Christmas Child*
Issue $25.00; High $30.00; Low $24.00;
Close $24.00; Down $6.00

22-S12-1.6
1976 *Sacred Journey*
Issue $27.50; High $40.00; Low $30.00;
Close $35.00; Down $5.00

22-S12-1.7
1977 *Herald Angel*
Issue $27.50; High $33.00; Low $22.00;
Close $22.00; Down $11.00

22-S12-1.8
1978 *Heavenly Trio*
Issue $32.50; High $30.00; Low $19.00;
Close $19.00; Down $11.00

22-S12-1.9
1979 *Starlight Angel*
Issue $38.00; High $28.00; Low $20.00;
Close $20.00; Down $8.00

22-S12-1.10
1980 *Parade into Toyland*
Issue $45.00; High $60.00; Low $35.00;
Close $39.00; Down $11.00

22-S12-1.11
1981 *A Time to Remember*
Issue $45.00; High $45.00; Low $30.00;
Close $30.00; Down $15.00

22-S12-1.12
1982 *Angelic Procession*
Issue $45.00; High $62.00; Low $45.00;
Close $45.00; Down $7.00

22-S12-1.13
1983 *Angelic Messenger*
Issue $45.00; High $65.00; Low $45.00;
Close $55.00; Up $10.00

22-S12-1.14
1984 *A Gift from Heaven*
Issue $45.00; High $80.00; Low $45.00;
Close $65.00; Up $20.00

22-S12-1.15
1985 *Heavenly Light*
Issue price: $45.00

Mother's Day Series

Artist: Berta Hummel. Artist's signature or initials appear on front from 1972 thru 1975, and 1977

Overglaze-decorated porcelain

Diameter: 19.7 centimeters (7³/4 inches)

Attached back hanger

Edition size undisclosed, limited by year of issue

Not numbered, without certificate

22-S12-2.1
1972 *Playing Hooky*
Issue $15.00; High $30.00; Low $20.00;
Close $20.00; Down $10.00

22-S12-2.2
1973 *The Little Fisherman*
Issue $15.00; High $65.00; Low $40.00;
Close $40.00; Down $25.00

22-S12-2.3
1974 *The Bumblebee*
Issue $18.50; High $30.00; Low $16.00;
Close $16.00; Down $14.00

22-S12-2.4
1975 *Message of Love*
Issue $25.00; High $31.00; Low $10.00;
Close $10.00; Down $21.00

22-S12-2.5
1976 *Devotion for Mother*
Issue $27.50; High $25.00; Low $15.00;
Close $15.00; Down $10.00

22-S12-2.6
1977 *Moonlight Return*
Issue $27.50; High $35.00; Low $25.00;
Close $25.00; Down $5.00

22-S12-2.7
1978 *Afternoon Stroll*
Issue $32.50; High $20.00; Low $15.00;
Close $15.00; Down $5.00

22-S12-2.8
1979 *Cherub's Gift*
Issue $38.00; High $18.00; Low $14.00;
Close $14.00; Down $4.00

22-S12-2.9
1980 *Mother's Little Helpers*
Issue $45.00; High $36.00; Low $30.00;
Close $33.00; Up $3.00

22-S12-2.10
1981 *Playtime*
Issue $45.00; High $45.00; Low $30.00;
Close $30.00; Down $15.00

22-S12-2.11
1982 *The Flower Basket*
Issue $45.00; High $45.00; Low $30.00;
Close $30.00; Down $15.00

22-S12-2.12
1983 *Spring Bouquet*
Issue $45.00; High $60.00; Low $45.00;
Close $46.00; Up $1.00

22-S12-2.13
1984 *A Joy to Share*
Issue $45.00; High $50.00; Low $40.00;
Close $40.00; Down $5.00

22-S12-2.14
1985 *A Mother's Journey*
Issue $45.00; High $55.00; Low $45.00;
Close $55.00; Up $10.00

22-T40-1.1 ''Blue Titmouse''
1985 Tirschenreuth *Band's Songbirds of Europe*
Evolving from her many years as a porcelain artist of some reknown, German artist Ursula Band's approach to nature painting is scrupulously accurate, yet highly personal. This is her first work in the medium of collector's plates.

Since production of Tirschenreuth china began in 1838, Porzellanfabrik Tirschenreuth has continued to create magnificent porcelain objects for discerning collectors on five continents, including royalty and heads of state.

Their first entry into the limited-edition plate field is the series entitled *Band's Songbirds of Europe.*

It was created by artist Ursula Band, a native of Meissen, Germany, who received her professional training at the prestigious Painting and Drawing School of the Meissen State Porcelain Factory. In her first series, Frau Band has chosen to portray the songbirds which surround her home in Germany.

The series is the first depicting birds in their natural habitats to be produced under the auspices of the World Wildlife Fund, whose international president is HRH The Duke of Edinburgh, Prince Philip, of Great Britain.

Band's Songbirds of Europe Series

Artist: Ursula Band. Artist's signature appears on front

Overglaze-decorated porcelain banded in 22k gold

Diameter: 19 centimeters (7½ inches)

No hanger

Edition size undisclosed, limited by announced period of issue

Numbered with certificate

22-T40-1.1
1985 *Blue Titmouse*
Issue price: $19.50

26-B18-1.1 "Castle Caldwell"
1970 Belleek *Christmas*
Translucent parian china in Belleek's
renowned white relief design.

GREAT BRITAIN
BELLEEK
Belleek, County Fermanagh

Belleek Pottery Ltd., maker of thin, translucent parian china, was established in 1857 by David McBirney and Robert W. Armstrong on the banks of the River Erne near the small village of Belleek in County Fermanagh, Northern Ireland. The site is near deposits of clay discovered when the owner of Castle Caldwell in Fermanagh became interested in the brilliant whitewash used on local cottages and found that his entire estate lay on a bed of feldspar clay.

When combined with metallic washes, this clay produces the unique iridescent effect for which Belleek is known—a mother-of-pearl luster that is used on tea sets, figurines, and tableware. Queen Victoria and her son, the Prince of Wales, are among those who commissioned elaborate table services from the firm. Belleek ware is still made today much as it was a century ago.

Belleek's *Christmas* series, based on Irish subjects, began in 1970 and ended in 1977. The *Irish Wildlife Christmas* series began in 1978.

Artists for Belleek plates are not disclosed.

Christmas Series

Artist: undisclosed

Parian china

Diameter: 21.6 centimeters
(8½ inches)

No hanger

Edition size limited to announced
quantity of 7,500

Not numbered, without certificate

26-B18-1.1
1970 *Castle Caldwell*
Issue $25.00; High $125.00; Low $88.00;
Close $88.00; Down $37.00

26-B18-1.2
1971 *Celtic Cross*
Issue $25.00; High $50.00; Low $37.00;
Close $37.00; Down $8.00

26-B18-1.3
1972 *Flight of the Earls*
Issue $30.00; High $50.00; Low $45.00;
Close $45.00; Down $5.00

26-B18-1.4
1973 *Tribute to W. B. Yeats*
Issue $38.50; High $70.00; Low $65.00;
Close $65.00; Down $5.00

26-B18-1.5
1974 *Devenish Island*
Issue $45.00; High $280.00; Low $250.00;
Close $250.00; No Change

26-B18-1.6
1975 *The Celtic Cross*
Issue $48.00; High $65.00; Low $55.00;
Close $60.00; Down $5.00

26-B18-1.7
1976 *Dove of Peace*
Issue $55.00; High $78.00; Low $40.00;
Close $40.00; Down $38.00

26-B18-1.8
1977 *Wren*
Issue $55.00; High $59.00; Low $54.00;
Close $54.00; Down $5.00
Series Closed

*Irish Wildlife Christmas
Series*

Artist: undisclosed

Parian china

Diameter: 22.9 centimeters
(9 inches)

No hanger

Edition size undisclosed

Not numbered, without certificate

26-B18-2.1
1978 A Leaping Salmon
Issue $55.00; High $70.00; Low $65.00;
Close $65.00; Down $5.00

26-B18-2.2
1979 Hare at Rest
Issue $58.50; High $70.00; Low $60.00;
Close $60.00; Down $10.00

26-B18-2.3
1980 Hedgehog
Issue $66.50; High $100.00; Low $90.00;
Close $100.00; Up $10.00

26-B18-2.4
1981 Red Squirrel
Issue $78.00; High $80.00; Low $78.00;
Close $78.00; No Change

26-B18-2.5
1982 Irish Seal
Issue $78.00; High $100.00; Low $70.00;
Close $70.00; Down $8.00

26-B18-2.6
1983 Red Fox
Issue: $85.00; High $90.00; Low $85.00;
Close $85.00; No Change
Series Closed

26-D8-1.1 ''Toby Fillpot''
1984 Davenport Pottery *Toby*
Created in the animated style of the famous character mugs of England, this portly, jovial fellow displays the careful modeling and hand painting that have contributed to the widespread popularity of these items. It was this selfsame Toby Fillpot who gave his name to the genre of character mugs, now called ''tobies.''

The Davenport Pottery was founded by Arthur Wood and Son, descendants of esteemed potters who made their name and fortune by crafting Toby jugs at the close of the eighteenth century. Davenport is committed to preserving the tradition of fine British pottery, still relying on techniques that have been carefully handed down through generations of craftsmen.

With its move into the medium of limited-edition plates, The Davenport Pottery introduced, in 1983, the first collector's plate series based on the 200-year-old Toby tradition with "Toby Fillpot," the first issue in the Toby Plate Collection. Each plate in this edition is hand-cast and hand-painted by artisans using techniques that date back to the eighteenth century.

W. A. Blandford was commissioned as master modeller to design the "Toby Fillpot" plate. Subsequent plates have been modelled by Douglas Tootle.

Toby Plate Collection

Artist: as indicated. Artist's
signature appears on front

Earthenware

Diameter: 21.6 centimeters
(8½ inches)

No hanger

Edition size undisclosed, limited
by period of issue

Numbered with certificate

26-D8-1.1
1984 *Toby Fillpot*
Artist: Wilfred Blandford
Issue $35.00; High $49.00; Low $35.00;
Close $38.00; Up $3.00

26-D8-1.2
1984 *Falstaff*
Artist: Douglas Tootle
Issue $35.00; High $35.00; Low $35.00;
Close $35.00; No Change

26-D8-1.3
1985 *Jack Tar*
Artist: Douglas Tootle
Issue price: $40.00

GREAT BRITAIN
LONGTON CROWN POTTERY
Longton, Stoke-on-Trent, Staffordshire

Longton Crown Pottery maintains a long tradition of quality English bone china manufacture. Josiah Spode perfected the process by which animal bone ash is added to china clay to produce bone china, which is creamy white and translucent. His formula came to be known as English bone china and remains the standard today.

Longton Crown Pottery began its first Baronet bone china collector's plate series in 1981 with *The Canterbury Tales* collection, interpreting Geoffrey Chaucer's literary classic of the same name, and with the sponsorship of the Centre for Medieval & Renaissance Studies of Oxford, England.

The artist for the series is G. A. Hoover.

*The Canterbury Tales
Collection*

Artist: G. A. Hoover. Artist's
signature appears on front

Baronet bone china

Diameter: 21.6 centimeters
(8½ inches)

No hanger

Edition size undisclosed, limited
by period of issue

Numbered with certificate

26-L46-1.1
1981 *The Man of Law's Tale*
Issue $29.80; High $30.00; Low $30.00;
Close $30.00; No Change

26-L46-1.2
1982 *The Franklin's Tale*
Issue $29.80; High $30.00; Low $30.00;
Close $30.00; No Change

26-L46-1.3
1982 *The Knight's Tale*
Issue $31.80; High $36.00; Low $30.00;
Close $30.00; Down $5.00

26-L46-1.4
1982 *The Wife of Bath's Tale*
Issue $31.80; High $45.00; Low $34.00;
Close $40.00; Up $6.00
Series Closed

GREAT BRITAIN
ROYAL DOULTON
Burslem, Stoke-on-Trent, Staffordshire

Royal Doulton dates to 1815, when a potter named John Doulton invested his life savings of £100 in a one-kiln pottery in the Lambeth section of London.

At the International Exhibition of 1871, John's son Henry Doulton exhibited many of his experimental art pieces. Their favorable reception led to the development of decorative ceramics whose extensive range of colors and decorative techniques ultimately established Doulton Lambethware as an art form.

In 1877, Henry Doulton turned his attention to the development of tableware. At a small earthenware factory in Burslem, Staffordshire, table services for everyday use were produced along with more costly services with raised gold and acid-etched decorations, often combined with the finest of hand painting. Queen Victoria conferred knighthood upon Henry Doulton in 1887 for his accomplishments in the area of ceramic techniques, thus making him the first potter in England to receive such an honor. In 1901 the company received the Royal warrant, giving it authority to use *Royal* with its name.

The *Beswick Christmas* series, sponsored by Royal Doulton's Beswick Potteries from 1972 to 1978, depicted Christmas traditions from around the world. The Collector's International Gallery of "Fine Art on Fine China" began with the *Mother and Child* series in 1973. These plates show mothers and children of various countries. Other series in the Collector's International group are by contemporary artists and include the *Commedia Dell'Arte* series begun in 1974 and ended in 1978, and *The Log of the "Dashing Wave"* series which began in 1976. The *Valentine's Day* series also began in 1976 with artwork from Victorian prints. In 1980 Royal Doulton began the *Portraits of Innocence* series.

Royal Doulton has recruited several important artists to design its collector's plates. Among them are John Stobart, Edna Hibel, LeRoy Neiman, and Francisco J. J. C. Masseria.

Beswick Christmas Series

Artist: as indicated

Earthenware in hand-cast bas-relief, hand-painted in 15 colors

Diameter: 20.5 centimeters
(8 inches square)

Pierced foot rim

Edition size limited to 15,000

Not numbered, without certificate

26-R62-1.1
1972 *Christmas in England*
Artist: Harry Sales
Issue $35.00; High $40.00; Low $25.00;
Close $25.00; Down $15.00

26-R62-1.2
1973 *Christmas in Mexico*
Artist: Chavela Castrejon
Issue $37.50; High $25.00; Low $15.00;
Close $15.00; Down $10.00

26-R62-1.3
1974 *Christmas in Bulgaria*
Artist: Dimitri Yordanov
Issue $37.50; High $40.00; Low $25.00;
Close $25.00; Down $15.00

26-R62-1.4
1975 *Christmas in Norway*
Artist: Alton Toby
Issue $45.00; High $54.00; Low $25.00;
Close $25.00; Down $29.00

26-R62-1.5
1976 *Christmas in Holland*
Artist: Alton Toby
Issue $50.00; High $45.00; Low $25.00;
Close $25.00; Down $19.00

26-R62-1.6
1977 *Christmas in Poland*
Artist: Alton Toby
Issue $50.00; High $100.00; Low $35.00;
Close $50.00; Down $40.00

26-R62-1.7
1978 *Christmas in America*
Artist: Alton Toby
Issue $55.00; High $60.00; Low $44.00;
Close $44.00; Down $8.00
Series Closed

Mother and Child Series

Artist: Edna Hibel. Artist's signature appears on front

Bone china banded in gold

Diameter: 21 centimeters (8¼ inches)

No hanger

Edition size limited to 15,000

Numbered since 1974, without certificate

26-R62-2.1
1973 *Colette and Child*
Issue $40.00; High $465.00; Low $375.00;
Close $375.00; Down $90.00

26-R62-2.2
1974 *Sayuri and Child*
Issue $40.00; High $150.00; Low $140.00;
Close $145.00; Down $5.00

26-R62-2.3
1975 *Kristina and Child*
Issue $50.00; High $125.00; Low $80.00;
Close $80.00; Down $45.00

26-R62-2.4
1976 *Marilyn and Child*
Issue $55.00; High $155.00; Low $85.00;
Close $85.00; Down $35.00

26-R62-2.5
1977 *Lucia and Child*
Issue $60.00; High $100.00; Low $85.00;
Close $85.00; Down $15.00

26-R62-2.6
1978 *Kathleen and Child*
Issue $85.00; High $100.00; Low $85.00;
Close $85.00; Down $5.00
Series Closed

Commedia Dell' Arte Series

Artist: LeRoy Neiman. Artist's signature appears on front

Bone china banded in gold

Diameter: 25.4 centimeters (10 inches)

No hanger

Edition size limited to 15,000

Numbered without certificate

26-R62-3.1
1974 *Harlequin*
Issue $50.00; High $70.00; Low $45.00;
Close $50.00; Down $20.00

26-R62-3.2
1975 *Pierrot*
Issue $60.00; High $65.00; Low $45.00;
Close $45.00; Down $20.00

26-R62-3.3
1977 *Columbine*
Issue $70.00; High $55.00; Low $40.00;
Close $40.00; Down $15.00

26-R62-3.4
1978 *Punchinello*
Issue $70.00; High $55.00; Low $40.00;
Close $40.00; Down $12.00
Series Closed

The Log of the "Dashing Wave" Series

Artist: John Stobart. Artist's signature appears on front

Bone china banded in gold

Diameter: 26.7 centimeters (10½ inches)

No hanger

Edition size limited to 15,000

Numbered without certificate

26-R62-6.1
1976 *Sailing with the Tide*
Issue $65.00; High $120.00; Low $85.00;
Close $89.00; Down $31.00

26-R62-6.2
1977 *Running Free*
Issue $70.00; High $135.00; Low $108.00;
Close $115.00; Down $20.00

26-R62-6.3
1978 *Rounding the Horn*
Issue $70.00; High $90.00; Low $65.00;
Close $65.00; Down $15.00

26-R62-6.4
1979 *Hong Kong*
Issue $75.00; High $110.00; Low $90.00;
Close $95.00; Up $3.00

26-R62-6.5
1981 *Bora Bora*
Issue $95.00; High $140.00; Low $90.00;
Close $90.00; Down $5.00

26-R62-6.6
1982 *Journey's End*
Issue $95.00; High $140.00; Low $99.00;
Close $130.00; Up $31.00
Series Closed

Valentine's Day Series

Artist: Unknown. Reproduced from nineteenth-century Victorian prints

Bone china banded in gold

Diameter: 21 centimeters (8¼ inches)

No hanger

Edition size undisclosed, limited by period of issue

Not numbered, without certificate

26-R62-7.1
1976 *Victorian Boy and Girl*
Issue $25.00; High $40.00; Low $25.00;
Close $30.00; Down $10.00

26-R62-7.2
1977 *My Sweetest Friend*
Issue $25.00; High $13.00; Low $10.00;
Close $10.00; Down $3.00

26-R62-7.3
1978 *If I Loved You*
Issue $25.00; High $40.00; Low $20.00;
Close $20.00; Down $20.00

26-R62-7.4
1979 *My Valentine*
Issue $29.95; High $30.00; Low $18.00;
Close $18.00; Down $12.00

26-R62-7.5
1980 *On a Swing*
Issue $32.95; High $30.00; Low $25.00;
Close $25.00; Down $5.00

26-R62-7.6
1981 *Sweet Music*
Issue $35.00; High $45.00; Low $40.00;
Close $40.00; No Change

26-R62-7.7
1982 *From My Heart*
Issue $40.00; High $55.00; Low $40.00;
Close $55.00; Up $13.00

26-R62-7.8
1983 *Cherub's Song*
Issue $40.00; High $55.00; Low $40.00;
Close $45.00; No Change

26-R62-7.9
1984 *Love in Bloom*
Issue $40.00; High $56.00; Low $40.00;
Close $56.00; Up $16.00

26-R62-7.10
1985 *With Loving Care*
Issue $40.00; High $45.00; Low $40.00;
Close $45.00; Up $5.00

Portraits of Innocence Series

Artist: Francisco Masseria. Artist's signature appears on front

Bone china banded in gold

Diameter: 20.3 centimeters (8 inches)

No hanger

Edition size limited to 15,000

Numbered without certificate

26-R62-11.1
1980 *Panchito*
Issue $75.00; High $175.00; Low $120.00;
Close $120.00; Down $55.00

26-R62-11.2
1981 *Adrien*
Issue $85.00; High $110.00; Low $70.00;
Close $70.00; Down $40.00

26-R62-11.3
1982 *Angelica*
Issue $95.00; High $110.00; Low $70.00;
Close $75.00; Down $35.00

26-R62-11.4
1983 *Juliana*
Issue $95.00; High $145.00; Low $70.00;
Close $70.00; Down $55.00
Series Closed

26-S63-1.1 "Partridge in a Pear Tree"
1970 Spode *Christmas*
The designs for this series were adapted from the artwork of Gillian West, a prominent 19th-century ceramics artist. The series also showcases the quality of Spode bone china, the first of its kind, famous throughout the world for its creamy whiteness, translucency and strength.

Josiah Spode I established the Spode Works at Stoke-on-Trent, England, in 1776 after spending nearly thirty years learning every facet of the pottery business. From the beginning, the Spode name was highly respected, and the firm has been awarded the Royal warrant by each English monarch since George III.

Josiah Spode perfected the process by which animal bone ash is added to china clay to produce bone china, which is creamy white and translucent. His formula came to be known as English bone china and remains the standard to this day.

Upon Spode's death in 1797, his son, Josiah Spode II, continued the trade, with William Copeland in charge of sales. Josiah Spode III in turn headed the business, but upon his death, Copeland became sole owner, and from 1827 his descendants operated the firm. Under their direction it was called W. T. Copeland & Sons, Ltd., but retained the Spode trademark. Between 1967 and 1976, the firm was owned by Carborundum Company, but in 1976 Spode merged with Royal Worcester of England. The Spode trademark has been retained, and the present factory is located on the site of the original pottery.

Spode's bone china *Christmas* series, which began in 1970 and ended in 1981, is based on old English carols. The plate body itself reproduces an original eighteenth-century Spode model; the designs are based on work by Gillian West, a prominent nineteenth-century British ceramics artist. The 1970 and 1971 plates are decorated in gold; thereafter, decorations are in gold plus a second color which is changed every two years.

Christmas Series

Artist: Gillian West

Bone china decorated in gold

Diameter: 20.3 centimeters (8 inches)

No hanger

Edition size undisclosed, limited by year of issue

Not numbered, without certificate

26-S63-1.1
1970 *Partridge in a Pear Tree*
Issue $35.00; High $60.00; Low $40.00;
Close $40.00; Down $20.00

26-S63-1.2
1971 *In Heaven the Angels Singing*
Issue $35.00; High $37.00; Low $37.00;
Close $37.00; No Change

26-S63-1.3
1972 *We Saw Three Ships A'Sailing*
Issue $35.00; High $46.00; Low $35.00;
Close $35.00; Down $11.00

26-S63-1.4
1973 *We Three Kings of Orient Are*
Issue $35.00; High $70.00; Low $55.00;
Close $55.00; Down $10.00

26-S63-1.5
1974 *Deck the Halls*
Issue $35.00; High $45.00; Low $40.00;
Close $40.00; Down $5.00

26-S63-1.6
1975 *Christbaum*
Issue $45.00; High $50.00; Low $35.00;
Close $35.00; Down $15.00

26-S63-1.7
1976 *Good King Wenceslas*
Issue $45.00; High $40.00; Low $30.00;
Close $30.00; Down $10.00

26-S63-1.8
1977 *The Holly and the Ivy*
Issue $45.00; High $47.00; Low $44.00;
Close $44.00; Down $3.00

26-S63-1.9
1978 *While Shepherds Watched*
Issue $45.00; High $50.00; Low $40.00;
Close $40.00; Down $10.00

26-S63-1.10
1979 *Away in a Manger*
Issue $50.00; High $45.00; Low $30.00;
Close $30.00; Down $15.00

26-S63-1.11
1980 *Bringing in the Boar's Head*
Issue $60.00; High $55.00; Low $40.00;
Close $40.00; Down $15.00

26-S63-1.12
1981 *Make We Merry*
Issue $65.00; High $55.00; Low $50.00;
Close $50.00; Down $5.00
Series Closed

26-W90-1.1 "Windsor Castle"
1969 Wedgwood *Christmas*
26-W90-2.1 "Sportive Love" and
26-W90-2.11 "Mare and Foal"
1971 and 1981 Wedgwood *Mothers*
Three examples of the varied colors that
Wedgwood's vitreous, unglazed stoneware
known as Jasper ware comes in. The white
or colored bas-relief decorations are applied
by hand.

Josiah Wedgwood I, Fellow of the Royal Society, is known as the "father of English potters." He founded the firm that bears his name in 1759 and built a new factory which he called "Etruria" ten years later.

Wedgwood himself developed many of the processes and materials used by the firm to this day. He is perhaps best known for his "Jasper ware" which he perfected in 1774. A vitreous, unglazed stoneware, Jasper is pure white in its original form but can be stained to produce a wide variety of colored backgrounds—green, lilac, yellow, maroon, black, and most popular of all, classic "Wedgwood blue"—onto which white or colored bas-relief decorations are applied by hand.

Although potters in England and abroad tried to duplicate Jasper ware, none was successful, and the Wedgwood name is so firmly linked with Jasper to this day that many people mistakenly think it is the only ware Wedgwood produces, and that it is made only in blue.

In 1940, having outgrown the pottery at Etruria, the firm moved to what has been described as the most up-to-date pottery in the world, near the village of Barlaston, Stoke-on-Trent, Staffordshire, England. There, in 1969, the firm celebrated the two-hundredth anniversary of the Etruria pottery by introducing a *Christmas* series of classic Wedgwood blue-and-white Jasper collector's plates commemorating famous English monuments. In 1971 Wedgwood began a series of *Mothers* plates, issued annually, made in black basalt ware and Jasper wares, and bearing designs created for Wedgwood in the late eighteenth century. The *Bicentennial of American Independence* series, also in blue-and-white Jasper, is a six-plate series which began in 1972 and closed in 1976. It commemorates events which led to American Independence. *The Blossoming of Suzanne* series on Wedgwood bone china, with designs by Mary Vickers, started in 1977. The *Mary Vickers My Memories* series began in 1981.

Artists for Wedgwood over the past two centuries have included some of the most distinguished names in plate design. William Hackwood was a modeler for Wedgwood from 1769 to 1832, and his eighteenth-century designs have been used on Wedgwood Jasper ware for generations. Lady Elizabeth Templetown was a designer for Wedgwood from 1783 to 1787. Most of her designs were modeled by William Hackwood. Among the staff artists of the Wedgwood Design Studio over the past thirty years are Rex Whistler, Eric Ravilious, Edward Bawden, Arnold Machin, Richard Guyatt, and Eduardo Paolozzi.

Christmas Series

Artist: Tom Harper until 1978; undisclosed thereafter

Jasper stoneware

Diameter: 20.3 centimeters (8 inches)

No hanger

Edition size undisclosed, limited by year of issue

Not numbered, with certificate

26-W90-1.1
1969 *Windsor Castle*
Issue $25.00; High $270.00; Low $200.00;
Close $250.00; No Change

26-W90-1.2
1970 *Christmas in Trafalgar Square*
Issue $30.00; High $30.00; Low $25.00;
Close $29.00; Up $2.00

26-W90-1.3
1971 *Piccadilly Circus, London*
Issue $30.00; High $45.00; Low $35.00;
Close $35.00; Down $5.00

26-W90-1.4
1972 *St. Paul's Cathedral*
Issue $35.00; High $36.00; Low $29.00;
Close $29.00; Down $7.00

26-W90-1.5
1973 *The Tower of London*
Issue $40.00; High $50.00; Low $40.00;
Close $40.00; Down $5.00

26-W90-1.6
1974 *The Houses of Parliament*
Issue $40.00; High $50.00; Low $37.00;
Close $37.00; No Change

26-W90-1.7
1975 *Tower Bridge*
Issue $45.00; High $38.00; Low $34.00;
Close $36.00; Up $2.00

26-W90-1.8
1976 *Hampton Court*
Issue $55.00; High $46.00; Low $38.00;
Close $38.00; Down $8.00

26-W90-1.9
1977 *Westminster Abbey*
Issue $55.00; High $35.00; Low $34.00;
Close $34.00; Down $1.00

26-W90-1.10
1978 *The Horse Guards*
Issue $60.00; High $45.00; Low $39.00;
Close $39.00; Down $2.00

26-W90-1.11
1979 *Buckingham Palace*
Issue $65.00; High $54.00; Low $35.00;
Close $35.00; Down $14.00

26-W90-1.12
1980 *St. James Palace*
Issue $70.00; High $70.00; Low $50.00;
Close $53.00; Down $12.00

26-W90-1.13
1981 *Marble Arch*
Issue $75.00; High $75.00; Low $65.00;
Close $65.00; Down $10.00

26-W90-1.14
1982 *Lambeth Palace*
Issue $80.00; High $100.00; Low $75.00;
Close $83.00; Down $7.00

26-W90-1.15
1983 *All Souls, Langham Palace*
Issue $80.00; High $85.00; Low $60.00;
Close $60.00; Down $20.00

26-W90-1.16
1984 *Constitutional Hill*
Issue $80.00; High $88.00; Low $75.00;
Close $80.00; No Change

Mothers Series

Artist: as indicated

Jasper stoneware in varying colors

Diameter: 16.5 centimeters
(6½ inches)

No hanger

Edition size undisclosed, limited
by year of issue

Not numbered, without certificate

26-W90-2.1
1971 *Sportive Love*
Artist: Lady Elizabeth Templetown
Issue $20.00; High $26.00; Low $14.00;
Close $25.00; Down $1.00

26-W90-2.2
1972 *The Sewing Lesson*
Artist: Emma Crewe
Issue $20.00; High $30.00; Low $12.00;
Close $30.00; Up $15.00

26-W90-2.3
1973 *The Baptism of Achilles*
Artist: Lady Elizabeth Templetown
Issue $25.00; High $16.00; Low $14.00;
Close $15.00; Down $1.00

26-W90-2.4
1974 *Domestic Employment*
Artist: Lady Elizabeth Templetown
Issue $30.00; High $40.00; Low $30.00;
Close $40.00; Up $7.00

26-W90-2.5
1975 *Mother and Child*
Artist: Lady Elizabeth Templetown
Issue $35.00; High $45.00; Low $36.00;
Close $36.00; Down $1.00

26-W90-2.6
1976 *The Spinner*
Artist: William Hackwood
Issue $35.00; High $35.00; Low $28.00;
Close $28.00; Down $5.00

26-W90-2.7
1977 *Leisure Time*
Artist: William Hackwood
Issue $35.00; High $33.00; Low $26.00;
Close $26.00; Down $7.00

26-W90-2.8
1978 *Swan and Cygnets*
Artist: Undisclosed
Issue $40.00; High $45.00; Low $38.00;
Close $40.00; Up $2.00

26-W90-2.9
1979 Deer and Fawn
Artist: Undisclosed
Issue $45.00; High $40.00; Low $36.00;
Close $40.00; Up $4.00

26-W90-2.10
1980 Birds
Artist: Undisclosed
Issue $47.50; High $50.00; Low $45.00;
Close $45.00; Down $5.00

26-W90-2.11
1981 Mare and Foal
Artist: Undisclosed
Issue $50.00; High $50.00; Low $49.00;
Close $49.00; Down $1.00

26-W90-2.12
1982 Cherubs with Swing
Artist: Undisclosed
Issue $55.00; High $55.00; Low $55.00;
Close $55.00; No Change

26-W90-2.13
1983 Cupid and Butterfly
Artist: Undisclosed
Issue $55.00; High $56.00; Low $50.00;
Close $56.00; Up $1.00

26-W90-2.14
1984 Cupid and Music
Artist: Undisclosed
Issue $55.00; High $55.00; Low $50.00;
Close $50.00; Down $5.00

26-W90-2.15
1985 Cupid and Doves
Issue price: $55.00

Bicentennial of American Independence Series

Artist: Undisclosed

Jasper stoneware

Diameter: 20.3 centimeters
(8 inches)

No hanger

Edition size undisclosed, limited
by year of issue

Not numbered, without certificate

26-W90-3.1
1972 *Boston Tea Party*
Issue $30.00; High $35.00; Low $30.00;
Close $30.00; Down $5.00

26-W90-3.2
1973 *Paul Revere's Ride*
Issue $35.00; High $100.00; Low $75.00;
Close $85.00; Down $15.00

26-W90-3.3
1974 *Battle of Concord*
Issue $40.00; High $45.00; Low $24.00;
Close $24.00; Down $21.00

26-W90-3.4
1975 *Across the Delaware*
Issue $45.00; High $82.00; Low $40.00;
Close $40.00; Down $42.00

26-W90-3.5
1975 *Victory at Yorktown*
Issue $45.00; High $42.00; Low $25.00;
Close $25.00; Down $17.00

26-W90-3.6
1976 *Declaration Signed*
Issue $45.00; High $40.00; Low $30.00;
Close $40.00; No Change
Series Closed

Blossoming of Suzanne Series

Artist: Mary Vickers. Artist's signature appears on front

Bone china banded in gold

Diameter: 23.5 centimeters (9¼ inches)

No hanger

Edition size limited to 17,000 in 1977; 24,000 thereafter

Numbered with certificate

26-W90-4.1
1977 *Innocence*
Issue $60.00; High $85.00; Low $60.00;
Close $60.00; Down $25.00

26-W90-4.2
1978 *Cherish*
Issue $60.00; High $62.00; Low $60.00;
Close $60.00; Down $2.00

26-W90-4.3
1979 *Daydream*
Issue $65.00; High $65.00; Low $63.00;
Close $63.00; Down $2.00

26-W90-4.4
1980 *Wistful*
Issue $70.00; High $85.00; Low $70.00;
Close $70.00; Down $6.00
Series Closed

Mary Vickers My Memories Series

Artist: Mary Vickers. Artist's signature appears on front

Queensware banded in gold

Diameter: 20.3 centimeters (8 inches)

No hanger

Edition size undisclosed, limited by period of issue

Numbered with certificate

26-W90-5.1
1981 *Be My Friend*
Issue $27.00; High $27.00; Low $27.00;
Close $27.00; No Change

26-W90-5.2
1982 *Playtime*
Issue $27.00; High $36.00; Low $27.00;
Close $27.00; Down $8.00

26-W90-5.3
1983 *Our Garden*
Issue $27.00; High $65.00; Low $32.00;
Close $47.00; Up $15.00

26-W90-5.4
1984 *The Recital*
Issue $27.00; High $50.00; Low $27.00;
Close $34.00; Up $7.00

26-W90-5.5
1985 *Mother's Treasures*
Issue price: $29.00

ITALY
ANRI
Santa Christina

The House of Anri, which claims to be the world's largest wood-carving manufactory, is a family firm established in 1916 by Anton Riffeser, Sr. and is headed by his grandson, Ernst Riffeser. The factory is located in the Tyrolean Alps, an area with a long tradition of wood carving.

Anri's *Christmas* series began in 1971. Using a process known as "toriart," the plates are molded and carved in wood material and hand-painted to produce a three-dimensional effect. Each plate is mounted in a circular European maple frame.

A master woodcarver from Saint Ulrich, Italy, Josef Malfertheiner is the artist until 1978; thereafter, the artist is undisclosed.

Christmas Series

Artist: Josef Malfertheiner until 1978; undisclosed thereafter

Hand-painted molded wood material

Diameter: 30.5 centimeters (12 inches)

Attached back hanger

Edition size limited to 10,000 until 1976; 6,000 thereafter

Numbered since 1972, without certificate

38-A54-1.1
1971 *St. Jakob in Groden*
Issue $37.50; High $93.00; Low $37.00;
Close $45.00; Down $48.00

38-A54-1.2
1972 *Pipers at Alberobello*
Issue $45.00; High $100.00; Low $90.00;
Close $100.00; No Change

38-A54-1.3
1973 *Alpine Horn*
Issue $45.00; High $375.00; Low $325.00;
Close $325.00; Down $50.00

38-A54-1.4
1974 *Young Man and Girl*
Issue $50.00; High $120.00; Low $75.00;
Close $90.00; Down $10.00

38-A54-1.5
1975 *Christmas in Ireland*
Issue $60.00; High $85.00; Low $52.00;
Close $52.00; Down $33.00

38-A54-1.6
1976 *Alpine Christmas*
Issue $65.00; High $210.00; Low $182.00;
Close $182.00; Down $23.00

38-A54-1.7
1977 *Legend of Heiligenblut*
Issue $65.00; High $125.00; Low $100.00;
Close $100.00; Down $25.00

38-A54-1.8
1978 *The Klöckler Singers*
Issue $80.00; High $75.00; Low $57.00;
Close $63.00; Down $12.00

38-A54-1.9
1979 *The Moss Gatherers of Villnoess*
Issue $135.00; High $110.00; Low $69.00;
Close $69.00; Down $41.00

38-A54-1.10
1980 *Wintry Church-going in Santa Christina*
Issue $165.00; High $160.00; Low $130.00;
Close $130.00; Down $30.00

38-A54-1.11
1981 *Santa Claus in Tyrol*
Issue $165.00; High $168.00; Low $110.00;
Close $130.00; Down $38.00

38-A54-1.12
1982 *Star Singers*
Issue $165.00; High $165.00; Low $125.00;
Close $150.00; Down $15.00

38-A54-1.13
1983 *Unto Us a Child Is Born*
Issue $165.00; High $200.00; Low $160.00;
Close $160.00; Down $5.00

38-A54-1.14
1984 *Yuletide in the Valley*
Issue $165.00; High $170.00; Low $150.00;
Close $150.00; Down $15.00

38-A54-1.15
1985 *Good Morning, Good Cheer*
Issue price: $165.00

38-K32-2.5 "Anemones"
1977 King's *Flowers of America*
These plates are among the few in the market to have such high-relief decoration, carefully hand-applied. They are also hand-painted. The level of handwork made them difficult to produce; they were issued in an extremely limited edition of 1,000.

ITALY
KING'S
Usmate, Milan

King's Porcelain was established in the original Giuseppe Cappe factory in the 1960s. The factory had been known for its Cappe figurines of which King's has retained the original molds.

King's *Flowers of America* series began in 1973 and ended in 1977.

Chief sculptor for King's Porcelain is the Italian artist Aldo Falchi, who studied sculpture in Milan and later collaborated with Bjørn Wiinblad on works for Rosenthal of Germany. Some of his pieces in terra cotta can be found in Verona, Mantova, and Bozzolo, Italy.

Flowers of America Series

Artist: Aldo Falchi. Artist's signature appears on back since 1975

High relief, hand-painted porcelain banded in gold

Diameter: 22.3 centimeters (8¾ inches)

Attached back hanger

Edition size limited to 1,000

Numbered without certificate

38-K32-2.1
1973 *Pink Carnation*
Issue $85.00; High $85.00; Low $85.00;
Close $85.00; No Change

38-K32-2.2
1974 *Red Roses*
Issue $100.00; High $165.00; Low $140.00;
Close $145.00; Up $5.00

38-K32-2.3
1975 *Yellow Dahlia*
Issue $110.00; High $175.00; Low $155.00;
Close $155.00; Down $20.00

38-K32-2.4
1976 *Bluebells*
Issue $130.00; High $168.00; Low $165.00;
Close $165.00; Down $3.00

38-K32-2.5
1977 *Anemones*
Issue $130.00; High $185.00; Low $175.00;
Close $175.00; No Change
Series Closed

ITALY
VENETO FLAIR
Treviso

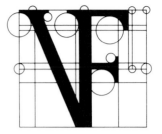

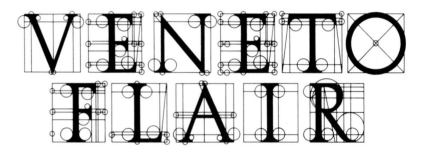

Veneto Flair was established in 1946 by a consortium of potters and painters. Creative World of White Plains, New York, acts as importer and distributor of the Veneto Flair collector's plates.

A centuries-old technique is used to create the Veneto Flair plates. The resulting decorated and glazed earthenware is known as majolica or faience pottery. In this ancient process, terra cotta is hand-thrown on a potter's wheel and the design is incised with a scalpel on the baked clay. Colors are then hand-applied and the plates undergo a series of paintings and firings before a final firing with a secret-formula glaze which produces Veneto Flair's unique mosaic-effect finish.

In 1971, Veneto Flair entered the limited-edition plate market with a single issue, the Bellini "Madonna" plate. The *Last Supper* series, based on Leonardo da Vinci's painting, started in 1973. Their *St. Mark's of Venice* series began in 1984.

Born in Torgiano, Italy, Vincente Tiziano is credited with reviving ancient Etruscan techniques of ceramic production, and his classical style was greatly influenced by the ceramic traditions of the sixteenth century. He is a recipient of the Amerigo Longhi Award from the International Ceramic Show of Deruta in the Italian province of Perugia. Many of his works are on display at the Deruta Ceramic Museum.

Bellini Plate

Artist: Vincente Tiziano (after Bellini's *Madonna*)

Terra cotta banded in gold

Diameter: 21.6 centimeters (8½ inches)

Pierced foot rim

Edition size limited to 500

Numbered with certificate

38-V22-1.1
1971 *Madonna*
Issue $45.00; High $400.00; Low $385.00;
Close $385.00; Down $15.00
Series Closed

Last Supper Series

Artist: Vincente Tiziano (after Leonardo da Vinci's *Last Supper*). Artist's signature appears on front

Terra cotta banded in gold

Diameter: 21.6 centimeters (8½ inches)

Pierced foot rim

Edition size limited to 2,000

Numbered with certificate

38-V22-6.1
1973 *Last Supper—Scene I*
Issue $100.00; High $75.00; Low $60.00;
Close $60.00; Down $15.00

38-V22-6.2
1973 *Last Supper—Scene II*
Issue $70.00; High $85.00; Low $78.00;
Close $78.00; Down $7.00

38-V22-6.3
1974 *Last Supper—Scene III*
Issue $70.00; High $87.00; Low $83.00;
Close $83.00; Down $4.00

38-V22-6.4
1975 *Last Supper—Scene IV*
Issue $70.00; High $135.00; Low $125.00;
Close $125.00; No Change

38-V22-6.5
1976 *Last Supper—Scene V*
Issue $70.00; High $95.00; Low $70.00;
Close $70.00; Down $24.00
Series Closed

St. Mark's of Venice Series •

Artist: Franco Lamincia. Artist's signature appears on front

Majolica-style earthenware, hand-painted and banded in gold

Diameter: 20.3 centimeters (8 inches)

Pierced foot rim

Edition size undisclosed, limited by year of issue

Numbered with certificate

38-V22-15.1
1984 *Noah and the Dove*
Issue $60.00; High $65.00; Low $60.00;
Close $65.00; Up $5.00

38-V22-15.2
1985 *Moses and the Burning Bush*
Issue price: $60.00

ITALY
STUDIO DANTE DI VOLTERADICI
Toscana

Located in Tuscany, world center for the mining and carving of alabaster, the Studio Dante di Volteradici continues the Italian tradition of alabaster sculpturing.

Di Volteradici's *Grand Opera* series, commissioned by the Museo Teatrale alla Scala to commemorate the two-hundredth anniversary of La Scala Opera House, began in 1976, and ended in 1982. *Madonne Viventi (Living Madonnas)*, its first proprietary series, began in 1978 and ended in 1984. Their *Ghiberti Doors* series began in 1983. In 1985, they introduced a series by contemporary sculptor Sergio Benvenuti, entitled *Benvenuti's Muses*.

Gino Ruggeri, a sculptor in the neo-classic tradition, is best known for his work "The Crucifix," sculpted from the Casa Serena Institute of Cecina Mare, and his two sculptures, "Memorials to the Fallen," which pay tribute to World War I victims. Now in his late 70s, Ruggeri's last completed work was the "Aida" plate. His successor as designer of the *Grand Opera* series was Franco Ingargiola, whom Ruggeri personally tutored and who worked in onyx and ceramics as well as alabaster. Alberto Santangela, current sculptor of the *Madonne Viventi* and *Ghiberti Doors* series, sculpts in the style of the Italian High Renaissance.

Grand Opera Series

Artist: Gino Ruggeri thru 1979;
Franco Ingargiola thereafter.
Artist's signature appears on front

Ivory alabaster

Diameter: 21.6 centimeters
(8½ inches)

Attached back hanger

Edition size undisclosed, limited
by period of issue

Numbered with certificate

38-V90-1.1
1976 Rigoletto
Issue $35.00; High $100.00; Low $45.00;
Close $45.00; Down $55.00

38-V90-1.2
1977 Madama Butterfly
Issue $35.00; High $50.00; Low $35.00;
Close $35.00; Down $15.00

38-V90-1.3
1978 Carmen
Issue $40.00; High $45.00; Low $40.00;
Close $40.00; Down $5.00

38-V90-1.4
1979 Aida
Issue $40.00; High $50.00; Low $40.00;
Close $40.00; Down $7.00

38-V90-1.5
1980 The Barber of Seville
Issue $40.00; High $55.00; Low $44.00;
Close $44.00; Down $11.00

38-V90-1.6
1981 Tosca
Issue $40.00; High $65.00; Low $40.00;
Close $42.00; Up $2.00

38-V90-1.7
1982 I Pagliacci
Issue $40.00; High $120.00; Low $85.00;
Close $115.00; Up $30.00
Series Closed

Madonne Viventi
(Living Madonnas)

Artist: Ado Santini in 1978;
Alberto Santangela thereafter.
Artist's signature appears on front

Ivory alabaster

Diameter: 21.6 centimeters
(8½ inches)

Attached back hanger

Edition size undisclosed, limited
by period of issue

Numbered with certificate

38-V90-2.1
1978 *Madonna Pensosa*
(The Pensive Madonna)
Issue $45.00; High $50.00; Low $45.00;
Close $45.00; Down $5.00

38-V90-2.2
1979 *Madonna Serena*
(The Serene Madonna)
Issue $45.00; High $65.00; Low $45.00;
Close $65.00; Up $20.00

38-V90-2.3
1980 *Madonna Beata*
(The Beatific Madonna)
Issue $45.00; High $50.00; Low $45.00;
Close $48.00; Up $3.00

38-V90-2.4
1981 *Madonna Profetica*
(The Prophetic Madonna)
Issue $45.00; High $70.00; Low $60.00;
Close $60.00; Down $10.00

38-V90-2.5
1982 *Madonna Modesta*
(The Demure Madonna)
Issue $45.00; High $80.00; Low $70.00;
Close $75.00; Up $5.00

38-V90-2.6
1983 *Madonna Saggio*
(The Wise Madonna)
Issue $45.00; High $100.00; Low $45.00;
Close $100.00; Up $55.00

38-V90-2.7
1984 *Madonna Tenera*
(The Tender Madonna)
Issue $45.00; High $70.00; Low $45.00;
Close $62.00; Up $17.00
Series Closed

Ghiberti Doors Series

Artist: Alberto Santangela.
Artist's signature appears on front

Ivory alabaster

Diameter: 21.6 centimeters
(8½ inches)

Attached back hanger

Edition size undisclosed, limited
by period of issue

Numbered with certificate

38-V90-3.1
1983 *Adoration of the Magi*
Issue $50.00; High $125.00; Low $50.00;
Close $120.00; Up $70.00

38-V90-3.2
1984 *The Nativity*
Issue $50.00; High $50.00; Low $50.00;
Close $50.00; No Change

38-V90-3.3
1985 *The Annunciation*
Issue price: $50.00

Benvenuti's Muses Series

Artist: Sergio Benvenuti. Artist's
signature appears on front

Ivory alabaster

Diameter: 21.6 centimeters
(8½ inches)

Attached black hanger

Edition size undisclosed, limited
by period of issue

Numbered with certificate

38-V90-4.1
1985 *Erato*
Issue price: $50.00

JAPAN
FUKAGAWA
Arita

Although the present Fukagawa Porcelain factory was organized in the 1880s in Arita by the Fukagawa family, the heritage of its Izumi-stone porcelain goes back some four centuries to the discovery of kaolin deposits on the island of Kyushu, Japan. It was there, on the slopes of Mount Izumi, that the Korean master potter Yi Samp'yöng ended his twenty-year search for a pure white clay base to be used in the manufacture of fine porcelain. As the direct result of his discovery, a number of small porcelain workshops—the first in all Japan—sprang up in the nearby town of Arita, and delicate plates and saucers were being shipped to the West from the harbor city of Imari decades before porcelain manufacture began in Europe.

The establishment of Fukagawa Porcelain was actually a merger of a number of small workshops whose standards and techniques dated to the time of Yi Samp'yöng. In 1913, Fukagawa was granted the title "Purveyor to the Imperial Household," which indicates patronage from the royal family of Japan. In recognition of this honor, all Fukagawa ceramics bear the imprint "Imperial." The factory, which is still in the hands of the Fukagawa family, continues to employ the original Izumiyama clay from Mount Izumi to give its porcelain a uniquely white body.

In 1977, Fukagawa began its first series of collector's plates—the *Warabe No Haiku (Haiku about Children)* series. The series ended in 1980.

Master of the traditional "Sea of Whiteness" style, Suetomi is the principal artist for Fukagawa and is the recipient of the Gold Prize from Japan's Ministry of International Trade and Industry.

Warabe No Haiku
(Haiku about Children)

Artist: Suetomi. Artist's signature and seal appear on front

Overglaze-decorated porcelain

Diameter: 26 centimeters (10¼ inches)

No hanger

Edition size undisclosed, limited by period of issue

Numbered with certificate

Original Haiku poem appears on front

42-F78-1.1
1977 Beneath the Plum Branch
Issue $38.00; High $44.00; Low $38.00;
Close $38.00; Down $6.00

42-F78-1.2
1978 Child of Straw
Issue $42.00; High $45.00; Low $42.00;
Close $42.00; No Change

42-F78-1.3
1979 Dragon Dance
Issue $42.00; High $45.00; Low $42.00;
Close $44.00; Up $2.00

42-F78-1.4
1980 Mask Dancing
Issue $42.00; High $115.00; Low $90.00;
Close $90.00; Down $22.00
Series Closed

Schmid

A Japanese subsidiary of Schmid (see Germany, SCHMID) produces several series of plates based on contemporary cartoon characters.

The *Peanuts Christmas* series and the *Peanuts Mother's Day* series began in 1972 and ended in 1982. The *Peanuts Valentine's Day* series began in 1977. The *Disney Christmas* series was introduced in 1973 and the *Disney Mother's Day* series in 1974—both ended in 1982. The *Raggedy Ann Annual* series started in 1980.

Cartoonist Charles Schulz, creator of the widely-syndicated cartoon strip "Peanuts," designed or approved all plates in the three *Peanuts* series. Walt Disney Productions staff artists designed both *Disney* series. Artists for the *Raggedy Ann* series are not disclosed.

Peanuts Christmas Series

Artist: Charles Schulz. Artist's signature appears on front

Overglaze-decorated porcelain

Diameter: 19 centimeters (7½ inches)

Attached back hanger

Edition size undisclosed, limited by year of issue thru 1978; 15,000 thereafter

Not numbered thru 1978; numbered thereafter, without certificate

42-S12-1.1
1972 *Snoopy Guides the Sleigh*
Issue $10.00; High $80.00; Low $55.00;
Close $80.00; Up $10.00

42-S12-1.2
1973 *Christmas Eve at the Doghouse*
Issue $10.00; High $199.00; Low $115.00;
Close $180.00; Up $65.00

42-S12-1.3
1974 *Christmas Eve at the Fireplace*
Issue $10.00; High $65.00; Low $49.00;
Close $49.00; Down $13.00

42-S12-1.4
1975 *Woodstock, Santa Claus*
Issue $12.50; High $16.00; Low $9.00;
Close $9.00; Down $7.00

42-S12-1.5
1976 *Woodstock's Christmas*
Issue $13.00; High $30.00; Low $18.00;
Close $18.00; Down $7.00

42-S12-1.6
1977 *Deck the Doghouse*
Issue $13.00; High $18.00; Low $13.00;
Close $17.00; Up $2.00

42-S12-1.7
1978 *Filling the Stocking*
Issue $15.00; High $28.00; Low $14.00;
Close $14.00; Down $3.00

42-S12-1.8
1979 *Christmas at Hand*
Issue $17.50; High $23.00; Low $15.00;
Close $15.00; Down $5.00

42-S12-1.9
1980 *Waiting for Santa*
Issue $17.50; High $50.00; Low $30.00;
Close $30.00; Down $15.00

42-S12-1.10
1981 *A Christmas Wish*
Issue $17.50; High $25.00; Low $20.00;
Close $20.00; No Change

42-S12-1.11
1982 *Perfect Performance*
Issue $18.50; High $35.00; Low $21.00;
Close $30.00; Up $8.00
Series Closed

Peanuts Mother's Day Series

Artist: Charles Schulz. Artist's signature appears on front except 1975

Overglaze-decorated porcelain

Diameter: 19 centimeters (7½ inches)

Attached back hanger

Edition size undisclosed, limited by year of issue thru 1978; 10,000 thereafter

Not numbered thru 1978; numbered thereafter, without certificate

42-S12-2.1
1972 *Linus*
Issue $10.00; High $13.00; Low $8.00;
Close $8.00; Down $5.00

42-S12-2.2
1973 *Mom?*
Issue $10.00; High $20.00; Low $8.00;
Close $10.00; Down $10.00

42-S12-2.3
1974 *Snoopy and Woodstock on Parade*
Issue $10.00; High $30.00; Low $20.00;
Close $30.00; Up $10.00

42-S12-2.4
1975 *A Kiss for Lucy*
Issue $12.50; High $18.00; Low $8.00;
Close $8.00; Down $10.00

42-S12-2.5
1976 *Linus and Snoopy*
Issue $13.00; High $15.00; Low $10.00;
Close $10.00; Down $5.00

42-S12-2.6
1977 *Dear Mom*
Issue $13.00; High $13.00; Low $8.00;
Close $8.00; Down $5.00

42-S12-2.7
1978 *Thoughts That Count*
Issue $15.00; High $14.00; Low $12.00;
Close $12.00; Down $1.00

42-S12-2.8
1979 *A Special Letter*
Issue $17.50; High $14.00; Low $12.00;
Close $14.00; Up $1.00

42-S12-2.9
1980 *A Tribute to Mom*
Issue $17.50; High $20.00; Low $13.00;
Close $20.00; Up $4.00

42-S12-2.10
1981 *Mission for Mom*
Issue $17.50; High $18.00; Low $10.00;
Close $10.00; Down $8.00

42-S12-2.11
1982 *Which Way to Mother?*
Issue $18.50; High $19.00; Low $12.00;
Close $12.00; Down $7.00
Series Closed

Disney Christmas Series

Artist: Undisclosed

Overglaze-decorated porcelain

Diameter: 19 centimeters
(7½ inches)

Attached back hanger

Edition size undisclosed, limited
by year of issue thru 1978; 15,000
thereafter

Not numbered thru 1978;
numbered thereafter, without
certificate

42-S12-3.1
1973 *Sleigh Ride*
Issue $10.00; High $340.00; Low $285.00;
Close $325.00; Up $10.00

42-S12-3.2
1974 *Decorating the Tree*
Issue $10.00; High $80.00; Low $60.00;
Close $72.00; Down $8.00

42-S12-3.3
1975 Caroling
Issue $12.50; High $20.00; Low $11.00;
Close $11.00; Down $7.00

42-S12-3.4
1976 Building a Snowman
Issue $13.00; High $18.00; Low $12.00;
Close $12.00; Down $3.00

42-S12-3.5
1977 Down the Chimney
Issue $13.00; High $29.00; Low $18.00;
Close $22.00; Up $4.00

42-S12-3.6
1978 Night Before Christmas
Issue $15.00; High $18.00; Low $14.00;
Close $14.00; Down $4.00

42-S12-3.7
1979 Santa's Surprise
Issue $17.50; High $20.00; Low $16.00;
Close $16.00; Down $4.00

42-S12-3.8
1980 Sleigh Ride
Issue $17.50; High $30.00; Low $22.00;
Close $22.00; Down $8.00

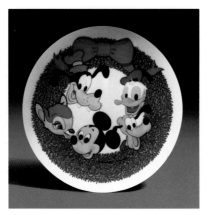

42-S12-3.9
1981 Happy Holidays
Issue $17.50; High $19.00; Low $11.00;
Close $11.00; Down $8.00

42-S12-3.10
1982 Winter Games
Issue $18.50; High $20.00; Low $14.00;
Close $14.00; Down $5.00
Series Closed

Disney Mother's Day Series

Artist: Undisclosed

Overglaze-decorated porcelain

Diameter: 19 centimeters
(7½ inches)

Attached back hanger

Edition size undisclosed, limited by year of issue thru 1978; 10,000 thereafter

Not numbered thru 1978; numbered thereafter, without certificate

42-S12-4.1
1974 Flowers for Mother
Issue $10.00; High $52.00; Low $43.00;
Close $43.00; Down $9.00

42-S12-4.2
1975 Snow White and the Seven Dwarfs
Issue $12.50; High $35.00; Low $25.00;
Close $32.00; Up $7.00

42-S12-4.3
1976 Minnie Mouse and Friends
Issue $13.00; High $23.00; Low $12.00;
Close $12.00; Down $11.00

42-S12-4.4
1977 Pluto's Pals
Issue $13.00; High $15.00; Low $13.00;
Close $15.00; Up $1.00

42-S12-4.5
1978 Flowers for Bambi
Issue $15.00; High $19.00; Low $14.00;
Close $14.00; Down $5.00

42-S12-4.6
1979 Happy Feet
Issue $17.50; High $17.00; Low $12.00;
Close $12.00; Down $5.00

42-S12-4.7
1980 Minnie's Surprise
Issue $17.50; High $18.00; Low $13.00;
Close $14.00; Down $4.00

42-S12-4.8
1981 Playmates
Issue $17.50; High $24.00; Low $10.00;
Close $10.00; Down $14.00

42-S12-4.9
1982 *A Dream Come True*
Issue $18.50; High $19.00; Low $15.00;
Close $15.00; Down $4.00
Series Closed

Peanuts Valentine's Day Series

Artist: Charles Schulz. Artist's signature appears on front

Overglaze-decorated porcelain

Diameter: 19 centimeters (7½ inches)

Attached back hanger

Edition size undisclosed, limited by year of issue

Not numbered, without certificate

42-S12-7.1
1977 *Home Is Where the Heart Is*
Issue $13.00; High $17.00; Low $9.00;
Close $9.00; Down $8.00

42-S12-7.2
1978 *Heavenly Bliss*
Issue $13.00; High $17.00; Low $13.00;
Close $13.00; Down $4.00

42-S12-7.3
1979 *Love Match*
Issue $17.50; High $17.00; Low $16.00;
Close $16.00; Down $1.00

42-S12-7.4
1980 *From Snoopy, with Love*
Issue $17.50; High $23.00; Low $18.00;
Close $18.00; Down $5.00

42-S12-7.5
1981 *Hearts-a-Flutter*
Issue $17.50; High $55.00; Low $25.00;
Close $28.00; Down $27.00

42-S12-7.6
1982 *Love Patch*
Issue $17.50; High $18.00; Low $10.00;
Close $14.00; Down $4.00
Series Closed

Raggedy Ann Annual Series

Artist: Undisclosed

Overglaze-decorated porcelain

Diameter: 19 centimeters
(7½ inches)

Attached back hanger

Edition size limited to 10,000

Numbered without certificate for
1980 plate; with certificate
thereafter

42-S12-9.1
1980 *The Sunshine Wagon*
Issue $17.50; High $60.00; Low $30.00;
Close $40.00; Down $20.00

42-S12-9.2
1981 *The Raggedy Shuffle*
Issue $17.50; High $21.00; Low $9.00;
Close $9.00; Down $12.00

42-S12-9.3
1982 *Flying High*
Issue $18.50; High $20.00; Low $14.00;
Close $14.00; Down $4.00

42-S12-9.4
1983 *Winning Streak*
Issue $22.50; High $42.00; Low $20.00;
Close $20.00; Down $18.00

42-S12-9.5
1984 *Rocking Rodeo*
Issue $22.50; High $30.00; Low $22.50;
Close $30.00; Up $7.50
Series Closed

NORWAY
PORSGRUND
Porsgrunn, Telemark County

Johan Jeremiason established Porsgrund, Norway's only porcelain factory, in 1885. Jeremiason began his business by importing English clay which was modeled by ceramist Carl Bauer. Porcelain tableware and decorative wares have been produced since then. Porsgrund's first collector's plate was a 1909 Christmas issue entitled "Christmas Flowers" (OTC). The series was abandoned after a single issue.

A *Christmas* series based on religious themes was introduced in 1968 and ended with the 1977 issue. The *Mother's Day* series began in 1970. In 1978 Porsgrund began a nostalgic Christmas series entitled the *Traditional Norwegian Christmas* series. The series closed in 1982.

Born in Fredrikstad, Norway, Gunnar Bratlie is a master of the traditional Norwegian folk art known as "rosemaling." He is the principal artist for Porsgrund.

Christmas Series

Artist: Gunnar Bratlie

Porcelain decorated in cobalt blue underglaze

Diameter: 17.8 centimeters (7 inches)

Pierced foot rim

Edition size undisclosed, limited by year of issue

Not numbered, without certificate

54-P62-1.1
1968 *Church Scene*
Issue $12.00; High $135.00; Low $90.00;
Close $110.00; Down $25.00

54-P62-1.2
1969 *Three Kings*
Issue $12.00; High $23.00; Low $16.00;
Close $16.00; Down $5.00

54-P62-1.3
1970 *Road to Bethlehem*
Issue $12.00; High $12.00; Low $7.00;
Close $10.00; Down $2.00

54-P62-1.4
1971 *A Child Is Born in Bethlehem*
Issue $12.00; High $16.00; Low $12.00;
Close $12.00; Down $4.00

54-P62-1.5
1972 *Hark, the Herald Angels Sing*
Issue $12.00; High $24.00; Low $17.00;
Close $17.00; Down $7.00

54-P62-1.6
1973 *Promise of the Savior*
Issue $15.00; High $45.00; Low $35.00;
Close $40.00; Up $5.00

54-P62-1.7
1974 *The Shepherds*
Issue $15.00; High $45.00; Low $25.00;
Close $25.00; Down $18.00

54-P62-1.8
1975 *Jesus on the Road to the Temple*
Issue $19.50; High $24.00; Low $15.00;
Close $15.00; Down $9.00

54-P62-1.9
1976 Jesus and the Elders
Issue $22.00; High $18.00; Low $14.00;
Close $14.00; Down $4.00

54-P62-1.10
1977 The Draught of Fish
Issue $24.00; High $22.00; Low $15.00;
Close $20.00; No Change
Series Closed

Mother's Day Series

Artist: Gunnar Bratlie thru 1982;
Thorstein Rittun thereafter

Porcelain decorated in cobalt blue
underglaze

Diameter: 12.7 centineters
(5 inches)

Pierced foot rim

Edition size undisclosed, limited
by year of issue

Not numbered, without certificate

54-P62-2.1
1970 Mare and Foal
Issue $7.50; High $15.00; Low $6.00;
Close $6.00; Down $9.00

54-P62-2.2
1971 Boy and Geese
Issue $7.50; High $10.00; Low $5.00;
Close $5.00; Down $3.00

54-P62-2.3
1972 Doe and Fawn
Issue $10.00; High $9.00; Low $5.00;
Close $5.00; Down $4.00

54-P62-2.4
1973 Cat and Kittens
Issue $10.00; High $11.00; Low $9.00;
Close $9.00; Down $2.00

54-P62-2.5
1974 Boy and Goats
Issue $10.00; High $20.00; Low $10.00;
Close $15.00; Up $1.00

54-P62-2.6
1975 *Dog and Puppies*
Issue $12.50; High $24.00; Low $15.00;
Close $15.00; Down $8.00

54-P62-2.7
1976 *Girl and Calf*
Issue $15.00; High $21.00; Low $15.00;
Close $15.00; Down $6.00

54-P62-2.8
1977 *Boy and Chickens*
Issue $16.50; High $25.00; Low $20.00;
Close $25.00; Up $3.00

54-P62-2.9
1978 *Girl and Pigs*
Issue $17.50; High $25.00; Low $25.00;
Close $25.00; No Change

54-P62-2.10
1979 *Boy and Reindeer*
Issue $19.50; High $21.00; Low $20.00;
Close $20.00; Down $1.00

54-P62-2.11
1980 *Girl and Lambs*
Issue $21.50; High $30.00; Low $14.00;
Close $30.00; Up $8.00

54-P62-2.12
1981 *Boy and Birds*
Issue $24.00; High $24.00; Low $24.00;
Close $24.00; No Change

54-P62-2.13
1982 *Girl and Rabbits*
Issue $26.00; High $27.00; Low $25.00;
Close $25.00; Down $2.00

54-P62-2.14
1983 *Mother and Kittens*
Issue $26.00; High $30.00; Low $24.00;
Close $24.00; Down $2.00

54-P62-2.15
1984 *By the Pond*
Issue $25.00; High $25.00; Low $25.00;
Close $25.00; No Change

Traditional Norwegian Christmas Series

Artist: Gunnar Bratlie. Artist's initials appear on back

Porcelain decorated in cobalt blue underglaze

Diameter: 17.8 centimeters (7 inches)

Pierced foot rim

Edition size undisclosed, limited by year of issue

Not numbered, without certificate

54-P62-5.1
1978 *Guests Are Coming for Christmas Eve*
Issue $27.00; High $30.00; Low $23.00;
Close $23.00; Down $7.00

54-P62-5.2
1979 *Home for Christmas*
Issue $30.00; High $30.00; Low $20.00;
Close $20.00; Down $10.00

54-P62-5.3
1980 *Preparing for Christmas*
Issue $34.00; High $40.00; Low $34.00;
Close $34.00; Down $6.00

54-P62-5.4
1981 *Christmas Skating*
Issue $38.00; High $42.00; Low $39.00;
Close $40.00; Up $1.00

54-P62-5.5
1982 *White Christmas*
Issue $42.00; High $50.00; Low $44.00;
Close $45.00; Up $1.00
Series Closed

72-L41-2.2 "Bird and Chicks"
1972 Lladró *Mother's Day*
Lladró's unique bas-relief plates feature bisque-fired centers and highly-glazed porcelain borders with a gold banded rim.

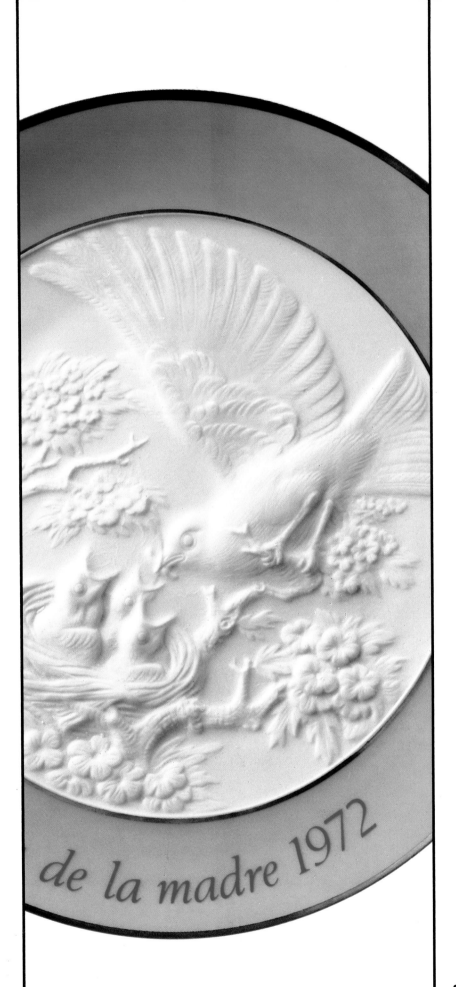

SPAIN
LLADRÓ
Tabernes Blanques, Valencia

LLADRÓ

The Lladró Porcelain factory was established in the 1950s by three Lladró brothers—Juan, Jose, and Vicente, sons of a peasant. At night, they studied porcelain designing, modeling, and firing and built their first kiln while in their teens. By 1970 their factory was one of the best-equipped in Europe and had become known for its vases and figurines.

Lladró initiated its limited-edition *Mother's Day* series in 1971. The series closed in 1979.

Artists for Lladró plates are not disclosed.

Mother's Day Series

Artist: Undisclosed

White bisque center in bas-relief with underglaze-decorated porcelain border and banded in gold

Diameter: 20.3 centimeters (8 inches)

No hanger

Edition size undisclosed, limited by year of issue

Not numbered, without certificate

72-L41-2.1
1971 *Kiss of the Child*
Issue $27.50; High $65.00; Low $30.00;
Close $30.00; Down $35.00

72-L41-2.2
1972 *Bird and Chicks*
Issue $27.50; High $20.00; Low $15.00;
Close $18.00; Down $2.00

72-L41-2.3
1973 Mother and Children
Issue $35.00; High $35.00; Low $25.00;
Close $35.00; Up $10.00

72-L41-2.4
1974 Mother Nursing
Issue $45.00; High $133.00; Low $128.00;
Close $128.00; Down $5.00

72-L41-2.5
1975 Mother and Child
Issue $60.00; High $55.00; Low $48.00;
Close $55.00; Up $2.00

72-L41-2.6
1976 Tender Vigil
Issue $60.00; High $60.00; Low $48.00;
Close $60.00; Up $12.00

72-L41-2.7
1977 Mother and Daughter
Issue $67.50; High $53.00; Low $52.00;
Close $52.00; Down $1.00

72-L41-2.8
1978 The New Arrival
Issue $80.00; High $55.00; Low $55.00;
Close $55.00; No Change

72-L41-2.9
1979 Off to School
Issue $90.00; High $80.00; Low $55.00;
Close $60.00; Down $20.00
Series Closed

Orrefors was originally established in 1726 as an ironworks. In 1898 they began manufacturing glass ink bottles and window glass. Although the ironworks was no longer profitable, Johan Ekman purchased the property in 1913. He was interested in improving the facilities for glassmaking and recognized the importance of the valuable forest land of the area as fuel for glass furnaces. He eventually built an entire community around the glassworks.

Orrefors crystal is made from a mixture of seashore sand and potash, plus a heavy lead content. The ornamentation is created by master blowers who apply liquid molten glass in desired shapes.

In 1970 Orrefors began its *Annual Cathedral* series, made in untinted crystal, depicting famous places of worship. This series ended in 1978. These plates are hand-made with the designs engraved in the crystal and filled with 24k gold.

John Selbing is regarded as one of the world's leading photographers of glass. He is credited with developing the technique which enabled production of inlaid-gold crystal plates. At the age of nineteen he joined Orrefors and for forty-six years handled their design, photography, and advertising projects. For the last several years he has been working independently in fine art.

Annual Cathedral Series

Artist: John Selbing

Leaded crystal with engraved designs inlaid in 24k gold

Diameter: 25.4 centimeters (10 inches)

No hanger

Edition size limited to 5,000 thru 1975; 3,000 thereafter

Numbered since 1975, without certificate

76-O74-1.1
1970 *Notre Dame Cathedral*
Issue $50.00; High $45.00; Low $40.00;
Close $45.00; Up $5.00

76-O74-1.2
1971 *Westminster Abbey*
Issue $50.00; High $42.00; Low $42.00;
Close $42.00; No Change

76-O74-1.3
1972 Basilica di San Marco
Issue $50.00; High $60.00; Low $60.00;
Close $60.00; No Change

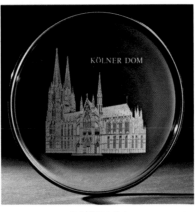

76-O74-1.4
1973 Cologne Cathedral
Issue $50.00; High $70.00; Low $60.00;
Close $60.00; Down $10.00

76-O74-1.5
1974 Temple Rue de la Victoire, Paris
Issue $60.00; High $75.00; Low $70.00;
Close $75.00; Up $3.00

76-O74-1.6
1975 Basilica di San Pietro, Rome
Issue $85.00; High $90.00; Low $90.00;
Close $90.00; No Change

76-O74-1.7
1976 Christ Church, Philadelphia
Issue $85.00; High $70.00; Low $60.00;
Close $60.00; Down $10.00

76-O74-1.8
1977 Masjid-E-Shah
Issue $90.00; High $120.00; Low $117.00;
Close $120.00; Up $2.00

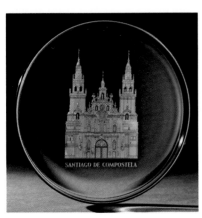

76-O74-1.9
1978 Santiago de Compostela
Issue $95.00; High $110.00; Low $90.00;
Close $110.00; Up $10.00
Series Closed

The Rörstrand Porcelain Factory is Sweden's oldest pottery and the second oldest in Europe. Originally founded in Stockholm in 1726 under government patronage, the plant was later moved inland to Lidkoping for safety during World War II.

Rörstrand is one of the few factories in the world that produces all three ceramic bodies—porcelain, stoneware, and high-fired earthenware. The output of the factory includes both dinnerware and decorative art, including collector's plates. Rörstrand's first collector's plate series was a *Christmas* series (OTC), started in 1904 and ended in 1926. In 1968 Rörstrand began its series of square *Christmas* plates with designs derived from Swedish folk tales and traditions.

Rörstrand artist Gunnar Nylund has exhibited at the Swedish National Museum and is widely known for his monumental ceramic reliefs.

Christmas Series

Artist: Gunnar Nylund

Porcelain decorated in Scandia blue underglaze

Diameter: 19 centimeters (7½ inches square)

Pierced foot rim

Edition size undisclosed, limited by year of issue

Not numbered, without certificate

76-R54-1.1
1968 Bringing Home the Tree
Issue $12.00; High $550.00; Low $550.00;
Close $550.00; No Change

76-R54-1.2
1969 Fisherman Sailing Home
Issue $13.50; High $60.00; Low $27.00;
Close $27.00; Down $33.00

76-R54-1.3
1970 Nils with His Geese
Issue $13.50; High $29.00; Low $18.00;
Close $18.00; Down $11.00

76-R54-1.4
1971 Nils in Lapland
Issue $15.00; High $28.00; Low $22.00;
Close $22.00; Down $6.00

76-R54-1.5
1972 Dalecarlian Fiddler
Issue $15.00; High $30.00; Low $18.00;
Close $18.00; Down $10.00

76-R54-1.6
1973 Farm in Smaland
Issue $16.00; High $100.00; Low $50.00;
Close $50.00; Down $50.00

76-R54-1.7
1974 Vadstena
Issue $19.00; High $60.00; Low $45.00;
Close $45.00; Down $15.00

76-R54-1.8
1975 Nils in Vastmanland
Issue $20.00; High $36.00; Low $25.00;
Close $28.00; Down $8.00

76-R54-1.9
1976 *Nils in Uppland*
Issue $20.00; High $35.00; Low $24.00;
Close $24.00; Down $6.00

76-R54-1.10
1977 *Nils in Värmland*
Issue $29.50; High $26.00; Low $20.00;
Close $20.00; Down $3.00

76-R54-1.11
1978 *Nils in Fjallbacka*
Issue $32.50; High $30.00; Low $30.00;
Close $30.00; No Change

76-R54-1.12
1979 *Nils in Vaestergoetland*
Issue $38.50; High $35.00; Low $30.00;
Close $35.00; Up $5.00

76-R54-1.13
1980 *Nils in Halland*
Issue $55.00; High $55.00; Low $45.00;
Close $45.00; Down $6.00

76-R54-1.14
1981 *Nils in Gotland*
Issue $55.00; High $60.00; Low $58.00;
Close $60.00; Up $2.00

76-R54-1.15
1982 *Nils at Skansen in Stockholm*
Issue $47.50; High $55.00; Low $50.00;
Close $50.00; No Change

76-R54-1.16
1983 *Nils in Oland*
Issue $42.50; High $45.00; Low $42.50;
Close $45.00; Up $2.50

76-R54-1.17
1984 *Nils in Angermanland*
Issue $42.50; High $50.00; Low $42.50;
Close $50.00; Up $7.50

84-A72-1.4 "Girl with Seashells"
1982 Artists of the World *Children of Aberdeen*
So named for the "floating city" of junks and barges anchored near Hong Kong, this series demonstrates the universal appeal of children in a highly naturalistic style. Artist Kee Fung Ng, a native Chinese, shows the influence of both Eastern and Western thinking in his work.

225

Initially organized as DeGrazia of Scottsdale, the company was founded by James LaFond to represent Arizona artist Ted De-Grazia. The present name, Artists of the World, was adopted in 1977 when the company's scope was enlarged to include additional artists.

DeGrazia plate issues produced by the company are today listed under the dual heading Fairmont/Artists of the World; they are found in this book under the Fairmont name, which was the company that originally manufactured them.

Children of Aberdeen, a proprietary series with artwork by Kee Fung Ng, began in 1979 and depicts the children who live on boats anchored at the fishing village of Aberdeen near Hong Kong.

Artist Kee Fung Ng was born in Canton, China, and educated at its Fu San Art School. His works have received critical acclaim for their subtle balancing of both Eastern and Western artistic concepts.

Children of Aberdeen Series

Artist: Kee Fung Ng. Artist's signature appears on front

China banded in gold

Diameter: 25.4 centimeters (10 inches)

No hanger

Edition size unannounced

Numbered with certificate

84-A72-1.1
1979 *Girl with Little Brother*
Issue $50.00; High $58.00; Low $50.00;
Close $50.00; Down $5.00

84-A72-1.2
1980 *Sampan Girl*
Issue $50.00; High $75.00; Low $55.00;
Close $55.00; Down $10.00

84-A72-1.3
1981 *Girl with Little Sister*
Issue $55.00; High $78.00; Low $55.00;
Close $55.00; Down $5.00

84-A72-1.4
1982 *Girl with Seashells*
Issue $60.00; High $80.00; Low $65.00;
Close $65.00; Down $5.00

84-A72-1.5
1983 *Girl with Seabirds*
Issue $60.00; High $88.00; Low $70.00;
Close $88.00; Up $8.00

84-A72-1.6
1984 *Brother and Sister*
Issue $60.00; High $75.00; Low $60.00;
Close $70.00; Up $10.00
Series Closed

UNITED STATES
CROWN PARIAN
South El Monte, California

perfection in porcelain

Crown Parian, Ltd. was incorporated in South El Monte, California in 1978 for the purpose of producing fine porcelain limited-edition plates and related products.

Crown Parian has introduced two series by well-known comedian Red Skelton: the *Freddie the Freeloader* series in 1979 and *Freddie's Adventures* series in 1982. The *American Folk Heroes* series began in 1983 with artwork by Gene Boyer.

Freddie the Freeloader Series

Artist: Red Skelton. Artist's signature appears on front

Overglaze-decorated porcelain banded in gold

Diameter: 21.6 centimeters (8½ inches)

No hanger

Edition size limited to 10,000

Numbered without certificate

84-C72-1.1
1979 *Freddie in the Bathtub*
Issue $55.00; High $250.00; Low $200.00;
Close $220.00; Down $5.00

84-C72-1.2
1980 *Freddie's Shack*
Issue $55.00; High $95.00; Low $65.00;
Close $70.00; Down $25.00

84-C72-1.3
1981 *Freddie on the Green*
Issue $60.00; High $83.00; Low $60.00;
Close $60.00; Down $15.00

84-C72-1.4
1982 *Love That Freddie*
Issue $60.00; High $63.00; Low $45.00;
Close $50.00; Down $13.00
Series Closed

American Folk Heroes Series

Artist: Gene Boyer. Artist's signature appears on front

Overglaze-decorated porcelain banded in gold

Diameter: 21.6 centimeters (8½ inches)

No hanger

Edition size undisclosed, limited by announced period of issue

Numbered with certificate

84-C72-2.1
1983 *Johnny Appleseed*
Issue $35.00; High $50.00; Low $35.00;
Close $38.00; Up $3.00

84-C72-2.2
1984 *Davy Crockett*
Issue $35.00; High $35.00; Low $35.00;
Close $35.00; No Change

84-C72-2.3
1985 *Betsy Ross*
Issue price: $35.00

Freddie's Adventures Series

Artist: Red Skelton. Artist's signature appears on front

Overglaze-decorated porcelain banded in gold

Diameter: 21.6 centimeters (8½ inches)

No hanger

Edition size limited to 15,000

Numbered without certificate

84-C72-3.1
1981 *Captain Freddie*
Issue $60.00; High $85.00; Low $50.00;
Close $50.00; Down $14.00

84-C72-3.2
1982 *Bronco Freddie*
Issue $60.00; High $55.00; Low $40.00;
Close $40.00; Down $15.00

84-C72-3.3
1983 *Sir Freddie*
Issue $62.50; High $62.50; Low $46.00;
Close $46.00; Down $16.50

84-C72-3.4
1984 *Gertrude and Heathcliffe*
Issue $62.50; High $63.00; Low $60.00;
Close $60.00; Down $2.50
Series Closed

84-E74-1.1 ''Stop and Smell the Roses''
1981 R. J. Ernst Enterprises *Seems Like Yesterday*
This popular plate introduced artist Rusty Money to the collector's plate market. It highlights her soft palette and unique painting style, giving a watercolor effect.

R. J. Ernst Enterprises was founded in 1976 by Ray and Marilyn Ernst. Originally operating from a collectibles gallery in Escondido, California, the company now has expanded offices in San Marcos. Ernst Enterprises produces a variety of limited-edition collectibles as well as collector's plates.

In 1982, the Ernst plate series *Seems Like Yesterday* introduced artist Rusty Money to the collector's market.

Seems Like Yesterday Series

Artist: Rusty Money. Artist's signature appears on front

Porcelain

Diameter: 21.6 centimeters (8½ inches)

No hanger

Edition size undisclosed, limited by announced period of issue

Numbered with certificate

84-E74-1.1
1981 *Stop and Smell the Roses*
Issue $24.50; High $25.00; Low $17.00;
Close $17.00; Down $8.00

84-E74-1.2
1982 *Home by Lunch*
Issue $24.50; High $25.00; Low $18.00;
Close $18.00; Down $7.00

84-E74-1.3
1982 *Lisa's Creek*
Issue $24.50; High $30.00; Low $21.00;
Close $25.00; Up $1.00

84-E74-1.4
1983 *It's Got My Name on It*
Issue $24.50; High $35.00; Low $24.50;
Close $25.00; Up $.50

84-E74-1.5
1984 *My Magic Hat*
Issue $24.50; High $25.00; Low $22.00;
Close $24.00; Down $.50

84-E74-1.6
1984 *Little Prince*
Issue $24.50; High $30.00; Low $24.50;
Close $30.00; Up $5.50
Series Closed

UNITED STATES
FAIRMONT
Pasadena, California

Fairmont

Perfect Porcelain

Fairmont China was established in 1976 to produce limited-edition plates. Two series began that year: the *Holiday* series with artwork by Ted DeGrazia, and the *Famous Clowns* series by comedian Red Skelton. In 1978, Fairmont issued the third plate in the *DeGrazia Children* series, originally started by Gorham (see United States, GORHAM). In 1978 Fairmont started their *Classical American Beauties* series by the artist Vincent and, in 1981, began their *Playful Memories* series with artwork by Sue Etém.

DeGrazia Holiday Series

Artist: Ted DeGrazia. Artist's signature appears on front; first 500 autographed on back

China banded in gold

Diameter: 26 centimeters (10¼ inches)

No hanger

Edition size limited to 10,000

Numbered since 1977, without certificate

84-F4-1.1
1976 *The Festival of Lights*
Issue $45.00; High $325.00; Low $260.00;
Close $300.00; Up $25.00

84-F4-1.2
1977 *The Bell of Hope*
Issue $45.00; High $180.00; Low $142.00;
Close $142.00; Down $38.00

84-F4-1.3
1978 *Little Madonna*
Issue $45.00; High $210.00; Low $160.00;
Close $160.00; Down $50.00

84-F4-1.4
1979 *The Nativity*
Issue $50.00; High $160.00; Low $139.00;
Close $139.00; Down $21.00

84-F4-1.5
1980 *Little Pima Indian Drummer Boy*
Issue $50.00; High $160.00; Low $135.00;
Close $135.00; Down $10.00

84-F4-1.6
1981 *Little Prayer—The Christmas Angel*
Issue $55.00; High $185.00; Low $130.00;
Close $130.00; Down $55.00

84-F4-1.7
1982 *The Blue Boy*
Issue $60.00; High $165.00; Low $150.00;
Close $150.00; No Change

84-F4-1.8
1983 *Heavenly Blessings*
Issue $65.00; High $140.00; Low $115.00;
Close $115.00; Down $25.00

84-F4-1.9
1984 *Navajo Madonna*
Issue $65.00; High $135.00; Low $65.00;
Close $120.00; Up $55.00

84-F4-1.10
1985 *Saguaro Dance*
Issue price: $65.00
Series Closed

Famous Clowns Series

Artist: Red Skelton. Artist's signature appears on front

China banded in gold

Diameter: 21.6 centimeters (8½ inches)

No hanger

Edition size limited to 10,000

Numbered without certificate

84-F4-2.1
1976 *Freddie the Freeloader*
Issue $55.00; High $410.00; Low $350.00;
Close $360.00; Down $50.00

84-F4-2.2
1977 *W. C. Fields*
Issue $55.00; High $66.00; Low $50.00;
Close $60.00; Down $6.00

84-F4-2.3
1978 *Happy*
Issue $55.00; High $70.00; Low $50.00;
Close $50.00; Down $15.00

84-F4-2.4
1979 *The Pledge*
Issue $55.00; High $90.00; Low $60.00;
Close $60.00; Down $30.00
Series Closed

DeGrazia Children Series

Artist: Ted DeGrazia. Artist's signature appears on front; first 500 autographed on back

China banded in gold

Diameter: 26 centimeters (10¼ inches)

No hanger

Edition size limited to 10,000

Numbered without certificate

84-F4-4.1
1978 *Flower Girl*
Issue $45.00; High $175.00; Low $150.00;
Close $170.00; Down $5.00

84-F4-4.2
1979 *Flower Boy*
Issue $45.00; High $165.00; Low $110.00;
Close $110.00; Down $55.00

Rockwell Christmas Series

Artist: Norman Rockwell. Artist's signature appears on front

Etched sterling silver

Diameter: 20.3 centimeters (8 inches)

No hanger

Edition size: as indicated

Numbered, with certificate since 1972

84-F64-1.1
1970 *Bringing Home the Tree*
Edition: 18,321
Issue $100.00; High $150.00; Low $140.00;
Close $140.00; Down $10.00

84-F64-1.2
1971 *Under the Mistletoe*
Edition: 24,792
Issue $100.00; High $100.00; Low $75.00;
Close $85.00; Down $15.00

84-F64-1.3
1972 *The Carolers*
Edition: 29,074
Issue $125.00; High $100.00; Low $75.00;
Close $80.00; Down $20.00

84-F64-1.4
1973 *Trimming the Tree*
Edition: 18,010
Issue $125.00; High $110.00; Low $75.00;
Close $75.00; Down $35.00

84-F64-1.5
1974 *Hanging the Wreath*
Edition: 12,822
Issue $175.00; High $110.00; Low $75.00;
Close $75.00; Down $35.00

84-F64-1.6
1975 *Home for Christmas*
Edition: 11,059
Issue $180.00; High $160.00; Low $100.00;
Close $100.00; Down $60.00
Series Closed

In 1831 Jabez Gorham, a silver-smith, established the Gorham Corporation. Today a division of Textron, the firm is one of the world's largest producers of sterling and hollowware, figurines, and ornaments.

Gorham Corporation acquired crystal and china manufacturing companies in 1970, enabling it to produce limited-edition plates in china as well as silver.

Gorham's *Rockwell Four Seasons* series, which began in 1971 and ended in 1980, was comprised of four plates each year (spring, summer, fall, and winter). A *Christmas* series, also with artwork by Norman Rockwell, was started in 1974. The *DeGrazia Children* series and the *Sugar and Spice* series, with artwork by Leo Jansen, began in 1976 with the latter ending in 1979. The *Prince Tatters* series was started in 1977 and ended in 1980.

Since 1978, Fairmont China has made the *DeGrazia Children* plates (see United States, FAIRMONT). The *Sugar and Spice* and *Prince Tatters* series are produced for Kern Collectibles by Gorham (see United States, KERN COLLECTIBLES).

Rockwell Four Seasons Series

Artist: Norman Rockwell. Artist's signature appears on front

China banded in 24k gold

Diameter: 26.7 centimeters (10½ inches)

No hanger

Edition size undisclosed, limited by year of issue

Not numbered, without certificate

Issued in sets of four

84-G58-1.1-1
1971 *A Boy and His Dog;*
A Boy Meets His Dog
Issue $50.00; High $360.00; Low $300.00;
Close $300.00; Down $25.00

84-G58-1.1-2
1971 *Adventurers Between Adventures*

84-G58-1.1-3
1971 *A Mysterious Malady*

84-G58-1.1-4
1971 *Pride of Parenthood*

84-G58-1.2-1
1972 *Young Love; Flying Colors*
Issue $60.00; High $150.00; Low $95.00;
Close $140.00; Up $30.00

84-G58-1.2-2
1972 *Beguiling Buttercup*

84-G58-1.2-3
1972 *A Scholarly Pace*

84-G58-1.2-4
1972 *Downhill Daring*

84-G58-1.3-1
1973 *The Ages of Love;*
Sweet Song So Young
Issue $60.00; High $190.00; Low $130.00;
Close $130.00; Down $45.00

84-G58-1.3-2
1973 *Flowers in Tender Bloom*

84-G58-1.3-3
1973 *Fondly Do We Remember*

84-G58-1.3-4
1973 *Gaily Sharing Vintage*

84-G58-1.4-1
1974 *Grandpa and Me; Day Dreamers*
Issue $60.00; High $115.00; Low $100.00;
Close $110.00; Down $5.00

84-G58-1.4-2
1974 *Goin' Fishin'*

84-G58-1.4-3
1974 *Pensive Pals*

84-G58-1.4-4
1974 *Gay Blades*

84-G58-1.5-1
1975 *Me and My Pal;*
Young Man's Fancy
Issue $70.00; High $140.00; Low $100.00;
Close $100.00; Down $40.00

84-G58-1.5-2
1975 Fisherman's Paradise

84-G58-1.5-3
1975 Disastrous Daring

84-G58-1.5-4
1975 A Lickin' Good Bath

84-G58-1.6-1
1976 Grand Pals; Soaring Spirits
Issue $70.00; High $180.00; Low $110.00;
Close $150.00; Down $30.00

84-G58-1.6-2
1976 Fish Finders

84-G58-1.6-3
1976 Ghostly Gourds

84-G58-1.6-4
1976 Snow Sculpture

84-G58-1.7-1
1977 Going on Sixteen; Sweet Serenade
Issue $75.00; High $175.00; Low $105.00;
Close $105.00; Down $70.00

84-G58-1.7-2
1977 Shear Agony

84-G58-1.7-3
1977 *Pilgrimage*

84-G58-1.7-4
1977 *Chilling Chore*

84-G58-1.8-1
1978 *The Tender Years; Spring Tonic*
Issue $100.00; High $100.00; Low $81.00;
Close $85.00; Down $10.00

84-G58-1.8-2
1978 *Cool Aid*

84-G58-1.8-3
1978 *Chilly Reception*

84-G58-1.8-4
1978 *New Year Look*

84-G58-1.9-1
1979 *A Helping Hand;*
Closed for Business
Issue $100.00; High $90.00; Low $55.00;
Close $60.00; Down $30.00

84-G58-1.9-2
1979 *Swatters Rights*

84-G58-1.9-3
1979 *The Coal Season's Coming*

84-G58-1.9-4
1979 Year End Count

84-G58-1.10-1
1980 Dad's Boy; In His Spirit
Issue $135.00; High $115.00; Low $75.00;
Close $75.00; Down $35.00
Series Closed

84-G58-1.10-2
1980 Trout Dinner

84-G58-1.10-3
1980 Careful Aim

84-G58-1.10-4
1980 Ski Skills
Series Closed

Rockwell Christmas Series

Artist: Norman Rockwell. Artist's signature appears on front

China banded in 24k gold

Diameter: 21.6 centimeters (8½ inches)

No hanger

Edition size undisclosed, limited by year of issue

Not numbered, without certificate

84-G58-3.1
1974 Tiny Tim
Issue $12.50; High $45.00; Low $30.00;
Close $40.00; Down $5.00

84-G58-3.2
1975 Good Deeds
Issue $17.50; High $50.00; Low $25.00;
Close $25.00; Down $25.00

84-G58-3.3
1976 *Christmas Trio*
Issue $19.50; High $38.00; Low $24.00;
Close $30.00; Down $8.00

84-G58-3.4
1977 *Yuletide Reckoning*
Issue $19.50; High $50.00; Low $26.00;
Close $50.00; Up $5.00

84-G58-3.5
1978 *Planning Christmas Visits*
Issue $24.50; High $25.00; Low $19.00;
Close $20.00; Down $5.00

84-G58-3.6
1979 *Santa's Helpers*
Issue $24.50; High $25.00; Low $19.00;
Close $19.00; Down $1.00

84-G58-3.7
1980 *Letter to Santa*
Issue $27.50; High $35.00; Low $20.00;
Close $20.00; Down $5.00

84-G58-3.8
1981 *Santa Plans His Visit*
Issue $29.50; High $30.00; Low $22.00;
Close $22.00; Down $8.00

84-G58-3.9
1982 *The Jolly Coachman*
Issue $29.50; High $30.00; Low $24.00;
Close $24.00; Down $6.00

84-G58-3.10
1983 *Christmas Dancers*
Issue $29.50; High $42.00; Low $25.00;
Close $28.00; Down $1.50

84-G58-3.11
1984 *Christmas Medley*
Issue $29.50; High $40.00; Low $29.50;
Close $35.00; Up $5.50

84-G58-3.12
1985 *Home for the Holidays*
Issue price: $29.50

DeGrazia Children Series

Artist: Ted DeGrazia. Artist's
signature appears on front

China banded in 24k gold

Diameter: 26.7 centimeters
(10½ inches)

No hanger

Edition size: as indicated

Not numbered, without certificate

84-G58-5.1
1976 *Los Niños*
Edition: 5,000
Issue $35.00; High $1500.00; Low $1300.00;
Close $1300.00; Down $100.00

84-G58-5.2
1977 *The White Dove*
Edition: 10,000
Issue $40.00; High $175.00; Low $160.00;
Close $175.00; Up $15.00
Series Closed

Sugar and Spice Series

Artist: Leo Jansen. Artist's
signature appears on front

China banded in 24k gold

Diameter: 21.6 centimeters
(8½ inches)

No hanger

Edition size limited to 7,500

Numbered without certificate

84-G58-6.1
1976 *Dana and Debbie*
Issue $40.00; High $135.00; Low $80.00;
Close $90.00; Down $40.00

84-G58-6.2
1977 *Becky and Baby*
Issue $42.50; High $60.00; Low $27.00;
Close $35.00; Down $25.00

84-G58-6.3
1978 Jeanette and Julie
Issue $47.50; High $50.00; Low $41.00;
Close $41.00; Down $9.00

84-G58-6.4
1979 Ramona and Rachel
Issue $50.00; High $110.00; Low $95.00;
Close $105.00; No Change
Series Closed

Prince Tatters Series

Artist: Leo Jansen. Artist's
signature appears on front

China banded in 24k gold

Diameter: 21.6 centimeters
(8½ inches)

No hanger

Edition size limited to 7,500

Numbered without certificate

84-G58-8.1
1977 Johnny and Duke
Issue $40.00; High $50.00; Low $35.00;
Close $35.00; Down $15.00

84-G58-8.2
1978 Randy and Rex
Issue $42.50; High $68.00; Low $59.00;
Close $59.00; Down $9.00

84-G58-8.3
1979 Furry Friends
Issue $47.50; High $40.00; Low $24.00;
Close $24.00; Down $16.00

84-G58-8.4
1980 Benji's Burro
Issue $50.00; High $150.00; Low $110.00;
Close $130.00; Up $5.00
Series Closed

84-I31-1.1 "She Walks in Beauty"
1977 Incolay *Romantic Poets*
The first incolay stone collector's plate; the sculptural technique closely resembles high-relief cameo.

UNITED STATES
INCOLAY
San Fernando, California

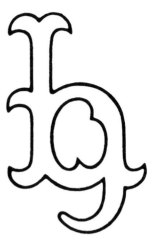

Incolay Studios of California

Incolay Studios has been creating cameo *objets d'art* in Incolay stone since 1965. The manufacturing process by which Incolay stone is created is a closely guarded secret, but it is acknowledged that the process includes the addition of a range of quartz-based minerals to replicate the coloring and weight of semi-precious stone cameos of the past.

Incolay Studios began its first series of collector's plates, the *Romantic Poets Collection,* in 1977. The series is inspired by the poetry of early nineteenth-century poets. In 1979, a second series of cameo plates, the *Great Romances of History Collection,* began. Their *Voyages of Ulysses* series began in 1984.

Gayle Bright Appleby is the designer of the first four issues in the *Romantic Poets Collection.* Roger Akers is the present sculptor. Carl Romanelli is the sculptor for the *Great Romances of History* series, and Alan Brunettin is the creator of *Voyage of Ulysses.*

Romantic Poets Collection

Artist: as indicated. Artist's signature appears on front

Incolay stone with high relief cameos

Diameter: 26 centimeters (10¼ inches)

Attached back hanger

Edition size undisclosed, limited by announced period of issue

Numbered with certificate

84-I31-1.1
1977 She Walks in Beauty
Artist: Gayle Bright Appleby
Issue $60.00; High $190.00; Low $95.00;
Close $95.00; Down $95.00

84-I31-1.2
1978 A Thing of Beauty Is a Joy Forever
Artist: Gayle Bright Appleby
Issue $60.00; High $68.00; Low $65.00;
Close $65.00; Down $3.00

84-I31-1.3
1979 *To a Skylark*
Artist: Gayle Bright Appleby
Issue $65.00; High $75.00; Low $65.00;
Close $65.00; No Change

84-I31-1.4
1980 *She Was a Phantom of Delight*
Artist: Gayle Bright Appleby
Issue $65.00; High $70.00; Low $65.00;
Close $65.00; Down $5.00

84-I31-1.5
1981 *The Kiss*
Artist: Roger Akers
Issue $65.00; High $75.00; Low $65.00;
Close $65.00; Down $1.00

84-I31-1.6
1982 *My Heart Leaps Up When I Behold*
Artist: Roger Akers
Issue $70.00; High $115.00; Low $73.00;
Close $73.00; Down $27.00

84-I31-1.7
1983 *I Stood Tiptoe*
Artist: Roger Akers
Issue $70.00; High $100.00; Low $70.00;
Close $75.00; Up $5.00

84-I31-1.8
1984 *The Dream*
Issue $70.00; High $80.00; Low $70.00;
Close $75.00; Up $5.00

84-I31-1.9
1985 *The Recollection*
Issue price: $70.00

Great Romances of History Collection

Artist: Carl Romanelli. Artist's signature appears on front

Incolay stone with high relief cameos

Diameter: 26 centimeters (10¼ inches)

Attached back hanger

Edition size undisclosed, limited by announced period of issue

Numbered with certificate

84-I31-3.1
1979 Antony and Cleopatra
Issue $65.00; High $67.00; Low $55.00;
Close $55.00; Down $12.00

84-I31-3.2
1980 The Taj Mahal Lovers
Issue $65.00; High $80.00; Low $60.00;
Close $60.00; Down $7.00

84-I31-3.3
1981 Lancelot and Guinevere
Issue $65.00; High $95.00; Low $65.00;
Close $65.00; No Change

84-I31-3.4
1982 Lord Nelson and Lady Hamilton
Issue $70.00; High $95.00; Low $70.00;
Close $70.00; No Change
Series Closed

Voyage of Ulysses Series

Artist: Alan Brunettin. Artist's signature appears on front

Incolay stone with high relief cameos

Diameter: 21.6 centimeters (8½ inches)

Pierced foot rim

Edition size undisclosed, limited by year of issue

Numbered with certificate

84-I31-4.1
1984 Isle of Circe
Issue $50.00; High $70.00; Low $50.00;
Close $62.00; Up $12.00

84-I31-4.2
1985 The Sirens
Issue price: $50.00

84-K20-7.2 "Future Farmer"
1981 Kern Collectibles *Leaders of To-morrow*
Artist Leo Jansen, a well-known studio portraitist, built a special following among collectors with his realistic portraits of children and animals. Today, some years after his untimely death at age 50, his plates maintain their popularity as well as their market value.

The story of Kern Collectibles dates to 1969 when Oscar L. Kern founded Commemorative Imports, a distributor of limited-edition collectibles. Mr. Kern expanded his business one step further in 1972 with the establishment of Kern Collectibles. In 1984, Kern Collectibles was purchased by the Consumer Products Division of 3M Company.

Kern Collectibles issues limited-edition plates produced especially for the company by several of the world's fine china manufacturers. *Leaders of Tomorrow* began in 1980 and comprised four issues by the late Leo Jansen.

Leaders of Tomorrow Series

Artist: Leo Jansen. Artist's signature appears on front

China banded in gold

Diameter: 21.6 centimeters (8½ inches)

No hanger

Edition size limited to 9,800

Numbered without certificate

84-K20-7.1
1980 *Future Physician*
Issue $50.00; High $60.00; Low $35.00;
Close $35.00; Down $25.00

84-K20-7.2
1981 *Future Farmer*
Issue $50.00; High $42.00; Low $30.00;
Close $30.00; Down $12.00

84-K20-7.3
1982 *Future Florist*
Issue $50.00; High $45.00; Low $30.00;
Close $30.00; Down $15.00

84-K20-7.4
1983 *Future Teacher*
Issue $50.00; High $50.00; Low $30.00;
Close $30.00; Down $20.00
Series Closed

NORTH AMERICA'S OLDEST
1854
Edwin M.
Knowles
NEWELL
W. VIRGINIA
U.S.A.
NAME IN FINE CHINA

The Edwin M. Knowles heritage of fine china can be traced to the early nineteenth century when Isaac Knowles, father of Edwin, established the family firm—Knowles, Taylor and Knowles—in East Liverpool, Ohio. The site was chosen for its proximity to deposits of high-quality kaolin clay. The firm became well known for its production of Lotus ware.

After apprenticing with Knowles, Taylor and Knowles, Edwin established his own company in Newell, West Virginia, and became a pre-eminent force in American china. He was honored by election to the presidency of the United States Potters Association.

After his death, the company ceased operations for a period of time until entering into an affiliation with The Bradford Exchange in order to preserve its time-honored name.

Since 1975 the Edwin M. Knowles name has appeared on issues certified by the Rockwell Society of America (see United States, ROCKWELL SOCIETY). The *Wizard of Oz*, first proprietary series to bear the name of Knowles, began in 1977 and ended in 1980, with artwork by James Auckland. The *Americana Holidays* series and the *Gone With the Wind* series, which is endorsed by Metro-Goldwyn-Mayer, began in 1978. Knowles began the *Csatari Grandparent Plate* series in 1980, and the *Annie Collector's Plate* series in 1983. The *Biblical Mothers* series began in 1983 with artwork by Eve Licea. The *Jeanne Down's Friends I Remember* series began in 1983 and their *Four Ancient Elements*, *Edna Hibel Mother's Day*, and *A Father's Love* series' began in 1984.

Also appearing in 1984 were the first of the new series based on the musical masterworks of Rodgers and Hammerstein: *The King and I*, recreated by William Chambers. This four-plate series was followed in 1985 by a second series, *Oklahoma!* by Mort Künstler. 1985 also witnessed the introduction of the first series ever sponsored by the prestigious *Encyclopaedia Britannica*, entitled *Birds of Your Garden*. This series introduced wildlife artist Kevin Daniel to collectors. And the year also saw the creation of the first Knowles series from the late artist Frances Hook: the *Legacy* series.

Knowles has commissioned a number of important contemporary artists to create its plates, including: James Auckland, Raymond Kursár, Don Spaulding, Joseph Csatari, William Chambers, Eve Licea and Edna Hibel.

Wizard of Oz Series

Artist: James Auckland. Artist's signature appears on front

China

Diameter: 21.6 centimeters (8½ inches) through 1979; 25.4 centimeters (10 inches) for 1980 plate

No hanger

Edition size undisclosed, limited by announced period of issue

Numbered with certificate

84-K41-1.1
1977 *Over the Rainbow*
Issue $19.00; High $140.00; Low $78.00;
Close $78.00; Down $52.00

84-K41-1.2
1978 *If I Only Had a Brain*
Issue $19.00; High $36.00; Low $32.00;
Close $33.00; Down $1.00

84-K41-1.3
1978 *If I Only Had a Heart*
Issue $19.00; High $45.00; Low $32.00;
Close $32.00; Down $8.00

84-K41-1.4
1978 *If I Were King of the Forest*
Issue $19.00; High $36.00; Low $32.00;
Close $33.00; Down $1.00

84-K41-1.5
1979 *The Wicked Witch of the West*
Issue $19.00; High $40.00; Low $35.00;
Close $35.00; No Change

84-K41-1.6
1979 *Follow the Yellow Brick Road*
Issue $19.00; High $40.00; Low $30.00;
Close $38.00; Up $8.00

84-K41-1.7
1979 *Wonderful Wizard of Oz*
Issue $19.00; High $55.00; Low $45.00;
Close $45.00; Down $5.00

84-K41-1.8
1980 *The Grand Finale*
(We're Off to See the Wizard)
Issue $24.00; High $50.00; Low $45.00;
Close $45.00; Down $5.00
Series Closed

Americana Holidays Series

Artist: Don Spaulding. Artist's signature appears on front

China

Diameter: 21.6 centimeters, (8½ inches)

No hanger

Edition size undisclosed, limited by period of issue

Numbered with certificate

84-K41-2.1
1978 Fourth of July
Issue $26.00; High $50.00; Low $35.00;
Close $50.00; Up $11.00

84-K41-2.2
1979 Thanksgiving
Issue $26.00; High $75.00; Low $37.00;
Close $40.00; Down $30.00

84-K41-2.3
1980 Easter
Issue $26.00; High $53.00; Low $40.00;
Close $40.00; Down $13.00

84-K41-2.4
1981 Valentine's Day
Issue $26.00; High $50.00; Low $26.00;
Close $30.00; Up $4.00

84-K41-2.5
1982 Father's Day
Issue $26.00; High $36.00; Low $28.00;
Close $30.00; Up $2.00

84-K41-2.6
1983 Christmas
Issue $26.00; High $45.00; Low $26.00;
Close $30.00; Up $4.00

84-K41-2.7
1984 Mother's Day
Issue $26.00; High $35.00; Low $26.00;
Close $30.00; Up $4.00
Series Closed

Gone With the Wind Series

Artist: Raymond Kursár. Artist's signature appears on front

China

Diameter: 21.6 centimeters (8½ inches)

No hanger

Edition size undisclosed, limited by period of issue

Numbered with certificate

84-K41-3.1
1978 Scarlett
Issue $21.50; High $250.00; Low $230.00;
Close $250.00; Up $25.00

84-K41-3.2
1979 Ashley
Issue $21.50; High $190.00; Low $150.00;
Close $160.00; Up $10.00

84-K41-3.3
1980 Melanie
Issue $21.50; High $70.00; Low $50.00;
Close $70.00; Up $10.00

84-K41-3.4
1981 Rhett
Issue $23.50; High $35.00; Low $29.00;
Close $30.00; Down $2.00

84-K41-3.5
1982 Mammy Lacing Scarlett
Issue $23.50; High $45.00; Low $40.00;
Close $40.00; Down $2.00

84-K41-3.6
1983 Melanie Gives Birth
Issue $23.50; High $55.00; Low $23.50;
Close $45.00; Up $21.50

84-K41-3.7
1984 Scarlett's Green Dress
Issue $25.50; High $25.50; Low $25.50;
Close $25.50; No Change

84-K41-3.8
1985 Rhett and Bonnie
Issue price: $25.50

Csatari Grandparent Plate Series

Artist: Joseph Csatari. Artist's signature appears on front

China

Diameter: 21.6 centimeters (8½ inches)

No hanger

Edition size undisclosed, limited by period of issue

Numbered with certificate

84-K41-4.1
1980 *Bedtime Story*
Issue $18.00; High $60.00; Low $30.00;
Close $30.00; Down $30.00

84-K41-4.2
1981 *The Skating Lesson*
Issue $20.00; High $22.00; Low $20.00;
Close $20.00; Down $2.00

84-K41-4.3
1982 *The Cookie Tasting*
Issue $20.00; High $60.00; Low $35.00;
Close $35.00; Down $15.00

84-K41-4.4
1983 *The Swinger*
Issue $20.00; High $32.00; Low $20.00;
Close $25.00; Up $5.00

84-K41-4.5
1984 *The Skating Queen*
Issue $22.00; High $22.00; Low $22.00;
Close $22.00; No Change

Annie Collector's Plate Series

Artist: William Chambers. Artist's signature appears on front

China

Diameter: 21.6 centimeters (8½ inches)

No hanger

Edition size undisclosed, limited by announced period of issue

Numbered with certificate

84-K41-5.1
1983 *Annie and Sandy*
Issue $19.00; High $60.00; Low $33.00;
Close $33.00; Down $27.00

84-K41-5.2
1983 *Daddy Warbucks*
Issue $19.00; High $35.00; Low $19.00;
Close $30.00; Up $11.00

84-K41-5.3
1983 *Annie and Grace*
Issue $19.00; High $40.00; Low $19.00;
Close $30.00; Up $11.00

84-K41-5.4
1984 *Annie and the Orphans*
Issue $21.00; High $35.00; Low $21.00;
Close $35.00; Up $14.00

84-K41-5.5
1985 *Tomorrow*
Issue price: $21.00

Biblical Mothers Series

Artist: Eve Licea. Artist's signature
appears on front

China banded in 24k gold

Diameter: 26 centimeters
(10¼ inches)

No hanger

Edition size undisclosed, limited
by announced period of issue

Numbered with certificate

84-K41-6.1
1983 *Bathsheba and Solomon*
Issue $39.50; High $150.00; Low $110.00;
Close $125.00; Up $15.00

84-K41-6.2
1984 *The Judgment of Solomon*
Issue $39.50; High $75.00; Low $39.50;
Close $70.00; Up $30.50

84-K41-6.3
1984 *Pharoah's Daughter and Moses*
Issue $39.50; High $65.00; Low $39.50;
Close $65.00; Up $25.50

84-K41-6.4
1984 *Mary and Jesus*
Issue $39.50; High $39.50; Low $39.50;
Close $39.50; No Change

Jeanne Down's Friends I Remember Series

Artist: Jeanne Down. Artist's signature appears on front

China

Diameter: 21.6 centimeters (8½ inches)

No hanger

Edition size undisclosed, limited by announced period of issue

Numbered with certificate

84-K41-7.1
1983 *Fish Story*
Issue $17.50; High $35.00; Low $17.50;
Close $30.00; Up $12.50

84-K41-7.2
1984 *Office Hours*
Issue $17.50; High $17.50; Low $17.50;
Close $17.50; No Change

84-K41-7.3
1984 *A Coat of Paint*
Issue $17.50; High $17.50; Low $17.50;
Close $17.50; No Change

84-K41-7.4
1985 *Here Comes the Bride*
Issue price: $19.50

84-K41-7.5
1985 *Fringe Benefits*
Issue price: $19.50

Four Ancient Elements Series

Artist: Georgia Lambert. Artist's signature appears on front

China

Diameter: 23.5 centimeters (9¼ inches)

No hanger

Edition size undisclosed, limited by year of issue

Numbered with certificate

84-K41-8.1
1984 *Earth*
Issue $27.50; High $65.00; Low $27.50;
Close $43.00; Up $15.50

84-K41-8.2
1984 *Water*
Issue $27.50; High $35.00; Low $27.50;
Close $35.00; Up $7.50

84-K41-8.3
1985 *Air*
Issue price: $29.50

Hibel Mother's Day Series

Artist: Edna Hibel. Artist's signature appears on front

China banded in burnished gold

Diameter: 21.6 centimeters (8½ inches)

No hanger

Edition size undisclosed, limited by year of issue

Numbered with certificate

84-K41-9.1
1984 *Abby and Lisa*
Issue $29.50; High $80.00; Low $29.50;
Close $68.00; Up $38.50

84-K41-9.2
1985 *Erica and Jamie*
Issue $29.50; High $40.00; Low $29.50;
Close $40.00; Up $10.50

A Father's Love Series

Artist: Betsey Bradley. Artist's signature appears on front

China

Diameter: 21.6 centimeters (8½ inches)

No hanger

Edition size undisclosed, limited by period of issue

Numbered with certificate

84-K41-10.1
1984 *Open Wide*
Issue $19.50; High $35.00; Low $19.50;
Close $32.00; Up $12.50

84-K41-10.2
1984 *Batter Up*
Issue $19.50; High $19.50; Low $19.50;
Close $19.50; No Change

84-K41-10.3
1985 *Little Shaver*
Issue price: $19.50

The King and I Series

Artist: William Chambers. Artist's signature appears on front

China

Diameter: 21.6 centimeters (8½ inches)

No hanger

Edition size undisclosed, limited by announced period of issue

Numbered with certificate

84-K41-11.1
1984 *A Puzzlement*
Issue $19.50; High $19.50; Low $19.50;
Close $19.50; No Change

84-K41-11.2
1985 *Shall We Dance?*
Issue price: $19.50

84-K41-11.3
1985 *Getting to Know You*
Issue price: $19.50

Birds of Your Garden Series

Artist: Kevin Daniel. Artist's signature appears on front

China

Diameter: 21.6 centimeters (8½ inches)

No hanger

Edition size undisclosed, limited by announced period of issue

Numbered with certificate

84-K41-12.1
1985 *The Cardinal*
Issue $19.50; High $19.50; Low $19.50;
Close $19.50; No Change

84-K41-12.2
1985 *The Blue Jay*
Issue $19.50; High $19.50; Low $19.50;
Close $19.50; No Change

84-K41-12.3
1985 *The Baltimore Oriole*
Issue price: $22.50

Frances Hook Legacy Series

Artist: Frances Hook. Artist's signature appears on front

China

Diameter: 21.6 centimeters (8½ inches)

No hanger

Edition size undisclosed, limited by announced period of issue

Numbered with certificate

84-K41-13.1
1985 *Fascination*
Issue price: $19.50

Edna Hibel Christmas Series

Artist: Edna Hibel. Artist's signature appears on front

China banded in 22k gold

Diameter: 26 centimeters (10¼ inches)

No hanger

Edition size undisclosed, limited by year of issue

Numbered with certificate

84-K41-15.1
1985 *The Angels' Message*
Issue price: $45.00

Oklahoma Series

Artist: Mort Künstler. Artist's signature appears on front

China

Diameter: 21.6 centimeters (8½ inches)

No hanger

Edition size undisclosed, limited by announced period of issue

Numbered with certificate

84-K41-17.1
1985 *Oh, What a Beautiful Mornin'*
Issue price: $19.50

84-L18-1.5 "Rufous Hummingbird"
1974 Lenox Boehm Bird
Although best-known for porcelain wild-life and flower sculptures based on his work, Edward Marshall Boehm was primarily a painter of nature. Here, Lenox has captured some of his best work, and frames it with an intricate gold filigree border.

LENOX

Walter Scott Lenox and his partner, Jonathan Coxon, Sr., established the Ceramic Art Company in Trenton, New Jersey, in 1889. In 1895 Lenox bought out Coxon and operated the business alone until it was reorganized in 1906 as Lenox, Inc. The plant later moved to Pomona. The firm's early products were bowls, vases, figurines, and later, tableware. All were made in "American Belleek," named for the town in Ireland where this creamy, ivory-tinted ware was first produced.

During World World I, Lenox was commissioned to supply President Wilson with a complete 1,700-piece dinner service, the first wholly American china ever used in the White House. Later, both Presidents Franklin Roosevelt and Harry Truman commissioned Lenox to make sets of dinnerware. In 1981, the Reagan administration commissioned Lenox to create a 4,372-piece dinnerware set for the White House.

In 1970 Lenox introduced its *Boehm Bird* series using paintings by artist Edward Marshall Boehm. The series ended in 1981. The *Boehm Woodland Wildlife* series began in 1973 with artwork adapted from original Boehm sculptures. The series ended in 1982.

Boehm Bird Series

Artist: Edward Marshall Boehm.
Artist's name appears on back

China with 24k gold design on border

Diameter: 26.7 centimeters (10½ inches)

No hanger

Edition size undisclosed

Not numbered, without certificate

84-L18-1.1
1970 *Wood Thrush*
Issue $35.00; High $230.00; Low $150.00;
Close $175.00; Down $55.00

84-L18-1.2
1971 *Goldfinch*
Issue $35.00; High $65.00; Low $50.00;
Close $45.00; Down $20.00

84-L18-1.3
1972 *Mountain Bluebird*
Issue $37.50; High $58.00; Low $35.00;
Close $35.00; Down $23.00

84-L18-1.4
1973 *Meadowlark*
Issue $41.00; High $50.00; Low $35.00;
Close $35.00; Down $15.00

84-L18-1.5
1974 *Rufous Hummingbird*
Issue $45.00; High $65.00; Low $45.00;
Close $45.00; Down $15.00

84-L18-1.6
1975 *American Redstart*
Issue $50.00; High $53.00; Low $40.00;
Close $40.00; Down $13.00

84-L18-1.7
1976 *Cardinal*
Issue $53.00; High $75.00; Low $50.00;
Close $55.00; Up $5.00

84-L18-1.8
1977 *Robins*
Issue $55.00; High $55.00; Low $40.00;
Close $48.00; Up $8.00

84-L18-1.9
1978 Mockingbirds
Issue $58.00; High $50.00; Low $45.00;
Close $45.00; Down $5.00

84-L18-1.10
1979 Golden-Crowned Kinglets
Issue $65.00; High $65.00; Low $50.00;
Close $55.00; Up $5.00

84-L18-1.11
1980 Black-Throated Blue Warblers
Issue $80.00; High $100.00; Low $80.00;
Close $80.00; Down $5.00

84-L18-1.12
1981 Eastern Phoebes
Issue $90.00; High $100.00; Low $93.00;
Close $93.00; Down $2.00
Series Closed

Boehm Woodland Wildlife Series

Artist: Edward Marshall Boehm.
Artist's name appears on back

China with 24k gold design on border

Diameter: 26.7 centimeters
(10½ inches)

No hanger

Edition size undisclosed

Not numbered, without certificate

84-L18-3.1
1973 Raccoons
Issue $50.00; High $70.00; Low $40.00;
Close $40.00; Down $30.00

84-L18-3.2
1974 Red Foxes
Issue $52.50; High $45.00; Low $35.00;
Close $40.00; Down $5.00

84-L18-3.3
1975 *Cottontail Rabbits*
Issue $58.50; High $70.00; Low $55.00;
Close $55.00; Down $15.00

84-L18-3.4
1976 *Eastern Chipmunks*
Issue $62.50; High $60.00; Low $50.00;
Close $50.00; Down $10.00

84-L18-3.5
1977 *Beaver*
Issue $67.50; High $62.00; Low $45.00;
Close $45.00; Down $17.00

84-L18-3.6
1978 *Whitetail Deer*
Issue $70.00; High $65.00; Low $50.00;
Close $50.00; Down $15.00

84-L18-3.7
1979 *Squirrels*
Issue $76.00; High $72.00; Low $50.00;
Close $50.00; Down $22.00

84-L18-3.8
1980 *Bobcats*
Issue $92.50; High $80.00; Low $60.00;
Close $60.00; Down $20.00

84-L18-3.9
1981 *Martens*
Issue $100.00; High $95.00; Low $85.00;
Close $90.00; No Change

84-L18-3.10
1982 *Otters*
Issue $100.00; High $120.00; Low $110.00;
Close $110.00; Down $10.00
Series Closed

CLASSICS IN THEIR TIME

Modern Masters, Ltd. was founded in 1980 by limited-edition collectibles dealer Richard J. Sitarski. The firm is located in Frankfort, Illinois, and produces not only limited-edition plates, but also limited-edition graphics. Although Modern Masters has produced several series under its own name, the *Family Treasures Collection*, first offered in 1982, was co-produced with Chicago-based Graphics Buying Service.

Richard Zolan is the creator of the *Family Treasures Collection*.

Family Treasures Collection

Artist: Richard Zolan. Artist's signature appears on front

China

Diameter: 21.6 centimeters (8½ inches)

No hanger

Edition size limited to 18,500

Numbered with certificate

84-M54-1.1
1981 *Cora's Recital*
Issue $39.50; High $35.00; Low $18.00;
Close $18.00; Down $17.00

84-M54-1.2
1982 *Cora's Tea Party*
Issue $39.50; High $38.00; Low $15.00;
Close $15.00; Down $23.00

84-M54-1.3
1983 *Cora's Garden Party*
Issue $39.50; High $40.00; Low $35.00;
Close $35.00; Down $5.00
Series Closed

Floyd Jones and his father founded the Monongahela Valley Cut Glass Company in 1912 at Morgantown, West Virginia. Their most famous design was an elegant pattern known as "Morgantown Rose." The company flourished under the direction of the Jones family for four generations. In 1977 John Heiner purchased the firm and renamed it Morgantown Crystal, recently expanding operations to include glass etching and engraving as well as cutting.

The first limited-edition collector's plates series to bear the Morgantown Crystal hallmark, *Yates' Country Ladies*, began in 1981.

Designs for issues in the series are by Michael Yates.

*Michael Yates' Country
Ladies Series*

Artist: Michael Yates. Artist's
signature appears on front

Full-lead crystal

Diameter: 22.6 centimeters
(8⅞ inches)

No hanger

Edition size limited to 30,000

Numbered with certificate

84-M58-1.1
1981 *Angelica*
Issue $75.00; High $75.00; Low $75.00;
Close $75.00; No Change

84-M58-1.2
1982 *Violet*
Issue $75.00; High $90.00; Low $75.00;
Close $80.00; Up $5.00

84-M58-1.3
1983 *Heather*
Issue $75.00; High $130.00; Low $75.00;
Close $110.00; Up $35.00

84-M58-1.4
1984 *Laurel*
Issue $75.00; High $75.00; Low $75.00;
Close $75.00; No Change
Series Closed

The Newell Pottery Company is a division of the Edwin M. Knowles China Company. The firm is best known for its Newellware, a variety of earthenware.

After having first produced the *Rockwell on Tour* series for the Rockwell Society of America in 1984, the Newell Pottery Company entered the limited-edition plate market under its own name with its *Sarah Stilwell Weber Calendar* series.

*Sarah Stilwell Weber
Calendar Series*

Artist: Sarah Stilwell Weber

Newellware

Diameter: 18.4 centimeters
(7¼ inches)

No hanger

Edition size undisclosed, limited
by announced period of issue

Numbered with certificate

© 1984 SEPCO

84-N18-1.1
1984 *June*
Issue $19.00; High $19.00; Low $19.00;
Close $19.00; No Change

84-N18-1.2
1985 *July*
Issue $19.00; High $19.00; Low $19.00;
Close $19.00; No Change

84-N18-1.3
1985 *August*
Issue $19.00; High $19.00; Low $19.00;
Close $19.00; No Change

84-N18-1.4
1985 *September*
Issue $19.00; High $19.00; Low $19.00;
Close $19.00; No Change

84-N18-1.5
1985 *October*
Issue price: $19.00

84-N18-1.6
1985 *November*
Issue price: $19.00

UNITED STATES
PEMBERTON & OAKES
Santa Barbara, California

Pemberton & Oakes was founded in 1977. Originally located in Evanston, Illinois, the firm moved to Santa Barbara, California in 1979 and opened a gallery for the display of original art works from its proprietary plate series.

The first two Bradex-listed series produced by the company, *Zolan's Children* and the *Nutcracker Ballet Plate Collection*, were both introduced in 1978; they are listed under the maker's name, Viletta China Co. (see United States, VILETTA). The two most-recent Bradex-listed series from the company are listed under the Pemberton & Oakes name. The *Children at Christmas Collection*, introduced in 1981, and *Wonder of Childhood Collection*, introduced in 1982, both feature the work of Donald Zolan, already well-known to collectors for his earlier *Zolan's Children* series.

Wonder of Childhood Collection

Artist: Donald Zolan. Artist's signature appears on front

China

Diameter: 21.6 centimeters (8½ inches)

No hanger

Edition size undisclosed, limited by announced period of issue

Numbered with certificate

84-P19-1.1
1982 *Touching the Sky*
Issue $19.00; High $42.00; Low $30.00;
Close $30.00; Down $10.00

84-P19-1.2
1983 *Spring Innocence*
Issue $19.00; High $38.00; Low $32.00;
Close $37.00; Up $2.00

84-P19-1.3
1984 *Winter Angel*
Issue $22.00; High $50.00; Low $22.00;
Close $50.00; Up $28.00

84-P19-1.4
1985 *Small Wonder*
Issue $22.00; High $22.00; Low $22.00;
Close $22.00; No Change

Children at Christmas Collection

Artist: Donald Zolan. Artist's signature appears on front

China banded in gold

Diameter: 26 centimeters (10¼ inches)

No hanger

Edition size limited to 15,000

Numbered with certificate

84-P19-2.1
1981 *A Gift for Laurie*
Issue $48.00; High $75.00; Low $55.00;
Close $60.00; Down $15.00

84-P19-2.2
1982 *A Christmas Prayer*
Issue $48.00; High $55.00; Low $50.00;
Close $50.00; No Change

84-P19-2.3
1983 *Erik's Delight*
Issue $48.00; High $60.00; Low $40.00;
Close $43.00; Down $5.00

84-P19-2.4
1984 *Christmas Secret*
Issue $48.00; High $50.00; Low $48.00;
Close $50.00; Up $2.00

84-P19-2.5
1985 *Christmas Kitten*
Issue price: $48.00

Children and Pets Series

Artist: Donald Zolan. Artist's
signature appears on front

China

Diameter: 19 centimeters
(7½ inches)

No hanger

Edition size undisclosed, limited
by announced period of issue

Numbered with certificate

84-P19-3.1
1984 *Tender Moment*
Issue $19.00; High $60.00; Low $19.00;
Close $60.00; Up $41.00

84-P19-3.2
1985 *Golden Moment*
Issue $19.00; High $40.00; Low $19.00;
Close $40.00; Up $21.00

84-P19-3.3
1985 *Making Friends*
Issue $19.00; High $19.00; Low $19.00;
Close $19.00; No Change

84-P19-3.4
1985 *Tender Beginning*
Issue price: $19.00

84-P29-1.3 "Mockingbird" and "Cardinal"
1972 Pickard *Lockhart Wildlife*
This two-plate set demonstrates both the illustration skill of noted naturalist James Lockhart, and the elegant rim embellishments for which Pickard issues are widely famous.

Pickard was established in Edgerton, Wisconsin, in 1894 by Wilder Austin Pickard, then moved to Chicago in 1897. For some forty years the Pickard China Studio, as the firm was then known, was a decorating company employing artists to hand-paint white blanks of bowls, pitchers, and other items obtained from factories in Europe.

In 1920 Pickard was incorporated and in 1938 moved to Antioch, Illinois, the site of the present pottery. Here the firm began making its own fine china. Today Pickard, Inc. is headed by Henry A. Pickard, a third generation descendant of the founder, making it the only American china company in the hands of the founding family.

In 1970 Pickard introduced its *Lockhart Wildlife* series, with artwork by James Lockhart. These plates were issued in pairs during the first four years of the series, but from 1974 individual plates were issued. The series ended in 1980. The *Christmas* series began in 1976, and in 1978 Pickard began the *Children of Renoir* series which ended in 1980. Pickard began its *Mother's Love* series in 1980 with artwork by Irene Spencer and in 1981 introduced *Oleg Cassini's Most Beautiful Women of All Time Collection.* The *Children of Mexico* series began in 1981 with artwork by Jorge Sanchez. In 1982, the *Symphony of Roses* series began with artwork by Irene Spencer.

Lockhart Wildlife Series

Artist: James Lockhart. Artist's signature appears on front

China banded in 24k gold

Diameter: as indicated

No hanger

Edition size: as indicated

Numbered with certificate

84-P29-1.1-1
1970 *Woodcock*
Edition: 2,000
Diameter: 26.7 cm. (10½ in.)
Pair Issue $150.00; High $290.00;
Low $290.00; Close $290.00; No Change

84-P29-1.1-2
1970 *Ruffed Grouse*

84-P29-1.2-1
1971 *Green-Winged Teal*
Edition: 2,000
Diameter: 26.7 cm. (10½ in.)
Pair Issue $150.00; High $220.00;
Low $200.00; Close $220.00; Up $20.00

84-P29-1.2-2
1971 *Mallard*

84-P29-1.3-1
1972 *Mockingbird*
Edition: 2,000
Diameter: 26.7 cm. (10½ in.)
Pair Issue $162.50; High $185.00;
Low $150.00; Close $170.00; Down $15.00

84-P29-1.3-2
1972 *Cardinal*

84-P29-1.4-1
1973 *Wild Turkey*
Edition: 2,000
Diameter: 26.7 cm. (10½ in.)
Pair Issue $162.50; High $260.00;
Low $140.00; Close $140.00; Down $35.00

84-P29-1.4-2
1973 *Ring-Necked Pheasant*

84-P29-1.5
1974 *American Bald Eagle*
Edition: 2,000
Diameter: 33 cm. (13 in.)
Issue $150.00; High $800.00; Low $700.00;
Close $700.00; Down $50.00

84-P29-1.6
1975 *White-Tailed Deer*
Edition: 2,500
Diameter: 27.9 cm. (11 in.)
Issue $100.00; High $130.00; Low $82.00;
Close $130.00; Up $30.00

84-P29-1.7
1976 *American Buffalo*
Edition: 2,500
Diameter: 33 cm. (13 in.)
Issue $165.00; High $170.00; Low $120.00;
Close $120.00; Down $50.00

84-P29-1.8
1977 *Great Horned Owl*
Edition: 2,500
Diameter: 27.9 cm. (11 in.)
Issue $100.00; High $100.00; Low $70.00;
Close $70.00; Down $30.00

84-P29-1.9
1978 *American Panther*
Edition: 2,000
Diameter: 33 cm. (13 in.)
Issue $175.00; High $190.00; Low $140.00;
Close $140.00; Down $35.00

84-P29-1.10
1979 *Red Fox*
Edition: 2,500
Diameter: 27.9 cm. (11 in.)
Issue $120.00; High $95.00; Low $55.00;
Close $60.00; Down $35.00

84-P29-1.11
1980 *Trumpeter Swan*
Edition: 2,000
Diameter: 33 cm. (13 in.)
Issue $200.00; High $150.00; Low $140.00;
Close $140.00; Down $10.00
Series Closed

Christmas Series

Artist: as indicated

China with 24k gold design on border

Diameter: 21 centimeters (8¼ inches)

No hanger

Edition size: as indicated

Numbered without certificate

84-P29-2.1
1976 *The Alba Madonna*
Artist: Raphael/Edition: 7,500
Issue $60.00; High $135.00; Low $75.00;
Close $75.00; Down $55.00

84-P29-2.2
1977 *The Nativity*
Artist: Lorenzo Lotto/Edition: 7,500
Issue $65.00; High $92.00; Low $50.00;
Close $55.00; Down $37.00

84-P29-2.3
1978 *The Rest on the Flight into Egypt*
Artist: Gerard David/Edition: 10,000
Issue $65.00; High $65.00; Low $40.00;
Close $40.00; Down $25.00

84-P29-2.4
1979 *Adoration of the Magi*
Artist: Botticelli/Edition: 10,000
Issue $70.00; High $45.00; Low $40.00;
Close $40.00; Down $5.00

84-P29-2.5
1980 *Madonna and Child with the Infant
Saint John*
Artist: Sodoma/Edition: 10,000
Issue $80.00; High $65.00; Low $46.00;
Close $46.00; Down $19.00

84-P29-2.6
1981 *Madonna and Child with Angels*
Artist: Hans Memling/Edition: 10,000
Issue $90.00; High $60.00; Low $45.00;
Close $45.00; Down $5.00
Series Closed

Children of Renoir Series

Artist: Pierre Auguste Renoir.
Artist's signature appears on front

China banded in 24k gold

Diameter: 21 centimeters
(8¼ inches)

No hanger

Edition size limited to 5,000. Two
annual issues

Numbered without certificate

84-P29-4.1
1978 *A Girl with a Watering Can*
Issue $50.00; High $150.00; Low $80.00;
Close $80.00; Down $70.00

84-P29-4.2
1978 *Child in White*
Issue $50.00; High $70.00; Low $55.00;
Close $55.00; Down $15.00

84-P29-4.3
1979 *Girl with Hoop*
Issue $55.00; High $65.00; Low $45.00;
Close $45.00; Down $20.00

84-P29-4.4
1979 *At the Piano*
Issue $55.00; High $65.00; Low $55.00;
Close $55.00; Down $10.00

84-P29-4.5
1980 *Two Little Circus Girls*
Issue $60.00; High $50.00; Low $30.00;
Close $30.00; Down $20.00

84-P29-4.6
1980 *The Artist's Son Jean*
Issue $60.00; High $50.00; Low $35.00;
Close $35.00; Down $10.00
Series Closed

Oleg Cassini's Most Beautiful Women of All Time Collection

Artist: Oleg Cassini. Artist's signature appears on front

China banded in 24k gold

Diameter: 26.7 centimeters (10½ inches)

No hanger

Edition size undisclosed, limited by year of issue

Numbered with certificate

84-P29-5.1
1981 *Helen of Troy*
Issue $75.00; High $75.00; Low $70.00;
Close $70.00; Down $5.00

84-P29-5.2
1982 *Marie Antoinette*
Issue $75.00; High $80.00; Low $67.00;
Close $67.00; Down $13.00

84-P29-5.3
1983 *Lillie Langtry*
Issue $75.00; High $110.00; Low $75.00;
Close $95.00; Up $20.00

84-P29-5.4
1984 *Salomé*
Issue $75.00; High $90.00; Low $75.00;
Close $90.00; Up $15.00
Series Closed

Mother's Love Series

Artist: Irene Spencer. Artist's signature appears on front

China banded in 24k gold

Diameter: 23.8 centimeters (9⅜ inches)

No hanger

Edition size limited to 7,500

Numbered without certificate

84-P29-6.1
1980 *Miracle*
Issue $95.00; High $160.00; Low $110.00;
Close $120.00; Down $30.00

84-P29-6.2
1981 *Story Time*
Issue $110.00; High $100.00; Low $75.00;
Close $75.00; Down $25.00

84-P29-6.3
1982 *First Edition*
Issue $115.00; High $110.00; Low $70.00;
Close $75.00; Down $35.00

84-P29-6.4
1983 *Precious Moment*
Issue $120.00; High $140.00; Low $110.00;
Close $125.00; Down $15.00
Series Closed

Children of Mexico Series

Artist: Jorge Sanchez. Artist's signature appears on front

China banded in 24k gold

Diameter: 26.7 centimeters (10½ inches)

No hanger

Edition size limited to 5,000

Numbered without certificate

84-P29-7.1
1981 *Maria*
Issue $85.00; High $130.00; Low $95.00;
Close $95.00; Down $35.00

84-P29-7.2
1981 *Miguel*
Issue $85.00; High $100.00; Low $65.00;
Close $65.00; Down $35.00

84-P29-7.3
1982 *Regina*
Issue $90.00; High $85.00; Low $75.00;
Close $75.00; Down $10.00

84-P29-7.4
1983 *Raphael*
Issue $90.00; High $95.00; Low $73.00;
Close $73.00; Down $22.00
Series Closed

Symphony of Roses Series

Artist: Irene Spencer. Artist's signature appears on front

China with scalloped, gold-rimmed border

Diameter: 23.8 centimeters (9³/₈ inches)

No hanger

Edition size limited to 10,000

Numbered without certificate

84-P29-8.1
1982 *Wild Irish Rose*
Issue $85.00; High $110.00; Low $75.00;
Close $75.00; Down $25.00

84-P29-8.2
1983 *Yellow Rose of Texas*
Issue $90.00; High $110.00; Low $95.00;
Close $100.00; Down $10.00

84-P29-8.3
1984 *Honeysuckle Rose*
Issue $95.00; High $100.00; Low $90.00;
Close $100.00; Up $5.00

84-P29-8.4
1985 *Rose of Washington Square*
Issue price: $100.00
Series Closed

Reco International was founded in 1967 by Heio W. Reich who continues as its president. From the beginning the firm has been an importer and maker of limited-edition plates.

World of Children, Reco International's first U.S. proprietary series, was introduced in 1977, with designs by John McClelland. The series ended in 1980. A second series with designs by the same artist, *McClelland's Mother Goose* series, was introduced in 1979. In 1981, Reco International began a third series, the *McClelland Children's Circus Collection*. The *Days Gone By* series, with artwork by Sandra Kuck, began in 1983.

World of Children Series

Artist: John McClelland. Artist's signature appears on front

China banded in 24k gold

Diameter: 26.7 centimeters (10½ inches)

No hanger

Edition size limited to 10,000 in 1977; 15,000 thereafter

Numbered with certificate since 1978

84-R60-1.1
1977 *Rainy Day Fun*
Issue $50.00; High $150.00; Low $75.00;
Close $75.00; Down $75.00

84-R60-1.2
1978 *When I Grow Up*
Issue $50.00; High $85.00; Low $50.00;
Close $50.00; Down $35.00

84-R60-1.3
1979 *You're Invited*
Issue $50.00; High $80.00; Low $45.00;
Close $45.00; Down $35.00

84-R60-1.4
1980 *Kittens for Sale*
Issue $50.00; High $55.00; Low $40.00;
Close $40.00; Down $15.00
Series Closed

McClelland's Mother Goose Series

Artist: John McClelland. Artist's signature appears on front

China

Diameter: 21.6 centimeters (8½ inches)

No hanger

Edition size undisclosed, limited by year of issue

Numbered with certificate

84-R60-2.1
1979 *Mary, Mary*
Issue $22.50; High $250.00; Low $200.00;
Close $220.00; Down $10.00

84-R60-2.2
1980 *Little Boy Blue*
Issue $22.50; High $110.00; Low $90.00;
Close $100.00; No Change

84-R60-2.3
1981 *Little Miss Muffet*
Issue $24.50; High $45.00; Low $32.00;
Close $39.00; Up $7.00

84-R60-2.4
1982 *Little Jack Horner*
Issue $24.50; High $50.00; Low $36.00;
Close $36.00; Down $9.00

84-R60-2.5
1983 *Little Bo Peep*
Issue $24.50; High $47.00; Low $24.50;
Close $44.00; Up $19.50

84-R60-2.6
1984 *Diddle, Diddle Dumpling*
Issue $24.50; High $45.00; Low $24.50;
Close $41.00; Up $16.50

84-R60-2.7
1985 *Mary Had a Little Lamb*
Issue $27.50; High $27.50; Low $27.50;
Close $27.50; No Change

McClelland Children's Circus Collection

Artist: John McClelland. Artist's signature appears on front

China

Diameter: 23.5 centimeters
(9¼ inches)

No hanger

Edition size undisclosed, limited by year of issue

Numbered with certificate

84-R60-3.1
1981 *Tommy the Clown*
Issue $29.50; High $32.00; Low $30.00;
Close $30.00; No Change

84-R60-3.2
1982 *Katie the Tightrope Walker*
Issue $29.50; High $31.00; Low $30.00;
Close $32.00; Up $1.00

84-R60-3.3
1983 *Johnny the Strongman*
Issue $29.50; High $36.00; Low $29.50;
Close $30.00; Up $.50

84-R60-3.4
1983 *Maggie the Animal Trainer*
Issue $29.50; High $40.00; Low $29.50;
Close $30.00; Up $.50
Series Closed

Days Gone By Series

Artist: Sandra Kuck. Artist's signature appears on front

China banded in 23K gold

Diameter: 23.5 centimeters (9¼ inches)

No hanger

Edition size undisclosed, limited by announced period of issue

Numbered with certificate

84-R60-8.1
1983 *Sunday Best*
Issue $29.50; High $90.00; Low $65.00;
Close $90.00; Up $20.00

84-R60-8.2
1983 *Amy's Magic Horse*
Issue $29.50; High $62.00; Low $30.00;
Close $62.00; Up $32.00

84-R60-8.3
1984 *Little Anglers*
Issue $29.50; High $45.00; Low $30.00;
Close $45.00; Up $15.00

84-R60-8.4
1984 *Afternoon Recital*
Issue $29.50; High $45.00; Low $29.50;
Close $43.00; Up $13.50

84-R60-8.5
1984 *Little Tutor*
Issue $29.50; High $40.00; Low $29.50;
Close $38.00; Up $8.50

84-R60-8.6
1984 Easter at Grandma's
Issue $29.50; High $40.00; Low $29.50;
Close $40.00; Up $10.50

84-R60-8.7
1985 Morning Song
Issue $29.50; High $40.00; Low $29.50;
Close $40.00; Up $10.50

84-R60-8.8
1985 Surrey Ride
Issue $29.50; High $35.00; Low $29.50;
Close $35.00; Up $5.50
Series Closed

Becky's Day Series

Artist: John McClelland. Artist's
signature appears on front

China

Diameter: 21.6 centimeters
(8½ inches)

No hanger

Edition size undisclosed, limited
by announced period of issue

Numbered with certificate

84-R60-10.1
1985 Awakening
Issue price: $24.50

84-R18-2.1 "A Partridge in a Pear Tree"
1970 Reed & Barton *Christmas*
Damascene silver—an electroplating process that combines copper, silver, bronze, and gold.

Reed & Barton Silversmiths traces its origin to a factory established by Isaac Babbitt in the early nineteenth century. In 1824 Babbitt developed an alloy, harder and more lustrous than pewter, which he named Britannia metal. Henry G. Reed and Charles E. Barton, artists working for Babbitt, acquired the firm in the 1830s and continued to manufacture Brittania ware. In the late 1840s, the factory began to produce plated silverware. Reed & Barton was incorporated in 1888 and started producing solid silver services. Sterling flatware and hollowware soon replaced plated ware as their largest line. In 1903 the firm began reproducing colonial pewter ware.

In 1970 Reed & Barton began their *Christmas* series which changes theme every three years. The first three plates are based on Christmas carols; the second three are based on fifteenth-century altar art; the next are based on American Christmas scenes; and the next depict nineteenth-century American illustrations. The series ended in 1981.

Artist Robert Johnson, whose works are in private collections throughout the United States, Europe, and the Far East, developed the patented electroplating process used in the creation of the Reed & Barton *Christmas* series. The medium, known as Damascene silver, combines silver, gold, copper, and bronze, and the electroplating process is derived from a hand-craft method perfected at Damascus in the middle ages.

Christmas Series

Artist: as indicated

Damascene silver

Diameter: 27.9 centimeters (11 inches) through 1978; thereafter, 20.3 centimeters (8 inches)

No hanger

Edition size: as indicated

Numbered without certificate through 1978; thereafter not numbered, accompanied with numbered certificate

84-R18-2.1
1970 *A Partridge in a Pear Tree*
Artist: Robert Johnson/Edition: 2,500
Issue $55.00; High $200.00; Low $150.00;
Close $150.00; Down $50.00

84-R18-2.2
1971 *We Three Kings of Orient Are*
Artist: Robert Johnson/Edition: 7,500
Issue $60.00; High $65.00; Low $45.00;
Close $45.00; Down $20.00

84-R18-2.3
1972 *Hark! The Herald Angels Sing*
Artist: Robert Johnson/Edition: 7,500
Issue $60.00; High $60.00; Low $38.00;
Close $38.00; Down $22.00

84-R18-2.4
1973 *Adoration of the Kings*
Artist: Rogier van der Weyden
Edition: 7,500
Issue $60.00; High $75.00; Low $75.00;
Close $75.00; No Change

84-R18-2.5
1974 *The Adoration of the Magi*
Artist: Fra Angelico and Fra Lippi
Edition: 7,500
Issue $65.00; High $65.00; Low $58.00;
Close $58.00; Down $7.00

84-R18-2.6
1975 *Adoration of the Kings*
Artist: Steven Lochner/Edition: 7,500
Issue $65.00; High $65.00; Low $65.00;
Close $65.00; No Change

84-R18-2.7
1976 *Morning Train*
Artist: Maxwell Mays/Edition: 7,500
Issue $65.00; High $60.00; Low $55.00;
Close $55.00; Down $5.00

84-R18-2.8
1977 *Decorating the Church*
Artist: Maxwell Mays/Edition: 7,500
Issue $65.00; High $60.00; Low $60.00;
Close $60.00; No Change

84-R18-2.9
1978 *The General Store at*
Christmas Time
Artist: Maxwell Mays/Edition: 7,500
Issue $65.00; High $70.00; Low $66.00;
Close $66.00; Down $4.00

84-R18-2.10
1979 *Merry Old Santa Claus*
Artist: Thomas Nast/Edition: 2,500
Issue $55.00; High $65.00; Low $63.00;
Close $63.00; No Change

84-R18-2.11
1980 *Gathering Christmas Greens*
Artist: Unknown/Edition: 2,500
Issue $65.00; High $75.00; Low $75.00;
Close $75.00; No Change

84-R18-2.12
1981 *The Shopkeeper at Christmas*
Artist: W. L. Sheppard/Edition: 2,500
Issue $75.00; High $75.00; Low $75.00;
Close $75.00; No Change
Series Closed

84-R69-1.1 "Lincoln"
1976 River Shore *Famous Americans*
The world's first copper collector's plate was
based on artwork by Norman Rockwell and
sculpted by Roger Brown.

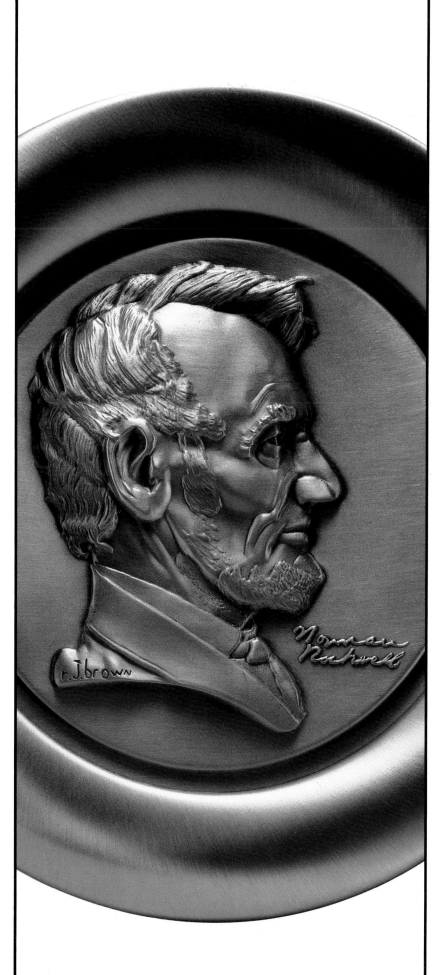

UNITED STATES
RIVER SHORE
Caledonia, Michigan

River Shore, Ltd.®

Museum Quality Limited Editions

River Shore, Ltd. was established in 1975 to market limited-edition collectibles.

In 1976 River Shore began its *Famous Americans* series, the first collector's plates crafted in copper, based on artwork by Norman Rockwell and sculpted by Roger Brown. The series ended in 1979. River Shore introduced its *Signs of Love* series in 1981 with artwork by Yin-Rei Hicks.

The company ceased production of collector's plates upon the completion of the *Signs of Love* series.

Famous Americans Series

Artist: Roger Brown (after works by Norman Rockwell). Artist's signature appears on front along with name of Norman Rockwell

Copper

Diameter: 20.3 centimeters (8 inches)

No hanger

Edition size limited to 9,500

Numbered with certificate

84-R69-1.1
1976 *Lincoln*
Issue $40.00; High $90.00; Low $65.00;
Close $65.00; Down $25.00

84-R69-1.2
1977 *Rockwell*
Issue $45.00; High $50.00; Low $39.00;
Close $39.00; Down $11.00

84-R69-1.3
1978 *Peace Corps*
Issue $45.00; High $30.00; Low $15.00;
Close $15.00; Down $15.00

84-R69-1.4
1979 *Spirit of Lindbergh*
Issue $50.00; High $40.00; Low $30.00;
Close $30.00; Down $10.00
Series Closed

Signs of Love Series

Artist: Yin-Rei Hicks. Artist's signature appears on front

China

Diameter: 21.6 centimeters (8½ inches)

No hanger

Edition size undisclosed, limited by announced period of issue

Numbered with certificate

84-R69-2.1
1981 *A Kiss for Mother*
Issue $18.50; High $22.00; Low $19.00;
Close $19.00; Down $3.00

84-R69-2.2
1981 *A Watchful Eye*
Issue $21.50; High $22.00; Low $22.00;
Close $22.00; No Change

84-R69-2.3
1982 *A Gentle Persuasion*
Issue $21.50; High $35.00; Low $22.00;
Close $22.00; No Change

84-R69-2.4
1983 *A Protective Embrace*
Issue $23.50; High $35.00; Low $28.00;
Close $28.00; Down $2.00

84-R69-2.5
1983 *A Tender Coaxing*
Issue $23.50; High $55.00; Low $38.00;
Close $46.00; Up $8.00

84-R69-2.6
1984 *A Reassuring Touch*
Issue $23.50; High $40.00; Low $23.50;
Close $40.00; Up $16.50

84-R69-2.7
1985 *A Trusting Hug*
Issue price: $23.50

84-R70-1.8 "Wrapped Up in Christmas"
1981 Rockwell Society *Christmas*
The Rockwell Society of America is recognized for its efforts to renew collector interest in obscure-but-worthy Rockwell works. Here, the simple elements of the overburdened boy and the playful dog demonstrate Rockwell's astounding storytelling ability and his gift at capturing the American character on canvas.

UNITED STATES
ROCKWELL SOCIETY
Ardsley, New York

The Rockwell Society of America is a chartered non-profit organization devoted to the study and appreciation of the works of Norman Rockwell. The Society's *Christmas* series began in 1974, with the first issue manufactured by Ridgewood. Subsequent issues have been made by the Edwin M. Knowles China Company (see United States, KNOWLES). The *Mother's Day* series started in 1976, the *Rockwell Heritage* series began in 1977, and *Rockwell's Rediscovered Women* series was introduced in 1981. The *Rockwell on Tour Collection* and *Rockwell's Light Campaign* series started in 1983.

In 1985, The Rockwell Society introduced the first Rockwell series to earn recognition and endorsement by the Norman Rockwell Family Trust, comprised of Norman Rockwell's heirs. The first series to bear the seals of The Rockwell Society, Knowles and The Rockwell Family Trust is entitled *Rockwell's American Dream*.

Christmas Series

Artist: Norman Rockwell. Artist's signature appears on front

China

Diameter: 21 centimeters (8¼ inches)

No hanger

Edition size undisclosed, limited by announced period of issue

Numbered with certificate

84-R70-1.1
1974 Scotty Gets His Tree
Issue $24.50; High $130.00; Low $100.00;
Close $115.00; Down $5.00

84-R70-1.2
1975 Angel with a Black Eye
Issue $24.50; High $90.00; Low $50.00;
Close $55.00; Down $35.00

84-R70-1.3
1976 Golden Christmas
Issue $24.50; High $58.00; Low $40.00;
Close $45.00; Down $13.00

84-R70-1.4
1977 Toy Shop Window
Issue $24.50; High $50.00; Low $35.00;
Close $35.00; Down $10.00

84-R70-1.5
1978 Christmas Dream
Issue $24.50; High $50.00; Low $30.00;
Close $32.00; Down $18.00

84-R70-1.6
1979 Somebody's Up There
Issue $24.50; High $30.00; Low $27.00;
Close $28.00; Up $1.00

84-R70-1.7
1980 Scotty Plays Santa
Issue $24.50; High $35.00; Low $28.00;
Close $28.00; Down $5.00

84-R70-1.8
1981 Wrapped Up in Christmas
Issue $25.50; High $35.00; Low $28.00;
Close $28.00; Down $2.00

84-R70-1.9
1982 *Christmas Courtship*
Issue $25.50; High $42.00; Low $30.00;
Close $30.00; Down $6.00

84-R70-1.10
1983 *Santa in the Subway*
Issue $25.50; High $40.00; Low $30.00;
Close $30.00; Up $4.50

84-R70-1.11
1984 *Santa in His Workshop*
Issue $27.50; High $33.00; Low $27.50;
Close $30.00; Up $2.50

Mother's Day Series

Artist: Norman Rockwell. Artist's
signature appears on front

China

Diameter: 21.6 centimeters
(8½ inches)

No hanger

Edition size undisclosed, limited
by announced period of issue

Numbered with certificate

84-R70-2.1
1976 *A Mother's Love*
Issue $24.50; High $125.00; Low $90.00;
Close $105.00; Up $15.00

84-R70-2.2
1977 *Faith*
Issue $24.50; High $75.00; Low $55.00;
Close $70.00; Up $5.00

84-R70-2.3
1978 *Bedtime*
Issue $24.50; High $90.00; Low $55.00;
Close $55.00; Down $35.00

84-R70-2.4
1979 *Reflections*
Issue $24.50; High $36.00; Low $35.00;
Close $35.00; Down $1.00

84-R70-2.5
1980 *A Mother's Pride*
Issue $24.50; High $38.00; Low $32.00;
Close $35.00; Up $3.00

84-R70-2.6
1981 After the Party
Issue $24.50; High $35.00; Low $32.00;
Close $35.00; Up $3.00

84-R70-2.7
1982 The Cooking Lesson
Issue $25.50; High $33.00; Low $30.00;
Close $33.00; Up $3.00

84-R70-2.8
*1983 Add Two Cups and a Measure
of Love*
Issue $25.50; High $75.00; Low $49.00;
Close $49.00; Down $9.00

84-R70-2.9
1984 Grandma's Courting Dress
Issue $25.50; High $50.00; Low $25.50;
Close $39.00; Up $13.50

84-R70-2.10
1985 Mending Time
Issue $27.50; High $40.00; Low $27.50;
Close $40.00; Up $12.50

Rockwell Heritage Series

Artist: Norman Rockwell. Artist's
signature appears on front

China

Diameter: 21.6 centimeters
(8½ inches)

No hanger

Edition size undisclosed, limited
by announced period of issue

Numbered with certificate

84-R70-3.1
1977 The Toy Maker
Issue $14.50; High $215.00; Low $195.00;
Close $200.00; Down $13.00

84-R70-3.2
1978 The Cobbler
Issue $19.50; High $160.00; Low $120.00;
Close $120.00; Down $20.00

84-R70-3.3
1979 *The Lighthouse Keeper's Daughter*
Issue $19.50; High $95.00; Low $65.00;
Close $65.00; Down $20.00

84-R70-3.4
1980 *The Ship Builder*
Issue $19.50; High $70.00; Low $55.00;
Close $55.00; No Change

84-R70-3.5
1981 *The Music Maker*
Issue $19.50; High $33.00; Low $30.00;
Close $32.00; Up $2.00

84-R70-3.6
1982 *The Tycoon*
Issue $19.50; High $40.00; Low $32.00;
Close $34.00; Up $2.00

84-R70-3.7
1983 *The Painter*
Issue $19.50; High $45.00; Low $25.00;
Close $45.00; Up $20.00

84-R70-3.8
1984 *The Storyteller*
Issue $19.50; High $35.00; Low $19.50;
Close $35.00; Up $15.50

84-R70-3.9
1985 *The Gourmet*
Issue $19.50; High $19.50; Low $19.50;
Close $19.50; No Change

Rockwell's Rediscovered Women Series

Artist: Norman Rockwell. Artist's signature appears on front

China

Diameter: 21.6 centimeters (8½ inches)

No hanger

Edition size undisclosed, limited by announced period of issue

Numbered with certificate

84-R70-4.1
1981 *Dreaming in the Attic*
Issue $19.50; High $40.00; Low $34.00;
Close $35.00; Up $1.00

84-R70-4.2
1982 *Waiting on the Shore*
Issue $22.50; High $50.00; Low $30.00;
Close $42.00; Up $12.00

84-R70-4.3
1983 *Pondering on the Porch*
Issue $22.50; High $40.00; Low $30.00;
Close $35.00; Up $5.00

84-R70-4.4
1983 *Making Believe at the Mirror*
Issue $22.50; High $40.00; Low $22.50;
Close $40.00; Up $17.50

84-R70-4.5
1983 *Waiting at the Dance*
Issue $22.50; High $40.00; Low $22.50;
Close $39.00; Up $16.50

84-R70-4.6
1983 *Gossiping in the Alcove*
Issue $22.50; High $22.50; Low $22.50;
Close $22.50; No Change

84-R70-4.7
1983 *Standing in the Doorway*
Issue $22.50; High $22.50; Low $22.50;
Close $22.50; No Change

84-R70-4.8
1983 *Flirting in the Parlor*
Issue $22.50; High $22.50; Low $22.50;
Close $22.50; No Change

84-R70-4.9
1984 Working in the Kitchen
Issue $22.50; High $22.50; Low $22.50;
Close $22.50; No Change

84-R70-4.10
1984 Meeting on the Path
Issue $22.50; High $22.50; Low $22.50;
Close $22.50; No Change

84-R70-4.11
1984 Confiding in the Den
Issue $22.50; High $22.50; Low $22.50;
Close $22.50; No Change

84-R70-4.12
1984 Reminiscing in the Quiet
Issue $22.50; High $22.50; Low $22.50;
Close $22.50; No Change
Series Closed

Rockwell on Tour Collection

Artist: Norman Rockwell. Artist's
signature appears on front

Newellware with raised border

Diameter: 19.7 centimeters
(7¾ inches)

No hanger

Edition size undisclosed, limited
by announced period of issue

Numbered with certificate

84-R70-5.1
1983 Walking through Merrie Englande
Issue $16.00; High $55.00; Low $44.00;
Close $45.00; Up $1.00

84-R70-5.2
1983 Promenade à Paris
Issue $16.00; High $30.00; Low $16.00;
Close $26.00; Up $10.00

84-R70-5.3
1983 When in Rome—
Issue $16.00; High $16.00; Low $16.00;
Close $16.00; No Change

84-R70-5.4
1984 Die Walk am Rhein
Issue $16.00; High $16.00; Low $16.00;
Close $16.00 No Change
Series Closed

Rockwell's Light Campaign Series

Artist: Norman Rockwell. Artist's signature appears on front

China banded in 14k gold

Diameter: 21.6 centimeters (8½ inches)

No hanger

Edition size undisclosed, limited by announced period of issue

Numbered with certificate

84-R70-6.1
1983 *This Is the Room That Light Made*
Issue $19.50; High $80.00; Low $19.50;
Close $80.00; Up $60.50

84-R70-6.2
1984 *Grandpa's Treasure Chest*
Issue $19.50; High $19.50; Low $19.50;
Close $19.50; No Change

84-R70-6.3
1984 *Father's Help*
Issue $19.50; High $19.50; Low $19.50;
Close $19.50; No Change

84-R70-6.4
1984 *Evening's Ease*
Issue $19.50; High $19.50; Low $19.50;
Close $19.50; No Change

84-R70-6.5
1984 *Close Harmony*
Issue $21.50; High $21.50; Low $21.50;
Close $21.50; No Change

84-R70-6.6
1984 *The Birthday Wish*
Issue $21.50; High $21.50; Low $21.50;
Close $21.50; No Change
Series Closed

Rockwell's American Dream Series

Artist: Norman Rockwell. Artist's signature appears on front

China banded in 14k gold

Diameter: 21.6 centimeters (8½ inches)

No hanger

Edition size undisclosed, limited by announced period of issue

Numbered with certificate

84-R70-7.1
1985 *A Young Girl's Dream*
Issue price: $19.90

313

UNITED STATES
ROMAN
Harwood Heights, Illinois

Roman founder Ronald T. Jedlinski grew up in a family business that sold religious goods, working himself through high school and college as a sales representative for his father's firm. After returning from the Navy at the end of World War II, he established his own company, Roman Religious Goods, and earned success as a producer and importer of fine quality religious items, including the famous Fontanini creches.

The company produced its first limited-edition porcelains in the mid-1970's under the Ceramica Excelsis name, later entering the collector's market with prints, plates and figurines designed by a number of well-known artists.

Roman's first Bradex-listed collector's plate series is *A Child's Play*, introduced in 1982. It features the well-known child portraiture of the late Frances Hook.

A Child's Play Series

Artist: Frances Hook. Artist's signature appears on front

China banded in 24k gold

Diameter: 21.6 centimeters (8½ inches)

No hanger

Edition size undisclosed, limited by announced period of issue

Numbered with certificate

84-R53-1.1
1982 *Kite Flying*
Issue $29.95; High $55.00; Low $29.95;
Close $40.00; Up $10.05

84-R53-1.2
1982 *Breezy Day*
Issue $29.95; High $45.00; Low $29.95;
Close $45.00; Up $15.05

84-R53-1.3
1984 *First Snow*
Issue $29.95; High $50.00; Low $29.95;
Close $50.00; Up $20.05

84-R53-1.4
1984 *Bathtub Sailor*
Issue $29.95; High $29.95; Low $29.95;
Close $29.95; No Change
Series Closed

UNITED STATES
ROYAL DEVON
Providence, Rhode Island

Royal Devon plates are manufactured by the Gorham Company (see United States, GORHAM). Both the *Christmas* series and *Mother's Day* series, bearing artwork by Norman Rockwell, began in 1975. Both series ended in 1980.

Christmas Series

Artist: Norman Rockwell. Artist's signature appears on front

China banded in gold

Diameter: 21.6 centimeters (8½ inches)

No hanger

Edition size undisclosed, limited by year of issue

Not numbered, without certificate

84-R61-1.1
1975 *Downhill Daring*
Issue $24.50; High $35.00; Low $16.00;
Close $16.00; Down $19.00

84-R61-1.2
1976 *The Christmas Gift*
Issue $24.50; High $60.00; Low $30.00;
Close $30.00; Down $30.00

84-R61-1.3
1977 *The Big Moment*
Issue $27.50; High $90.00; Low $45.00;
Close $45.00; Down $45.00

84-R61-1.4
1978 *Puppets for Christmas*
Issue $27.50; High $40.00; Low $34.00;
Close $36.00; Down $4.00

84-R61-1.5
1979 *One Present Too Many*
Issue $31.50; High $35.00; Low $30.00;
Close $35.00; Up $2.00

84-R61-1.6
1980 *Gramps Meets Gramps*
Issue $33.00; High $33.00; Low $28.00;
Close $28.00; Down $5.00
Series Closed

Mother's Day Series

Artist: Norman Rockwell. Artist's signature appears on front

China banded in gold

Diameter: 21.6 centimeters (8½ inches)

No hanger

Edition size undisclosed, limited by year of issue

Not numbered, without certificate

84-R61-2.1
1975 *Doctor and the Doll*
Issue $23.50; High $65.00; Low $45.00;
Close $60.00; Down $5.00

84-R61-2.2
1976 *Puppy Love*
Issue $24.50; High $75.00; Low $45.00;
Close $55.00; Down $20.00

84-R61-2.3
1977 *The Family*
Issue $24.50; High $112.00; Low $70.00;
Close $78.00; Down $34.00

84-R61-2.4
1978 *Mother's Day Off*
Issue $27.00; High $60.00; Low $40.00;
Close $43.00; Down $17.00

84-R61-2.5
1979 *Mother's Evening Out*
Issue $30.00; High $30.00; Low $25.00;
Close $25.00; Down $5.00

84-R61-2.6
1980 *Mother's Treat*
Issue $32.50; High $35.00; Low $30.00;
Close $35.00; Up $5.00
Series Closed

84-V3-2.1 "Chief Sitting Bull"
1979 Vague Shadows *The Chieftains I*
This first issue by artist Gregory Perillo established him as a master of Western art in the eyes of plate collectors everywhere. Eagerly sought on the secondary market, "Sitting Bull" commands lofty prices whenever it is traded.

Vague Shadows, Ltd. was established in 1977 to produce limited-edition works by Gregory Perillo. His *The Chieftains I* series was introduced in 1979.

Several other plate series with Indian themes—or covering such subjects as wildlife and children—are listed in the "Over-the-Counter" section of this book under the Vague Shadows name.

The Chieftains I Series

Artist: Gregory Perillo. Artist's signature appears on front

Overglaze-decorated porcelain banded in 24K gold

Diameter: 26 centimeters (10¼ inches)

No hanger

Edition size limited to 7,500

Numbered with certificate

84-V3-2.1
1979 *Chief Sitting Bull*
Issue $65.00; High $550.00; Low $310.00;
Close $550.00; Up $240.00

84-V3-2.2
1979 *Chief Joseph*
Issue $65.00; High $100.00; Low $50.00;
Close $90.00; Up $40.00

84-V3-2.3
1980 *Chief Red Cloud*
Issue $65.00; High $135.00; Low $85.00;
Close $100.00; Up $15.00

84-V3-2.4
1980 *Chief Geronimo*
Issue $65.00; High $80.00; Low $65.00;
Close $73.00; Up $3.00

84-V3-2.5
1981 *Chief Crazy Horse*
Issue $65.00; High $150.00; Low $125.00;
Close $130.00; Up $5.00
Series Closed

Viletta China Company was started in 1959 in Roseberg, Oregon, by Viletta West, who hand-painted china and sold it through stores in the Pacific Northwest. The firm is involved in many areas of the giftware and fine china field, including commemorative china items and limited-edition collector's plates.

In 1979 Viletta China moved from Roseberg to Houston, Texas.

The *Zolan's Children* series, by Donald Zolan, began in 1978 and was completed in 1981. The *Nutcracker Ballet Plate Collection* began in 1978 and ended in 1980. The artist for this series was Shell Fisher.

Zolan's Children Series

Artist: Donald Zolan. Artist's signature appears on front

China

Diameter: 21.6 centimeters (8½ inches)

No hanger

Edition size undisclosed, limited by period of issue

Numbered with certificate

84-V36-1.1
1978 Erik and Dandelion
Issue $19.00; High $180.00; Low $100.00;
Close $135.00; Up $15.00

84-V36-1.2
1979 Sabina in the Grass
Issue $22.00; High $150.00; Low $95.00;
Close $100.00; Down $25.00

84-V36-1.3
1980 By Myself
Issue $24.00; High $35.00; Low $22.00;
Close $25.00; Down $10.00

84-V36-1.4
1981 For You
Issue $24.00; High $27.00; Low $20.00;
Close $20.00; Down $7.00
Series Closed

Nutcracker Ballet Plate Collection

Artist: Shell Fisher. Artist's signature appears on front

China

Diameter: 21.6 centimeters (8½ inches)

No hanger

Edition size undisclosed, limited by year of issue

Numbered with certificate

84-V36-2.1
1978 Clara and Nutcracker
Issue $19.50; High $30.00; Low $12.00;
Close $15.00; Down $15.00

84-V36-2.2
1979 A Gift from Godfather
Issue $19.50; High $25.00; Low $12.00;
Close $15.00; Down $10.00

84-V36-2.3
1979 *The Sugarplum Fairy*
Issue $19.50; High $30.00; Low $17.00;
Close $20.00; Down $10.00

84-V36-2.4
1979 *The Snow King and Queen*
Issue $19.50; High $30.00; Low $22.00;
Close $30.00; No Change

84-V36-2.5
1980 *The Waltz of the Flowers*
Issue $19.50; High $29.00; Low $19.00;
Close $19.00; Down $5.00

84-V36-2.6
1980 *Clara and the Prince*
Issue $19.50; High $30.00; Low $20.00;
Close $25.00; Down $5.00
Series Closed

BRADEX-LISTED
PLATE ARTIST INFORMATION

AKERS, Roger Roger Aker's artwork ranges from massive wooden sculpture to the delicately rendered cameos of Incolay's *Romantic Poets Collection*. Akers was educated at the Cooper School of Art in Cleveland, the Art Institute of Chicago and the American Academy of Art in Chicago. Akers' awards include Best of Show at the Excellence in Woodcarving Show in 1981. The American Numismatic Association commissioned him for "Coin of the Year" in 1974. He is a freelance artist in Chicago and his works hang in midwestern galleries and have been selected for permanent museum display by the Illinois Arts Council. He was born in 1940 and grew up in Cleveland.

APPLEBY, Gayle Bright Gayle Bright Appleby is designer of the first four issues in Incolay's *Romantic Poets Collection*. She was born in 1949 and studied at San Fernando Valley State College in California and at Otis Art School. Her works have appeared in exhibits at Mari's of Hawaii in Lahaina and Alchemists Garden, Kihei, Hawaii. She is widely known for the intricate detail of her sculptures in bronze, silver and gold.

ARD, Kurt Kurt Ard's career got off to an inauspicious start when a bomb in wartime Denmark destroyed both his artwork and the publisher for his first major commission. But Ard has enjoyed international success in the four decades since. His illustrations have appeared in virtually every printed form, including magazines, posters, greeting cards and calendars. His credits include cover and story illustrations in such magazines as *The Saturday Evening Post*, *Redbook*, *McCalls*, *Modern Maturity* and equally prestigious publications in Germany, France and Scandinavia. He shares with Norman Rockwell an uncanny ability to capture the trauma and adventure of growing up, as shown in his *Moments of Truth* series for Bing & Grøndahl. Ard is a self-taught artist. He was born in 1925.

AUCKLAND, James James Auckland, creator of the *Wizard of Oz* series produced by Edwin M. Knowles, was copying Van Gogh prints at the age of six, using his mother's palette and brushes. He was born in 1946 and studied at the Art Center College of Design in Los Angeles and privately with Richard Huebnes, Lorser Feitelson, Joe Hehnigar and Harry Carmen.

BAHNSEN, Frode Frode Bahnsen's training in sculpture, ceramics and drawing is evident in the plates he designed for Grande Copenhagen's *Christmas* series, with bas-relief scenes from the fairy tales of Hans Christian Andersen. He was born in 1923 and studied at the Copenhagen Royal Academy of Art and subsequently worked for the Royal Mint in Copenhagen, rising to the position of head sculptor in 1968. His works hang in the Denmark National Museum and have been exhibited in many places, including the Charlottenborg Art Exhibition in Copenhagen and F.I.D.M.E. (Federal International National Danish Medal Exhibitions). The Queen of Denmark titled him knight of Dannebrog in 1978. Bahnsen died in 1983.

BAND, Ursula Born in Meissen, Germany, Alt Tirschenreuth artist Ursula Band displayed talent for painting and drawing in her early childhood. As a young woman she attended the Painting and Drawing School of the Meissen State Porcelain Manufactury. After her rigorous training she was selected to be among the handful of people who hand-paint Meissen china. In 1964, she established her own atelier. She portrayed the songbirds of the woodlands surrounding her home in Germany in her first collector's plate series, *Songbirds of Europe*.

BARKER, Cicely Mary Heinrich/ Villeroy & Boch artist Cicely Mary Barker was born in 1895 and published the first of her numerous "Flower Fairy" books in 1923. A largely self-taught artist, she also had formal training at the Croyden School of Art. A stained glass window of her design hangs in St. Andrew's Church in Croyden. Her works have been exhibited at the Royal Institute and are in the collection of the British royal family. Barker died in 1973.

BARRER, Gertrude With her husband Frank Russell, Gertrude Barrer has produced art displayed in some of the United States' most prestigious museums, including the Whitney Museum of American Art and the Art Institute of Chicago, and in the private collections of Cyrus Vance and Helmut Schmidt and the United Nations Interfaith Chapel in New York. Together they created the *Triptych* and *Romantic Love* series for Anna-Perenna. Barrer and Russell first met at the Art Student's League in New York. Five years later, they reunited in New York's art center, Greenwich Village, to work jointly on photographs, lithographs, frescoes, serigraphs and sculpture.

BEDAL, Karl The man whose illustrations of West Germany's classic half-timbered farmhouses appear on *Deutsches Fachwerk* plates is well-known throughout Bavaria for his architecture research and literature on German folk history. His artistic creations range from wall-size paintings to delicate water colors and linocut book illustrations. Bedal has been a freelance artist since 1958. He travels throughout Germany in search of his country's finest regional architecture, making his sketches on the spot to capture the patterns of wooden beams and braces on houses built centuries ago. He was born in 1914.

BENVENUTI, Sergio The designer of the *Muses* plate series for Studio Dante di Volteradici is an Italian master who gained international prominence in 1984 with two important commissions for bronze sculptures. He created his Beato Angelico statue at the request of the Dominican monks for the Church of San Marco in Florence. Italian National Television covered the statue's unveiling, which was attended by His Eminence, the Archbishop of Florence. Americans were introduced to Benvenuti with the critically acclaimed fountain he executed for the First International Bank Plaza in San Diego, California. Benvenuti has won numerous awards in his thirty-year career.

BLANDFORD, W.A. W.A. Blandford's career in the British ceramics industry began in the 1930s, when he was apprenticed to Wood & Sons, the Staffordshire ceramics house that produced many of the earliest Toby jugs. Since then he has modeled thousands of intricate ceramic pieces. In order to create the "Toby Fillpot" collector's plate for Davenport Pottery, Blandford spent hours examining antique Toby pieces before sketching his own design, true to the eighteenth century ceramics that inspired it.

BOEHM, Edward Marshall From a background as farmer and veterinarian, the artist for Lenox's *Boehm Bird* and *Boehm Woodland Wildlife* series became a full-time sculptor in 1949. At his death in 1969, the self-taught Boehm was recognized

as one of America's greatest wildlife artists. His faithful replication of nature scenes won a substantial following and his work has appeared in the collections of Dwight D. Eisenhower, John F. Kennedy, Lyndon B. Johnson, Queen Elizabeth II and Pope John XXIII. Boehm won numerous awards and his art is displayed in the Smithsonian Institution, the Metropolitan Museum of Art and other museums. He was born in 1914.

BOULMÉ, Claude When Gerard Boyer of D'Arceau-Limoges approached the great porcelain artist Claude Boulmé about a plate series capturing the porcelain style of the Sèvres Empire, Boulmé knew the subject of the plates must be the Emperor Napoleon, whose patronage permitted the Sèvres art to flower. In the *Joséphine et Napoléon* series, he portrays, in neo-Classical style, the passion of Napoleon for his Empress Josephine.

BOYER, Gene Crown Parian artist Gene Boyer is best known for more than 45 illustrations that appeared in the *Saturday Evening Post* between 1975 and 1978. Boyer got his first big break when Norman Rockwell awarded him second place in a cover contest for the new magazine. Although his portrait assignments for the Post included such contemporary celebrities as Elizabeth Taylor and Jimmy Carter, Boyer was attracted to the history and integrity offered by the past. In his portraits of such legends as Johnny Appleseed and Davy Crockett in the *American Folk Heroes* plate series, Boyer strives to capture with almost photographic realism the courage and qualities of heroes. Self-taught Boyer has done numerous portrait commissions and exhibited primarily in the Denver, Colorado and Washington, D.C. areas. He was born in 1948.

BRADLEY, Betsey Edwin M. Knowles artist Betsey Bradley first realized she had talent when her fifth grade profiles of classmates

showed a striking likeness to their subjects. She has been doing portraits ever since in pastels, pencil, acrylic and oils, and more recently began doing landscapes and still lifes. Bradley studied art at Smith College for Women in Massachusetts, the Minneapolis School of Art and the Rocky Mountain School of Art. Her paintings have been shown in several exhibitions. To her collector's plate series *A Father's Love* Bradley brings a softer version of her strikingly realistic artwork, inspiration from her own happy family, and support for the increasingly active role today's fathers take with their children.

BRATLIE, Gunnar Born in Fredrikstad, Norway in 1918, Gunnar Bratlie is a master of the traditional Norwegian folk art known as "rosemaling." He has worked in such diverse styles as oil, tempera, aquarelle and etching. Among his many awards are the Scandinavian book prize for illustration, a contest-winning design for Fredrikstad's 400th-year jubilee and a special stipend from the Norwegian Design Organization. His work is represented in many museums around the world, most notably at the Commune of Oslo, the Art Society of Fredrikstad and the Museo del Arte in Pisoia, Italy. Sole artist since 1967 for Porsgrund Pottery, his plates in the *Christmas, Mother's Day* and *Traditional Norwegian Christmas* series primarily depict Norwegian country scenes.

BROWN, Roger Roger Brown studied under Dorothea Denslow at the New York Sculpture Center and is a member of the New York Sculpture Center and the National Sculpture Center. Brown's works are in the collections of the Whitney Museum of American Art and the Remington Museum in New York, the Studebaker Museum in South Bend, Indiana, the Lyndon Baines Johnson Memorial Library and the Teterboro Aviation Museum, among others. He was born in 1933, and he is sculptor of the *Famous Americans* series for River Shore, Ltd.

BRUNETTIN, Alan Incolay artist Alan Brunettin mastered the art of traditional sculpture in a nine-year apprenticeship to his father, internationally celebrated sculptor Alfred Brunettin. Today his art in several media ranges from striking photorealism to cartoon-like surrealism. In *Voyage of Ulysses*, his first collector's plate series, Brunettin uses traditional sculptural techniques to render scenes from the Greek epic in cameo-carved high relief. Brunettin earned a Bachelor of Fine Arts degree with an emphasis in painting at Northern Illinois University and also studied at the American Academy of Art in Chicago. He has exhibited at Chicago-area art fairs and won prizes two consecutive years at the National Exhibit of Italian-American Art in Chicago.

CAMBIER, Guy Self-taught artist Guy Cambier, born in 1923, had his first one-man show at age 19 and has been exhibiting ever since in Belgium, France and at the Zantman Art Galleries in Carmel, California. He has won numerous

awards and honors through the years, from the *Prix de la Jeune Peinture Méditerranée* in 1955 to the *Laureate de la Médaille International des Artes* in 1977. He designed the *Girls of the Seasons* and *Cambier Mother's Day* series in a neo-Classical style for D'Arceau-Limoges.

CASSINI, Oleg Oleg Cassini is one of the best-known names in contemporary fashion—his name has appeared on everything from sunglasses to perfume—as well as an accomplished artist. Born to Countess Loiewski Cassini in Paris in 1913, Cassini renounced his right to the title of Count to become an American citizen after immigrating to the United States in the late 1930s. He designed film costumes in Hollywood for such celebrities as Gene Tierney and Grace Kelly before going to New York to put his name on a par with Dior and Cardin. Jacqueline Kennedy named Cassini her official couturier during her White House years. He received a law degree from the University of Florence and graduated from Florence's prestigious Academia delle Belle Artes. For *Oleg Cassini's Most Beautiful Women of All Time Collection* for Pickard, Cassini explored the historical and cultural aspects of the lives of women such as Helen of Troy.

CHAMBERS, William William Chambers came to the plate world almost by accident and became an overnight success in the midst of his career as a well-known illustrator and prize-winning portraitist. He had never heard of collector's plates when he got a letter from an Edwin M. Knowles art representative inviting him to discuss the *Annie Collector's Plate* series. Soon afterwards his debut plate, "Annie and Sandy," made history when it walked off with two of the most coveted awards, Plate of the Year and New Edition of the Year for 1983—the first time a single plate has won both honors. Chambers paid his dues as an illustrator and photographer before he came to the realization that he could both make a living and satisfy his artistic needs painting portraits. He has exhibited in the American Society of Illustrators' annual show, The American Show at Marshall Field's and the Mongerson Galleries (both in Chicago), and won first prize in the John Howard Sanden portrait competition. His works hang in various homes and businesses and at Ron De Bouver Fine Arts in Chicago. Chambers was born in 1940 and studied at Northeastern Illinois University and the American Academy of Art in Chicago.

CSATARI, Joseph Joseph Csatari, long-time friend and protégé of the late master of realism Norman Rockwell, is one of the most highly regarded realist painters of today. He and Rockwell collaborated on the annual calendars published by the Boy Scouts of America for a decade until 1975, when Rockwell turned the calendar commission over to Csatari, who has continued it. Edwin M. Knowles commissioned him for the *Csatari Grandparent Plate* series. His other important recent commissions include cover illustrations for numerous books and a commemorative stamp for the U.S. Postal Service. Csatari was born in 1929 and studied at the Academy of Art in Newark, New Jersey and the Pratt Institute in New York City. His awards include a Gold Medal from the Society of Illustrators.

DALI, Louis A noted Impressionist, Louis Dali is a Fellow of the *Salon de l'Ecole Française* and of the *Salon des Indépendants*, and winner of the *Prix Dessin de Briton*. Dali is a self-taught artist whose works hang in many private collections and salons, including the *Salon de la Marine, Salon de la Nationale des Beaux-Artes*, and the *Salon de l'Ecole Française des Indépendants*. Dali designed his *Twelve Parisian Places of Louis Dali* for D'Arceau-Limoges. He was born in 1906.

DANIEL, Kevin For Edwin M. Knowles artist Kevin Daniel, painting is a way of preserving wildlife. He used to hunt with a gun; now he combs the wilds with his camera, collecting photographs from which to paint highly accurate, detailed portrayals of animals from pheasants to fishes. For his *Birds of Your Garden* series, Daniel erected a camera on the birdfeeder in the backyard of his house near Minneapolis. Daniel, who learned to paint by studying the work of other artists, was named Artist of the Year by the Indiana Chapter of Ducks Unlimited, a waterfowl conservation group, in 1984, and won second place in the Minnesota Duck Stamp art competition the same year. Proceeds from the sale of his prints have helped save the endangered blue heron in Minnesota.

DEGRAZIA, Ted Ted DeGrazia, one of America's most popular and instantly-recognizable artists, was a man of contrasts and paradoxes. Born in Morenci, Arizona, in 1909, the son of an Italian copper miner, he didn't attend school for the first

11 years of his life but later earned three degrees in art and music from the University of Arizona. He studied with great Mexican muralists Diego Rivera and Jose Clemente Orozco and spent long hours of research and hard work on his paintings, yet he acquired the image of a drunken carouser. A millionaire in the last years of his life, his art was always of the people and for the people, and he strove to keep it affordable. His stylized paintings of Southwestern themes first came to international attention in 1960 when UNICEF sold 100 million Christmas cards bearing the image of his painting "Los Niños." Since then, they have appeared on everything from stained glass to figurines and in collector's plates series for Fairmont/Artists of the World and Gorham, including *DeGrazia Holiday* series and *DeGrazia Children* series. DeGrazia died of cancer in 1982.

DOWN, Jeanne Artist Jeanne Down uses her palette and brushes to tell stories—especially of her childhood days in Altoona, Pennsylvania. Though she grew up during the Great Depression, her memories are happy ones. Among other things, she learned to paint at the knee of her grandfather, Pennsylvania realist E.E. Wilt. After graduating high school she temporarily abandoned her avocation to spend 16 years raising a family. But after studying oil painting, watercolor and etching techniques under private teachers she began to offer instruction herself throughout California's San Fer-

nando Valley. In 1975 she opened her own gallery and studio. In her *Friends I Remember* series, Down uses an "impressionistic realist" style to impart feelings as well as images.

DURAND, Paul Paul Durand achieved an international reputation for his illustrations of such children's classics as *The Three Musketeers* and *Treasure Island*. General Charles De Gaulle chose Durand's art to illustrate his 1969 Christmas message to French children. Durand was influenced in Paris by Christian Berard, Jacques DeMachy, René Gruau and André Dignimont. He exhibited at the *Festival Cannes* in 1965, was presented as a candidate for the Hans Christian Andersen Prize in 1970, and did illustrations for numerous French and U.S. publications, including Hachette, Delagrave and Flammarion editions, *Reader's Digest*, *Le Figaro* and *Paris Presse*. He was the artist for the Limoges-Turgot plate series *Durand's Children Collection*. He was born in 1925 and died in 1977.

DUTHEIL, Jean D'Arceau-Limoges artist Jean Dutheil experimented with pigments for more than a year and a half to try to duplicate the rich colors of the medieval French manuscript on which *The Very Rich Hours* plate series is based. Dutheil was born in 1927 and studied at *L'École de Beaublance* in Limoges, France. His many awards and honors include the *Prix de la Ville de Limoges*, *Prix du Min-*

istre, *Grand Prix de Porcelaine de Limoges* and the *Meilleur Ouvrier de France*.

ETÉM, Sue Self-taught painter Sue Etém's first plate, "Renee," which launched the *Playful Memories* series by Fairmont, sold out in two hours at a gallery open house when it was first introduced. It also won NALED's Plate of the Year and Collectible of the Year for 1981. Etém herself was named NALED's Artist of the Year for 1981 and 1982. Like many of Etém's paintings, "Renee" began as a snapshot—in this case, of a little neighbor girl who came to the house for chewing gum and ended up playing with a drinking hose. Etém, who now designs for Derbyshire Collection, began drawing at age 3. After a year of formal art training at Arlington State College, she joined an advertising agency as a commercial artist. In the early 1950s she moved to Huntington Beach, California, where she taught art to neighborhood children. She has exhibited throughout the United States and Canada.

BRADEX-LISTED PLATE ARTIST INFORMATION

FAURE, Renée Granddaughter of the great American Impressionist Edmund Greacen and daughter of prominent painter Nan Greacon, Renée Faure has demonstrated talent and versatility as an artist in her own right. In the *Once Upon a Rhyme* collector's plate series she created for Heinrich/Villeroy & Boch, Faure captures the charm and appeal of age-old nursery rhymes. Scenes from such favorites as "A Tisket, a Tasket" come alive in Faure's subtle pastels and earth tones. Faure renders the fine detail with superb drafting skill.

FISHER, Shell Shell Fisher's work, as seen on the plates he has created for Viletta, represents some of the finest examples of contemporary realism. But Fisher is a versatile artist whose credits include interpretive canvasses, portraits commissioned by Queen Elizabeth II and Sammy Davis, Jr., and cartoons for several men's magazines. In his *Nutcracker Ballet Plate Collection*, he depicts the favorite Christmas ballet in vivid colors. Fisher studied at the Art Institute of Chicago, where his work is on display, other places, and has exhibited widely.

GANEAU, François François Ganeau was one of Europe's leading costume and set designers and resident consultant to the *Theatre Comedie Français*. He was widely acclaimed in 1937 for the *Pavillon de l'Elegance*, a mural he created for the Paris World's Fair. As a sculptor and painter he decorated many public buildings and private homes throughout France. He was commissioned by D'Arceau-Limoges to create the *Women of the Century* series bearing the United Nations' emblem for the International Women's Year. The twelve plates in the series picture the progression of 19th and 20th century Paris fashion. Ganeau studied at L'École Boulle, Paris. His works hang in the *Comédie Français*, Paris Opera House and the Louvre. Ganeau died in 1983 at the age of 71.

GEHM, Charles Charles Gehm is a prominent member of the Society of Illustrators and has gained a wide audience through his cover designs for Saul Bellow books. Gehm created the *Grimm's Fairy Tales* collector's plate series for

Königszelt Bayern in 1981 to commemorate the two-hundredth anniversary of the Grimm brothers' birth. The plates bear vivid illustrations of such Grimm classics as *Rapunzel* and *Rumplestilzchen*. Gehm is a graduate of the Columbus Art School. He has exhibited at the James Marks Gallery in California and has works hanging in private collections in the United States.

GUIDOU, Jean-Claude This young French painter won an international reputation with his sensitive pastel portraits and his studies of ballet dancers and race horses. Important personalities who have commissioned Guidou to execute their portraits include the late General Charles De Gaulle. In "Gigi," the first issue in Guidou's first collector's plate series, he captured his subject's *joie de vivre* on D'Arceau-Limoges porcelain with the pastel soft-focus technique an Impressionist master might have used. Guidou studied at the Louvre and the Royal Museum of Belgium and has exhibited widely.

HALLETT, Charlotte and William In their unique art Charlotte and William Hallett draw upon a rich tradition of myth and ornament to create a world of unicorns, dragons and maidens in love. This husband-and-wife team has collaborated on everything from Greek-inspired sterling flatware to crystal and paintings. Like the *Love For All Seasons* series they designed for Hutschenreuther, all their plates are joint creations. They met as staff

331

designers for a silver company and began to explore the world of color together, having already studied Egyptian, Baroque and Rococo ornamentation, history, fine art and symbolism. Charlotte studied at the University of Connecticut in Bridgeport; William, at Vesper George School of Art in Boston. They have exhibited in local, regional and national shows and their art is in the collections of the Archdiocese of New York and the royal families of Saudi Arabia and Spain, among others.

HÉTREAU, Remy Adept in a variety of styles, French painter Remy Hétreau is the principal artist for Haviland's collector's plates, with two distinctively different series to his credit—from historical chronicle to delightful yuletide fancy in *The Twelve Days of Christmas* series.

HIBEL, Edna Edna Hibel is one of the most respected American painters of her time, and a pioneer in porcelain as a fine-art medium. The plates in her series—which include the *Nobility of Children* and *Oriental Gold* series for Rosenthal, *Hibel's Mother's Day* series for Edwin M. Knowles, and the *Mother and Child* series for Royal Doulton—demonstrate her ability to capture the beauty she sees in life and her love for human beings. Hibel was born in 1917, and at 22 became the youngest living artist to have a painting in a major American museum when the Boston Museum purchased one of her canvasses. She is one of the few living female artists with a U.S.

museum—the Hibel Museum of Art in Florida—devoted to her works. She is an elected member of the Royal Society of Arts in London. She has held numerous one-woman shows since 1962 in the United States, England, Monaco, Germany and Argentina and recently became the first American woman to exhibit in Jerusalem. Her works hang in museums across the country. Hibel studied at the Boston Museum of Fine Arts with Carl Zerbe and Jacovleff from 1934 to 1939, and privately with Gregory Michaels in Boston.

HICKS, Yin-Rei Yin-Rei Hicks, a native of mainland China, was born during the Maoist takeover. Her family later fled to Taiwan, where her artistic ability first gained recognition. She won two scholarships from the University of Louisville in Kentucky and graduated with a Master's Degree in Creative Art. She has since become a prominent illustrator and designer of limited-edition collectibles. In 1981 River Shore introduced her *Signs of Love* series, in which Hick's paintings convey the tenderness between wild animals and their young. She has exhibited at the J.B. Speed Gallery in Kentucky, the Floyd County Museum, the University of Louisville, and other galleries in Kentucky and southern Indiana. Her works hang in private collections in the United States.

HOOK, Frances Her exquisite understanding of both children and art distinguishes the work of Frances Hook, one of America's

premier child portraitists. Her soft pastel style captures dreamy-eyed children in commercial illustrations, prints, lithographs and figurines as well as collector's plates. The public discovered her with her illustrations of the Northern Bath Tissue children—so popular they were sold on 30 million prints. With her late husband Richard, she illustrated *The Children's Living Bible* for Tyndale House Publishers. Her first collector's plate issue was in 1980 for Roman, and her first Bradex-listed series, *A Child's Play*, also for Roman, began in 1982. She also designed the *Frances Hook Legacy* series for Edwin M. Knowles. Hook studied at the Pennsylvania Museum School of Art. She was born in 1913 and died in 1983.

HOOVER, G.A. In *The Canterbury Tales Collection*, Longton Crown Pottery artist G.A. Hoover carries on a family tradition of artists which began with his grandfather. Hoover holds a Master of Fine Arts degree and is considered a master of the style known as Romantic Realism. He was born in 1943 and studied at Tulane University in New Orleans and at the John Herron School of Art in Indianapolis. He has executed designs and drawings for Little Brown & Company, McGraw-Hill, Playboy Press, MacMillan and Co., *Reader's Digest*, Harper & Row and Harcourt, Brace and Jovanovich. He has had three one-man shows at Bienville Gallery in New Orleans, participated in an invitational show in Colom-

bia, and has works hanging in several museums and in private collections.

INGARGIOLA, Franco Franco Ingargiola studied privately with sculptor Gino Ruggeri, from whom he took over design of the *Grand Opera* series for Studio Dante di Volteradici. Ingargiola worked in onyx and ceramics as well as in the ivory alabaster from which he sculpted the plates in this collection. Ingargiola also studied at Boy's Town in Rome and won first prize at the Craftsmen Arts Show in Cicena, Italy. He was born in 1944.

JANSEN, Leo Leo Jansen was born in The Hague, The Netherlands in 1930. He spent his youth in Indonesia, where he developed his skills as a portrait painter by sketching the bronze-skinned Malay children. He returned to The Netherlands to study at the Academy of Fine Arts and later refined his work in the famous "Pigalle" section of Paris. Before his death in 1980, Jansen designed plates for Kern Collectibles, including the *Leaders of Tomorrow* series, and Royal Bayreuth. In 1970 he won CALED's Plate of the Year award, in Canada. His art has been exhibited at the Avron Brothers Corporation in Los Angeles, California, and hangs in private collections in the United States.

JOHNSON, Robert Artist Robert Johnson, whose works are in private collections throughout the United States, Europe and the Far East, developed the patented electroplating process used in the creation of the Reed & Barton *Christmas* series. The medium, known as Damascene silver, combines silver, gold, copper and bronze. The process is derived from a hand-crafted method perfected at Damascus in the middle ages. Johnson designed the 1970, 1971 and 1972 plates in the series.

KELLER, Hedi Hedi Keller was born in 1916 in Tuttlingen, a village near the Black Forest. She studied for three years at the Kunstakademie in Stuttgart, learning about the great masters—Titian, Rembrandt and Breughel—but later was influenced by Van Gogh and the French Impressionists, who discarded conventional ideas to seek a more personal style. Keller shows her own colorful style in the *Hedi Keller Christmas* series produced by Königszelt Bayern. Keller's work has been exhibited in galleries in Berlin, Munich and Dusseldorf.

KRUMEICH, Thaddeus Thaddeus Krumeich is a master of the style known as *trompe l'oeil*, which he calls "magic realism." His magical, clear-eyed cats seem ready to leap off the plates in Anna-Perenna's *Uncle Tad's Cats* series. Krumeich, who studied at New York University and Columbia University, has created illustrations for publications such as *Reader's Digest*, *Time-Life Books* and *Family Circle*. His work was selected for UNICEF greeting cards in 1981 and 1982. Krumeich has had shows throughout the United States and is represented in collections such as those of Mrs. Paul Mellon, "Doc" Severinson and His Excellency Seydou Traori, Mali Ambassador to the United States. He was born in 1930.

KUCK, Sandra To capture the spontaneous moments in children's lives, Reco artist Sandra Kuck often rounds up a group of neighborhood kids and takes them off to play in the setting she wants to paint. Her "Sunday Best," first issue in Reco's *Days Gone By* series, captured the Plate of the Show

award at the 1983 South Bend Convention and was one of the most popular plates that year. Kuck, whose plate career began in 1979, studied art for one year at the University of California at Los Angeles before moving to Manhattan to be close to the great museums. She attended the Art Students' League in Manhattan and studied portraiture and anatomy with established artists. She has shown her work in galleries in New York City, Brooklyn and Long Island.

KÜNSTLER, Mort Mort Künstler's paintings chronicle American history from the time of the Indians through the space program. He paints with both high realism and imagination. His passion for detail—and respect for history—is showcased in his first collector's plate series, *Oklahoma!*, produced by Edwin M. Knowles, featuring scenes from the classic Rodgers and Hammerstein musical that tells the story of the last frontier land rush. Künstler attended the Pratt Institute in New York City. In his career as an illustrator he has published more than 2,000 illustrations for books, advertisements and magazines, including *Newsweek*, *National Geographic*, *The Saturday Evening Post*, *True*, *Sports Afield* and *Outdoor Life*. His paintings hang in the permanent collections of museums across the country.

KURSÁR, Raymond Until 1978, when "Scarlett," the first plate in Edwin M. Knowles' *Gone With the Wind* series was issued, Raymond Kursár had earned his reputation primarily in the field of commercial illustration. His original paintings for covers for Random House and Ballantine Books have been widely exhibited. He has won awards for his New York theater posters and published illustrations in such magazines as *Ladies Home Journal*, *Better Homes and Gardens* and *Good Housekeeping*. His corporate clients include RCA Records, McDonald's and Coca-Cola. Kursár was educated at the School of Advertising Art, the University of Oregon and the Museum of Modern Art in Portland, Oregon. He came to New York with his portfolio in hand, and, remarkably, has never had to work for a company as an employee. He was born in 1944.

LALIQUE, Marie-Claude Chief designer and president of the firm founded by her grandfather, René Lalique, Marie-Claude Lalique created the *Annual* series of Lalique crystal collector's plates which began in 1965 and ended in 1976. The third generation in a family of artists, Lalique is know for her versatility. She is an accomplished painter, sculptor, glass-blower and jewelry designer. She is a graduate of the *Grand Chaumiere* and *L'École Normale Superiore des Arts Decoratifs de Paris* where she concentrated on painting until her teacher, Andre Arbus, developed her appreciation of the decorative arts.

LAMBERT, Georgia As the child of an Air Force colonel, Georgia Lambert lived for much of her youth in Europe, where she spent countless hours in the great art museums, learning about the techniques of the Old Masters. She most admired the depth of color and sense of glowing light they achieved with numerous layers of paint and varnish. Today she uses the techniques she admired in the medium of china painting, raising a craft to an art form. Instead of simply tracing designs onto china or porcelain and filling them in, she paints originals directly onto porcelain "canvasses." For her first collector's plate series, *The Four Ancient Elements*, produced by Edwin M. Knowles, she applied 20 or more layers of paint to master plates to show the mythological figures of Earth, Air, Fire and Water.

LAMINCIA, Franco Born into a family whose artistic heritage spans generations, Franco Lamincia grew up in Deruta, Italy, an ancient village on the Tiber River near Perugia, renowned since the 16th cen-

BRADEX-LISTED PLATE ARTIST INFORMATION

tury for its fine majolica, also known as faience. He studied drawing at the local professional school under the great Alpinolo Maguini, who revived the production of true Deruta majolica in the early 1900s. Lamincia reproduced the majolica style when he designed "Noah and the Dove," first issue in Veneto Flair's *St. Mark's of Venice* series. Each plate is a hand-painted recreation of the great mosaics of St. Mark's Cathedral, which chronicle the Old Testament.

LANGE, Kai Artist Kai Lange has been with Royal Copenhagen since the age of 17, and after more than half a century with the firm is regarded as one of the most knowledgable artists working in the porcelain medium. The first Lange design selected for the annual *Christmas* plate was for the 1940 issue, and since 1963 every plate except the 1976 issue has been a Lange creation. Lange studied drawing under Carl Schwenn. He is the recipient of several grants and an illustrator for several Danish newspapers. He has created wall hangings for many official institutions. His works hang in the Folkets Hus, Copenhagen. He was born in 1905.

LICEA, Eve Eve Licea's art and life are a study in contrasts. She was born in 1928 to a poor working-class family in New York's Bronx area, and her family could not afford art lessons. Yet today she lives and works in a fashionable loft in Greenwich Village and her artworks are exhibited in such pres-

tigious galleries as Lever House, Pindar Gallery and Les Mouches in New York City. A painter, sculptor and lithographer, she is best known for her embossed lithographs and large cast-paper sculptures. Her style is a unique blend of contrasting elements: geometric patterns and rounded natural forms, color and white, matte and gloss surfaces, raised and flat areas. To her first collector's plate series, *Biblical Mothers*, produced by Edwin M. Knowles, she brings a sculptor's feel for light and shadow along with a painter's feel for line. A creator rather than a recorder, her treatment of subjects the Old Masters painted in a traditional way is very contemporary, and yet realistic. Licea studied at Parson's School of Design in New York. She has done illustrations for numerous publications, including *Good Housekeeping* and *Women's Day*.

LOCKHART, James James Lockhart, an ardent naturalist and conservationist, is widely known for his realistic portrayals of wild animals in their natural habitats. His *Lockhart Wildlife* series for Pickard commemorates vanishing forms of American fauna. His paintings and drawings also have appeared in limited edition prints, books, calendars, gift items and magazines, including *Collier's*, *The Saturday Evening Post* and *Sports Afield*. He is a member of the Board of Governors of Brookfield Zoo and of Chicago's Shedd Aquarium and a trustee of Duck's Unlimited, a waterfowl conservation group. He was born in 1912.

MALFERTHEINER, Josef A master woodcarver from Saint Ulrich, Italy, Josef Malfertheiner studied at the Ortesi Academy of Art and in 1966 became Master Carver for Anri, for whom he designed the *Christmas* series. He is best known for his portrayals of Tyrolean history and three-dimensional replication of Renoir, Van Eyck and Rembrandt. He has works in private collections in Italy, Austria, Germany and Australia.

MASSERIA, Francisco J.J.C. Francisco Masseria won his first gold medal at the age of fourteen in the *Salon Annuale de Entre Rios* in his native Argentina. He emigrated to Italy in 1936, made his home in Rome, and studied the works of the Italian and Spanish Renaissance masters. Today he studies the faces of people he sees on the streets. In Royal Doulton's *Portraits of Innocence* series, Masseria mixes two distinct techniques to form his own style, painting classically smooth faces against boldly Impressionistic backgrounds. His numerous awards include NALED's Lithograph of the Year in 1982. He has exhibited in South, Central and North America and in Europe.

MAYS, Maxwell Maxwell Mays, designer of the 1976, 1977 and 1978 plates in Reed & Barton's *Christmas* collector's plate series, specializes in Americana. His art has appeared in such magazines as *Collier's*, *Yankee*, *Cosmopolitan* and *New England*.

McCLELLAND, John In 1980, Reco artist John McClelland's plate "Mary, Mary," first in the *McClelland's Mother Goose* series, outperformed all others on the Bradford Exchange and was named Plate of the Year. It was also named "Best All-Around Collectible" and "Best Plate" by the National Association of Limited Edition Dealers, and McClelland won their "Best Artist" title as well. But he made his mark as a magazine illustrator and portraitist of politicians and artists long before he designed his first collector's plate. McClelland works almost exclusively from live models, whom he may meet by chance, to capture the individuality of children—he saw the model for "Mary, Mary" at a church daycare center. He studied at Auburn University and at Grand Central Art School and Art Career School, in New York, but considers portrait artist Jerry Farnsworth his most valuable teacher. He is the author of books on flower and portrait painting and has had numerous exhibits, primarily on the East Coast. His other plate series include *McClelland Children's Circus Collection* and *Becky's Day*, for Reco. He was born in 1919.

MONEY, Rusty In 1981, the Ernst plate series *Seems Like Yesterday* introduced artist Rusty Money to the collector's market. Money was born in Oak Park, Illinois and now lives and paints in Escondido, California. She studied at Arizona State University and the Washington School of Art. Her favorite subjects are children and turn-of-the-cen-

tury period scenes. Her work is characterized by the use of delicate pastels in a semi-Impressionistic style. She won the International Fine Arts Award competition in 1980. Her works hang in numerous private collections.

MUELLER, Hans Hans Mueller, born in Waldsassen, Bavaria, in 1934, was the son of a Bareuther artist. He studied engraving and painting at the porcelain academy in Selb and the Porcelain Trade School of Bavaria and in 1952 joined Bareuther as a porcelain painter. He was promoted to chief designer for the firm in 1968. In the *Christmas* and *Father's Day* series Mueller painted castles and country scenes in blue and white.

NEIMAN, LeRoy The creator of Royal Doulton's *Commedia Dell' Arte Series* also created the Olympian murals at the 1976 and 1980 Olympics and was named official artist for the 1984 Olympics. He was a gold medalist at the *Salon d'Arte Moderne* in Paris and an illustrator for such magazines as *Vogue, Harper's Bazaar, Glamour, Time, Newsweek* and *The Saturday Evening Post*. His works hang in some of the world's great museums, including the Hermitage Museum in Leningrad, and in private collections. Neiman attended the St. Paul Art Center, the University of Chicago and the Art Institute of Chicago. He was born in 1927.

NEUBACHER, Gerda The creator of Kaiser's *Classic Fairy Tales Collection* also introduced Austrians to moccasins. Gerda Neubacher was born in the small Austrian mountain village of Pols in 1945, and intended to make fashion design her career. She studied for four years at the Grace Kelly School of Art in Zurich and has designed shoes, perfume ads and shopping bags. Now she is a realist painter well-known for her scenes of forests, children and wildlife. She moved to Canada with her husband, Fred, also a painter, and has won numerous awards in the many Canadian shows where she has exhibited. Her work, on canvas and on porcelain, is in galleries and private homes all over the world.

BRADEX-LISTED PLATE ARTIST INFORMATION

NIGHTINGALE, Sandy British artist Sandy Nightingale is known in her native country as a book illustrator for a number of well-established British publishing houses, including Pan, McMillan and Hamlyn, and has exhibited her works in numerous British galleries. In the *Alice in Wonderland* series—Porcelaine Georges Boyer's first collector's series for the United States market—she incorporated scenes from her parents' garden and memories of her childhood. Nightingale studied in England and in the south of France and is a member of the Chelsea Society of Illustrators. She was born in 1953.

NITSCHKE, Detlev Berlin Design artist Detlev Nitschke is widely known throughout Europe for his historically accurate paintings of turn-of-the-century Berlin. He was born in that city in 1935 and studied lithography before receiving formal training as a painter and graphic artist. After studying with painter Ehrenfried Viola, Nitschke attended the Masters School for Printing and Graphics in Berlin and the State Institute for Graphics. Creator of the *Holiday Week of the Family Kappelmann* plate series, he has exhibited his work in galleries throughout Germany and the rest of Europe.

OLSEN, Ib Spang Ib Spang Olsen, artist for Royal Copenhagen's *Mother's Day* series, is a recipient of the Danish Children's Book Prize.

PELTRIAUX, Bernard Renowned throughout the international art world for his paintings and lithographs, Bernard Peltriaux also dedicated himself, until his recent retirement, to educating artists from all over the world at the *Lycee Technique d'Etat* in Reims, the cathedral town where he was born and raised. He attended the *Ecole des Beaux-Arts* in Reims and the *Atelier Rene Jaudon* in Paris. He has numerous prizes and more than fifty solo exhibitions to his credit. *The Children of the Turn of the Century Collection*, produced by Limoges-Turgot, is his first collector's plate series.

PERILLO, Gregory Gregory Perillo has been an artist fascinated by the Old West since his father, an Italian immigrant, told him stories of the Indian Wars and Perillo sketched the details in crayon. Today he is a successful oil painter who paints proud, strong Plains Indians as they used to be. He was born in 1932 in New York City. He studied at the Pratt Institute, the School of Visual Arts and the Art Student's League. He is also the only living artist to have studied under renowned Western painter William R. Leigh. His collector's plate series for Kern Collectibles and Vague Shadows include *The Professionals*, *The Storybook Collection*, *The Chieftains I* series, a Christmas series and a wildlife series.

PETER, Nori Nori Peter, well-known for her portrayals of life in the Arctic, became entranced with the Innuit people when she saw them and their carvings at an art show. She makes frequent trips to the North from her Ontario, Canada home. Born in Hungary, she fled her country at the age of 21 after the Budapest uprising of 1956. Soon after arriving in Toronto, she began doing children's portraits. Her first collector's plate series was *People of the Midnight Sun* for Kaiser; her second, for Anna-Perenna, was *Arctic Spring*. She also has done *Mother's Day* series plates and twelve figurines for Kaiser. She studied at the Academy of Fine Arts in Budapest.

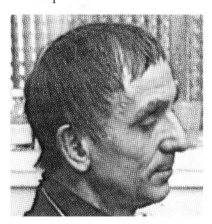

QUELLIER, André André Quellier, creator of *Quellier's Morals of Perrault* series for Limoges-Turgot, was born in Paris in 1925. He received his classical training at *L'École des Beaux Arts* and studied under the direction of Jean Dupas and Edmond Heuze. His work has been shown in the major cities of the world—in the United States, Japan, the Soviet Union, Spain and France, including one of the first exhibits at the Theatre des Champs

Elysees in Paris. His portrait of Jean Cocteau is in the home of Jean Marais. His numerous prizes include the *Prix Internationale du Gemmeil d'Art Sacré à Lourdes*, the *Médaille d'Or des Artists Français*, *Pris Casa Vealsquez, a Madrid*, and, in 1945, *Prix de l'Institute*.

RESTIEAU, André André Restieau is a world authority on the techniques of re-creating medieval stained-glass coloration in porcelain, as seen in his *Stained Glass Christmas (Noel Vitrail)* series for D'Arceau-Limoges. He studied with such masters as Lavelle and Fournier. His commissions also include *The Lafayette Legacy Collection* for D'Arceau-Limoges. In 1966 he exhibited at the *Cercle de la Librairie* in Paris.

ROCKWELL, Norman One of the most widely-known artists of the twentieth century, Norman Rockwell possessed an uncanny—and perhaps unmatched—ability to capture the spirit of American life in its most ordinary and its most festive moments. Rockwell created

well over 3,000 works in his long and illustrious career. He drew his first *Saturday Evening Post* cover in 1916, followed by more than 300 more. He also drew numerous illustrations for *Life*, *Look* and *Boy's Life*, and was well-known for his annual Boy Scouts calendar illustrations. Rockwell studied at Chase School of Fine and Applied Arts, the National Academy of Design and the Art Student's League, all in New York. He had a one-man show in 1941 at the Milwaukee Art Institute and a one-man exhibition at the Dannenberg Galleries in New York City. His works hang in the Smithsonian Institution, the Metropolitan Museum of Art, the Corner House Museum in Stockbridge, Massachusetts, and in other museums throughout the United States. In addition to the well-known and very popular collector's plate series by The Rockwell Society of America, Rockwell's work is also featured on collector's plates by Franklin Mint, Gorham and Royal Devon. Rockwell died in 1978 at the age of 84.

ROLLER, Carole The first American artist to design plates for Danish company Bing & Grøndahl, Carole Roller has also designed printed fabrics, dinnerware, rugs, towels, Christmas ornaments and stationery. She earned a bachelor's degree in fine arts at the Pratt Institute in New York City. Her plate series include *Children's Day* for Bing & Grøndahl. The company has also produced her figurines and pendants.

ROMANELLI, Carl The sculptor of Incolay's *Great Romances of History Collection* has works on display in memorials, churches, galleries and private collections throughout the world. Romanelli learned his art in a five-year apprenticeship with his father, sculptor Carlo Romanelli. One of his most famous works is a bronze bust of John Henry Cardinal Newman on display in the Vatican. His other commissions include a life-size bronze of Elvis Presley for the Las Vegas

Hilton. He has exhibited in galleries across the United States and is a board member of the California Art Club and the American Institute of Fine Arts.

RUGGERI, Gino Gino Ruggeri, a sculptor in the neo-Classical tradition, is best known for his work "The Crucifix," sculpted from the Casa Serena Institute of Cecina Mare, and his two sculptures "Memorials to the Fallen," which pay tribute to World War I victims. He sculpted the 1976-1980 issues in Studio Dante di Volteradici's *Grand Opera Series*. Ruggeri studied at the Academy of Fine Arts in Sienna and the Art Institute in Volterra, Italy. His awards include three first prizes from the Academy of Fine Arts. He has been director of the Cooperative Artien since 1942.

RUSSELL, Frank Frank Russell and his wife Gertrude Barrer have blended their talents to become a successful art-producing team. They met at the Art Student's League in New York and five years later were reunited in New York's art center, Greenwich Village. Together they have created lithographs, photographs, frescos, serigraphs, ceramics, sculptures and two plate series for Anna-Perenna, the *Triptych* and *Romantic Love* series. Their work has been exhibited at the Art Institute of Chicago and the Whitney Museum of American Art, and hangs in the private collections of Cyrus Vance, Helmut Schmidt and the U.N. Interfaith Chapel in New York.

SANCHEZ, Jorge Painter Jorge Sanchez was born in Mexico City in 1926 and studied to be a lawyer before beginning his art career. He studied art at the Art Academy of San Carlos. In 1978 the Museum of Mexico City exhibited his series of 21 paintings depicting the life of poet, philanthropist and religious figure Sor Jauna Ines de la Cruz. Sanchez' first plate was "Maria" in Pickard's *Children of Mexico* series, beginning in 1981. He has had many one-man shows at museums and galleries in Mexico.

SANTANGELA, Alberto When Alberto Santangela was an art student in Florence he was so captivated by the baptistery doors sculpted by 15th-century artist Lorenzo Ghiberti that they inspired him to become a sculptor instead of a painter. Years later he recreated scenes from Ghiberti's doors on collector's plates in the *Ghiberti's Doors* series for Studio Dante di Volteradici. He also sculpted the *Living Madonnas* series. He was born in Italy in 1936. Santangela apprenticed to his uncle, Amilcare Santini, at an early age before studying informally in Florence.

SCHOENER, Toni Toni Schoener's first love was porcelain. He was born in 1913 and at the end of elementary school was appointed chief designer for Altrohlauer Porzellanfabrik, one of the best-known Bavarian porcelain houses of the time. This "non-essential" industry came to a halt in 1939, and after the war Schoener wandered across Europe restoring war-damaged paintings before returning to Bavaria in 1955, when he joined Kaiser as chief designer. His Kaiser creations include *Christmas* and *Mother's Day* plates. Schoener died in 1978.

SCHULZ, Charles Cartoonist Charles Schulz' "Peanuts" characters have endeared themselves to millions of Americans through comic strips, television specials, a *Time* magazine cover, and many other media, including collector's plate series produced by Schmid. Schulz's television creations have won various Peabody and Emmy awards; the "Peanuts" strip won Best Humor Strip of the Year from the National Cartoonists Society in 1962; Yale University voted Schulz Humorist of the Year in 1958; and as governor of California Ronald Reagan proclaimed a Charles Schulz Day in 1967. Schulz studied at Art Instruction, Inc. in Minneapolis and has been awarded honorary degrees by Anderson College in Indiana and St. Mary's College in California. He was Grand Marshal of the Tournament of Roses Parade in 1976. He also won the National Cartoonists' Society "Reuben" Award in 1955 and 1964, the School Bell Award from the National Education Society in 1960 and the Big Brother of the Year Award in California in 1973.

SKELTON, Red Many people regard film, stage and television comedian and artist Red Skelton as a vital part of America's entertainment heritage. He has made Americans laugh for decades with his portrayals of such characters as Freddie the Freeloader, Clem Kadiddlehopper, Willie Lump-Lump, Sheriff Deadeye, Bolivar Shagnasty, San Fernando Red, George Appleby and Junior the Mean Widdle Kid. Skelton is also a photographer and filmmaker, a recorded composer, a children's fiction writer (with 40 published titles to his credit) and, of course, a painter whose works, reproduced on collector's plates, have endeared him to thousands. His plate series include the *Freddie the Freeloader* and *Freddie's Adventures* series for Crown Parian and the *Famous Clowns* series for Fairmont. Born in 1913 in Vincennes, Indiana, the son of a clown who died before he was born, Skelton began his career dancing for pennies on the street and joined a traveling medicine show at age ten. Since then he has entertained on vaudeville, stage, screen, radio and television. He is a self-taught artist who paints anytime, anyplace—even on airplanes.

SPAULDING, Don Edwin M. Knowles artist Don Spaulding is a Norman Rockwell protege and a leading exponent of authentic historical detail in painting. He began study at New York City's Art Student's League on the G.I. Bill when he was fresh out of World War II and in his early 20's. He was

among half a dozen students chosen to study and live with Rockwell for a summer, and Rockwell became one of his heroes and an example for his approach to Western art. Each of the props and costumes in his seven-plate *Americana Holidays* series is handpicked and true to the 19th century. He has won several awards at shows of Western painting.

SPENCER, Irene Irene Spencer received her training at the American Academy of Art and the Art Institute of Chicago, where she developed her distinctive style, reminiscent of the Old Masters. In addition to her accomplishments as a fine artist, she has written and illustrated children's books and worked as a newspaper cartoonist. Her collector's plates include the *Mother's Love* and *Symphony of Roses* series for Pickard and plates for Fairmont and Gorham. In 1979 she won NALED's "Lithograph of the Year" award and in 1980, NALED's "Plate of the Year" award, as well as The Bradford Exchange's award for New Edition of the Year.

STOBART, John John Stobart, artist for Royal Doulton's *The Log of the "Dashing Wave"* series, grew up in the English shipping town of Liverpool. He attended Derby College of Arts and won a scholarship to the Royal Academy of Art in London. He has traveled extensively by sea and some of the most exotic ports in the world have served as settings for his paintings. His works hang in such prestigious collections as the Marine Museum

of Upper Canada in Toronto, the National Maritime Museum in Greenwich, England, and the Royal Naval College. His paintings have been featured as cover art for many magazines.

TELLIER, Liliane Noted watercolorist Liliane Tellier, creator of Haviland's *1001 Arabian Nights* series, has an extensive following among connoisseurs of the medium. A native Parisienne, she studied watercolor and gouache at L'École Camondo in Paris and refined her techniques in Sweden. Later she worked for the International Society for Education through Art as a consultant to UNESCO.

THELANDER, Henry Artist Henry Thelander's association with Bing & Grøndahl is unparalleled on the collector's plate market. The 1984 issue marked his twenty-second consecutive design for the *Christmas* series. He also has designed every Bing & Grøndahl *Mother's Day* issue. A self-taught artist, Thelander has spent his five-decade-long career living and working in Copenhagen, London and Stockholm, benefiting from the variety of cultures and artistic influences. Known as the "equivalent of the poet laureate" in the Danish visual arts, he has designed government-sponsored postage stamps and posters. He was born in 1902.

TOOTLE, Douglas Davenport Pottery artist Douglas Tootle was born and raised in Staffordshire, England, and schooled at one of

the region's finest institutions, the Burslen College of Art. He was awarded a number of scholarships and left Staffordshire to study fine art and sculpture in London and Florence. Since returning to his native region he has done extensive modeling for some of its most prestigious potteries, including Coalport, a division of Wedgwood, and Hereford. He modeled "Jack Tar" for the *Toby Plate Collection*.

UOSIKKINEN, Raija Born in Hollola, Finland, Raija Uosikkinen is widely regarded as a master ceramicist. She studied at the Institute of Industrial Arts in Helsinki. In 1947 she joined the Arabia design department, and in 1952 she received a grant scholarship from the Arabia-Decora factory to study in Germany. She has taken subsequent study trips to Australia, Turkey, England and Indonesia. A 1954 Helsinki exhibit was devoted exclusively to her creations. Her distinctive contemporary folk art style is exemplified in her plate series *Kalevala*.

VESTERGAARD, Sven As head artist and chief designer for Royal Copenhagen, Sven Vestergaard is a guardian of the centuries-old tradition of hand-painted ceramics. He enrolled with Royal Copenhagen as an apprentice decorator in 1948 at the age of 16 and four years later had attained the pinnacle of the decorator's art. In 1976, when he was head of the drawing department, his artwork was chosen for the annual Christmas plate, "Danish Watermill." His works of

the last decade include the Historical Plates, the Olympic Plates, the *Motherhood* series and the *Hans Christian Andersen* series. Beginning in 1985, Vestergaard has been responsible for the *Christmas* series.

VICKERS, Mary Wedgwood artist Mary Vickers credits a German bomb that fell on London during World War II as her inspiration for becoming an artist. Born in 1940 in a war-torn suburb of London, she soon set out to create beauty in an often violent, ugly world. Today she is one of the leading contemporary Romantic painters, and is also accomplished in lithographs and etching. She studied at England's St. Martin's School of Art, the New York Art Student's League and the Pratt Institute. Her works are exhibited in major galleries on both sides of the Atlantic and in private collections such as that of the Duke and Duchess of Marlborough. Her collector's plates include *The Blossoming of Suzanne* and *My Memories* series.

WEBER, Sarah Stilwell Sarah Stilwell Weber was born near Philadelphia, Pennsylvania in 1878. She studied art at the Drexel Institute in Philadelphia under the tutelage of American illustrator Howard Pyle and was one of the founders of the American Realist movement. Between 1900 and 1930, Weber's work appeared in children's books and on the covers of such magazines as *Collier's* and the *Saturday Evening Post*. Her artwork appears on the plates in Newell Pottery's *Sarah Stilwell Weber Calendar* series.

WIINBLAD, Bjorn Danish artist Bjorn Wiinblad graduated from the Royal Academy of Art in 1944 and worked for *Nymolle Art Fajance* Factory from 1946 to 1956. His creations attracted the attention of Philipp Rosenthal, Jr., head of the Rosenthal company, who, after extensive negotiation, persuaded Wiinblad to design works for the German maker. He was assigned to create products for the Studio-Linie, a high quality, high-priced line of Rosenthal ware. His distinc-

tive collector's plates are world renowned, and the ''Lotus'' pattern of dinnerware he designed won the 1965 American Interior Design Award. His creations include the *Wiinblad Christmas* series produced by Rosenthal. His works are in the collections of museums throughout Europe.

WÜLFING, Sulamith Sulamith Wülfing was born in 1901 in Elberfeld (now part of Wuppertal) Germany and has lived in that area all of her life. She studied at the Art College in Wuppertal and is known for her art that has been reproduced on numerous cards, books and calendars. Much of her original work was lost during World War II, but this did not discourage her long and distinguished career. Her collector's plates include *Sulamith's Love Song* series and the new *Christmas* series for Königszelt Bayern. She has exhibited at the Spring Fair in Frankfurt.

XARAS, Ted Theodore "Ted" Xaras has been enamored of the steam engine since he was a child, when his father told him bedtime tales of building locomotives in Eddystone, Pennsylvania, and took him in borrowed cars to chase their clouds of smoke across the countryside—a pastime he still enjoys. Xaras' plate "Symphony in Steam: Canadian Pacific Railway," first issue in Christian Bell's *Age of Steam* series, won CALED's 1981 Plate of the Year title and became the first Bradex-listed plate produced in Canada. Xaras holds a B.F.A. in illustration from Philadelphia College of Art and an M.F.A. in painting from the Tyler School of Art in Philadelphia. He is a professor and chairman of the art department at Ursinus College in Pennsylvania. His credits include a cover for *Time* magazine and illustrations for various other books and railroad magazines. Xaras was born in 1945.

YATES, Michael Michael Yates was born in Pennsylvania in 1927. He studied at the Art Institute of Pittsburgh. His works appear in numerous public buildings and churches throughout America as well as in many private collections. His art has been commissioned for the homes of such prominent figures as Gerald Ford, Golda Meir, Johnny Cash and former First Lady Pat Nixon. He designed *Michael Yates' Country Ladies* series, Morgantown Crystal's first limited-edition collector's plate series, in double intaglio-carved crystal.

ZOLAN, Donald Donald Zolan is consistently rated one of the most popular collector's plate artists living in the United States, for his poignant pictures of special moments in the lives of contemporary children. His first plate, "Erik and Dandelion" in Viletta's *Zolan's Children* series, was released in 1978. In 1979 "Sabina in the Grass" made history when it became the first non-first-issue to receive the Bradford Exchange's "Plate of the Year" award. Zolan's *Wonder of Childhood Collection, Children at Christmas Collection,* and *Children and Pets* series are produced by Pemberton & Oakes. He and his brother, Richard Zolan (who has produced plates for Modern Masters), are the fifth generation of artists in their family. He studied at the Art Institute of Chicago and won a scholarship to the American Academy of Art. His works hang in numerous galleries throughout the United States and in private collections in Mexico, Australia, France, Italy, South Korea and Colombia.

ZOLAN, Richard Richard Zolan, the creator of Modern Masters/GBS' *Family Treasures Collection,* is descended from four generations of artists and is the brother of prominent collector's plate artist Donald Zolan. He was born in Chicago and now works in the Palm Desert area of California. His works are exhibited in numerous corporate art collections and owned by a number of celebrities. He has exhibited in one-man shows, and at major museums and galleries, including the Art Institute of Chicago.

ZVORYKIN, Boris Russian artist Boris Vasilevich Zvorykin was born in Moscow in 1872 and was one of the last great book illustrators of Tsarist Russia. He was also noted for his murals in the Cathedral at Simferopol. Forced to leave Russia during the 1917 revolution, he settled in Paris in 1920 and became an integral figure in an expatriate movement to retain Imperial Russia's cultural heritage. He elaborately illustrated four books of Russian fairy tales, later published as *The Firebird and Other Russian Fairy Tales* when they caught the eye of book editor Jaqueline Kennedy Onassis. Some of his illustrations appear on collector's plates in Heinrich/Villeroy & Boch's *Russian Fairy Tales* series.

MAKERS AND SPONSORS
OF OVER-THE-COUNTER ISSUES

Abbey Press (Viletta) **U.S.A.**
Accent on Art **U.S.A.**
Addams Family (Schmid) **U.S.A.**
Allison **U.S.A.**
American Archives (International Silver)
  U.S.A.
American Artists **U.S.A.**
American Arts Services (Viletta) **U.S.A.**
American Commemorative (Gorham) **U.S.A.**
American Express (Gorham) **U.S.A.**
American Express (Lenox) **U.S.A.**
American Heritage Art (Crown Parian) **U.S.A.**
American Historical Plates (Castleton China)
  U.S.A.
American Preservation Guild (Gorham) **U.S.A.**
American Rose Society (Gorham) **U.S.A.**
Anna-Perenna **Ger.**
Anri **Italy**
Antique Trader **U.S.A.**
Arabia **Finland**
Arizona Artisan **U.S.A.**
Arlington Mint **U.S.A.**
Armstrong's **U.S.A.**
Arta **Austria**
Artists of the World **U.S.A.**
Audubon Crystal **U.S.A.**
Avondale **U.S.A.**
  See also: Judaic Heritage Society
Aynsley **G.B.**

B & J Art Designs **U.S.A.**
Bareuther **Ger.**
Barthmann **Ger.**
Bayel of France **Fr.**
Bengough **Can.**
Berlin Design **Ger.**
Betourne Studios **Fr.**
Bing & Grøndahl **Den.**
  See also: Ghent Collection
Blue Delft (Schoonhaven) **Neth.**
Boehm Studios **G.B.**
  See also: Hamilton Collection
Bohemia **Czech.**
Bonita Silver **Mex.**
Brantwood Collection **U.S.A.**
Braymer Hall **U.S.A.**
Brentwood Fine Arts (Fairmont) **U.S.A.**
Briarcrest **U.S.A.**
John Brindle Fine Arts **U.S.A.**

Caithness Glass **G.B.**

Calhoun's Collectors Society **U.S.A.**
Calhoun's Collectors Society (Schumann)
  U.S.A.
California Porcelain and Bronze **U.S.A.**
Canadian Collector Plates **Can.**
Capo Di Monte **Italy**
Carlo Monti **Italy**
Carmel Collection **U.S.A.**
Carson Mint (Viletta) **U.S.A.**
Cartier **Fr.**
Castleton China **U.S.A.**
  See also: American Historical Plates
Castleton China (Shenango) **U.S.A.**
Caverswall, see: Ghent Collection
Certified Rarities **U.S.A.**
Chilmark **U.S.A.**
Christian Bell (Schumann) **Can.**
Cleveland Mint **U.S.A.**
Coalport **G.B.**
Collector Creations (Reed & Barton) **U.S.A.**
Collector's Heirlooms (Fairmont) **U.S.A.**
Collector's Heirlooms (Viletta) **U.S.A.**
Collectors Weekly **U.S.A.**
Continental Mint **U.S.A.**
Count Agazzi **Italy**
Creative World **U.S.A.**
Cristal D'Albret **Fr.**
Crown Delft **Neth.**
Crown Parian **U.S.A.**
  See also: American Heritage Art
Crown Staffordshire **G.B.**
Curator Collection **U.S.A.**

Danbury Mint **U.S.A.**
Danish Church **Ger.**
Daum **Fr.**
Derby Collection **U.S.A.**
Designers Collection **U.S.A.**
Stuart Devlin Silver **U.S.A.**
Walt Disney Productions **U.S.A.**
Dresden **Ger.**

Ebeling & Reuss **U.S.A.**
Enesco **U.S.A.**
R. J. Ernst Enterprises (Viletta) **U.S.A.**

Fairmont **U.S.A.**
  See also:
  Brentwood Fine Arts
  Collector's Heirlooms
  Ghent Collection

  Mistwood Designs
Fenton Glass **U.S.A.**
Firehouse **U.S.A.**
Fleetwood Collection (Gorham) **U.S.A.**
Fostoria **U.S.A.**
Franklin Crystal **U.S.A.**
Franklin Mint **U.S.A.**
Franklin Porcelain **U.S.A.**
Frankoma **U.S.A.**
Fürstenberg **Ger.**

Ghent Collection **U.S.A.**
Ghent Collection (Bing & Grøndahl) **U.S.A.**
Ghent Collection (Caverswall) **U.S.A.**
Ghent Collection (Fairmont) **U.S.A.**
Ghent Collection (Gorham) **U.S.A.**
Ghent Collection (Kaiser) **U.S.A.**
Ghent Collection (Viletta) **U.S.A.**
Glaskunst/Schott Zwiesel **Ger.**
Gnomes United **U.S.A.**
Goebel **Ger.**
Gold Crown Ceramics **Can.**
Golf Digest **U.S.A.**
Gorham **U.S.A.**
  See also:
  American Commemorative
  American Express
  American Preservation Guild
  American Rose Society
  Fleetwood Collection
  Ghent Collection
  Hoyle Products
  Lincoln Mint
  Volair
Gourinat-Dolan **Fr.**
Grafburg **Ger.**
Grande Copenhagen **Den.**
Grande Danica **Den.**
Graphics Buying Service,
  see: Modern Masters/GBS
Greentree Potteries **U.S.A.**
Dave Grossman Designs **U.S.A.**

Hackett American Collectors **U.S.A.**
Hamilton Collection **U.S.A.**
Hamilton Collection (Boehm Studios) **U.S.A.**
Hamilton Collection (Hutschenreuther) **U.S.A.**
Hamilton Collection (Porcelaine Ariel) **U.S.A.**
Hamilton Collection (Royal Devon) **U.S.A.**
Hamilton Collection (Viletta) **U.S.A.**
Hamilton Mint **U.S.A.**

343

Haviland **Fr.**
Haviland & Parlon **Fr.**
   See also: Kern Collectibles
Heinrich **Ger.**
Hibel Studio (Kaiser) **Ger.**
Hibel Studio (Rosenthal) **Ger.**
Historic Providence Mint **U.S.A.**
Ralph Homan Studios (Viletta) **U.S.A.**
Home Plates (Mingolla) **U.S.A.**
Hornsea **G.B.**
Hoyle Products (Gorham) **U.S.A.**
Hudson Pewter **U.S.A.**
Hutschenreuther **Ger.**
   See also: Hamilton Collection

Imperial **U.S.A.**
Incolay Studios **U.S.A.**
International Museum **U.S.A.**
International Silver **U.S.A.**
   See also: American Archives
Interpace **U.S.A.**

J M Company **U.S.A.**
Georg Jensen **Den.**
Svend Jensen **Den.**
Josair **Fr.**
Joys (Viletta) **U.S.A.**
Judaic Heritage Society **U.S.A.**
Judaic Heritage Society (Avondale) **U.S.A.**
Judaic Heritage Society (Viletta) **U.S.A.**

KPM-Royal Berlin **Ger.**
Kaiser **Ger.**
   See also:
    Ghent Collection
    Hibel Studio
David Kaplan Studio **U.S.A.**
Keller & George (Reed & Barton) **U.S.A.**
Kensington **U.S.A.**
Kera **Den.**
Kern Collectibles **U.S.A.**
Kern Collectibles (Haviland & Parlon) **U.S.A.**
Kern Collectibles (Pickard) **U.S.A.**
Kern Collectibles (Rosenthal) **U.S.A.**
Kern Collectibles (Royal Bayreuth) **U.S.A.**
Kern Collectibles (Sango) **U.S.A.**
Kilkelly **U.S.A.**
Kings **Italy**
Kirk **U.S.A.**
Koschevak Bros. **Czech.**
Kosta **Swed.**
Kurz (Shuler International) **Neth.**

Lake Shore Prints **U.S.A.**
Lapsys **U.S.A.**
Lenox **U.S.A.**
   See also: American Express
Lihs-Lindner **Ger.**
Lincoln Mint **U.S.A.**
Lincoln Mint (Gorham) **U.S.A.**
Litt **U.S.A.**
Lladró **Spain**
Lund & Clausen **Den.**
Lynell Studios **U.S.A.**

Mallek Studios **U.S.A.**
Manjundo **Japan**
Marigold **U.S.A.**
Marmot **Ger.**
Mason **G.B.**
Master Engravers of America **U.S.A.**
McCalla Enterprises (Viletta) **U.S.A.**
Meissen **Ger.**
Metal Arts **U.S.A.**
Metawa **Neth.**

Metlox Potteries, see: Vernonware
Metropolitan Museum of Art **U.S.A.**
Mingolla, see: Home Plates
Mistwood Designs (Fairmont) **U.S.A.**
Modern Concepts **U.S.A.**
Modern Masters **U.S.A.**
Modern Masters/GBS **U.S.A.**
Moser **Czech.**
Moussalli **U.S.A.**
Mueller **Ger.**
Museum Editions (Ridgewood) **U.S.A.**
Museum Editions (Viletta) **U.S.A.**

Noritake **Japan**
Nostalgia Collectibles **U.S.A.**

OK Collectibles **U.S.A.**
Ohio Arts **U.S.A.**
Orrefors **Swed.**

Pacific Art **U.S.A.**
Palisander **Den.**
Paramount Classics (Pickard) **U.S.A.**
Pemberton & Oakes (Viletta) **U.S.A.**
Pickard **U.S.A.**
   See also:
    Kern Collectibles
    Paramount Classics
Poillerat **Fr.**
Poole Pottery **G.B.**
Porcelaine Ariel, see: Hamilton Collection
Porcelain Limited **U.S.A.**
Porcelana Granada **Arg.**
Porsgrund **Nor.**
Puiforcat **Fr.**

Ram **U.S.A.**
Raynaud-Limoges **Fr.**
Reco International **U.S.A.**
Reed & Barton **U.S.A.**
   See also:
    Collector Creations
    Keller & George
Rhea Silva **G.B.**
Ridgewood **U.S.A.**
   See also: Museum Editions
River Shore **U.S.A.**
Rockwell Collectors Club **U.S.A.**
Rockwell Museum **U.S.A.**
Roman **U.S.A.**
Roman Ceramica Excelsis **Mex.**
Rörstrand **Swed.**
Rosenthal **Ger.**
   See also:
    Hibel Studio
    Kern Collectibles
Royal Bayreuth, see: Kern Collectibles
Royal Copenhagen **Den.**
Royal Cornwall **China/Taiwan, U.S.A.**
Royal Delft **Neth.**
Royal Devon, see: Hamilton Collection
Royal Doulton **Can., G.B.**
Royal Grafton **G.B.**
Royal Limoges **Fr.**
Royal Oaks **U.S.A.**
Royal Orleans **U.S.A.**
Royal Tettau **Ger.**
Royal Worcester **G.B., U.S.A.**
Royale **Ger.**
Royale Germania **Ger.**
Royalwood **U.S.A.**
John A. Ruthven **U.S.A.**

Sabino **Fr.**
Sango **Japan**

   See also: Kern Collectibles
Santa Clara **Spain**
Sarna **India**
Schmid **Ger., Japan**
   See also: Addams Family
Schoonhaven, see: Blue Delft
Schumann **Ger.**
   See also:
    Calhoun's Collectors Society
    Christian Bell
Sebastian **U.S.A.**
Seeley's Doll Plates **U.S.A.**
Seven Seas **U.S.A.**
Shenango, see: Castleton China
Shuler International, see: Kurz
Sierra Productions **U.S.A.**
Signature Collection **U.S.A.**
Silver Creations **U.S.A.**
Smith Glass **U.S.A.**
Sorrina **Can.**
Southern Living Gallery **U.S.A.**
Spode **G.B.**
Sterling America **U.S.A.**
Stieff **U.S.A.**
Stratford Collection **U.S.A.**
Stuart International **U.S.A.**
Stumar **Ger.**
Syracuse China **U.S.A.**

Tirschenreuth **Ger.**
Towle Silversmiths **U.S.A.**

U.S. Historical Society **U.S.A.**

Vague Shadows **U.S.A.**
Val St. Lambert **Belg.**
Veneto Flair **Italy**
Vernonware (Metlox Potteries) **U.S.A.**
Viletta **U.S.A.**
   See also:
    Abbey Press
    American Arts Services
    Carson Mint
    Collector's Heirlooms
    R. J. Ernst Enterprises
    Ghent Collection
    Hamilton Collection
    Ralph Homan Studios
    Joys
    Judaic Heritage Society
    McCalla Enterprises
    Museum Editions
    Pemberton & Oakes
    Warwick
    Westbury
    Edward Weston Editions
Villeroy & Boch **Ger.**
Volair (Gorham) **U.S.A.**

WMF Geislingen **Ger.**
Waldenburg Porcelain **Can.**
Warwick (Viletta) **U.S.A.**
George Washington Mint **U.S.A.**
Wedgwood **G.B.**
Wendell August Forge **U.S.A.**
Westbury (Viletta) **U.S.A.**
Westminster Collectibles **U.S.A.**
Westmoreland **U.S.A.**
Edward Weston Editions (Viletta) **U.S.A.**
Wheaton **U.S.A.**
Whitehall China **U.S.A.**
Wildlife Internationale **U.S.A.**

Zenith Delftware **Neth.**

OVER-THE-COUNTER ISSUES

Over-the-counter plates may be traded, but are not listed, on The Bradford Exchange along with "Bradex" plates, which generally trade with greater regularity and frequency. They are, nonetheless, true collector's plates issued in editions usually limited either to an announced number or to the year of issue as indicated. All editions repetitious of previous editions are excluded.

Over-the-counter issues are arranged alphabetically by country, then alphabetically by maker or maker/sponsor, then chronologically by series. Each entry includes the series name, the year and name of the plate, the edition limit, and the U.S. issue price whenever available.

	Edition Limit	Issue Price (US)
ARGENTINA		
Porcelana Granada		
Peace on Earth		
1971 Annunciation	9,300	$ 12.00
1972 Mary and Elizabeth	6,000	13.00
1973 Road to Bethlehem	5,000	14.00
1974 No Room at Inn	5,000	15.00
1975 Shepherds in Field	5,000	16.50
1976 Nativity	5,000	17.50
1977 Three Kings	5,000	18.00
1978 Young Carpenter	5,000	18.00
1979 Calling of Disciples	5,000	19.00
1980 Loaves and Fishes	5,000	20.00
1981 Suffer Little Children	5,000	21.00
1982 Triumphal Entry	5,000	22.50
1983 Gethsemane	5,000	23.50
1984 Golgotha	5,000	24.00
1985 Ascension	5,000	24.50
AUSTRIA		
Arta		
Mother's Day		
1973 Family with Puppy	1,500	50.00
Christmas		
1973 Nativity–In Manger	1,500	50.00
BELGIUM		
Val St. Lambert		
American Heritage		
1969 Pilgrim Fathers	500	200.00
1970 Paul Revere's Ride	500	200.00
1971 Washington on Delaware	500	200.00
Annual Old Masters		
1969 Rubens & Rembrandt (Pair)	5,000	50.00
1969 Van Gogh & Van Dyck (Pair)	5,000	50.00
1970 Da Vinci & Michelangelo (Pair)	5,000	50.00

	Edition Limit	Issue Price (US)
1971 El Greco & Goya (Pair)	5,000	$ 50.00
1972 Reynolds & Gainsborough (Pair)	5,000	50.00
(Single issue)		
1970 Rembrandt	Year	25.00
CANADA		
Canadian Collector Plates		
Discover Canada		
1980 Sawmill-Kings Landing	10,000	98.00
1981 Quebec Winter	10,000	98.00
1981 Before Bath	10,000	125.00
1982 Grist Mill, Delta	10,000	125.00
1982 Anglican Church at Magnetawan	10,000	125.00
1983 Majestic Rockies	10,000	125.00
1983 Habitants Driving Sleigh	10,000	125.00
1984 Autumn Memories	10,000	125.00
1984 After Bath	10,000	125.00
1985 Postman	10,000	125.00
1985 Pedlar	10,000	125.00
Children of Classics		
1982 Anne of Green Gables	15,000	70.00
1983 Tom Sawyer	15,000	70.00
Days of Innocence		
1982 He Loves Me . . .	15,000	70.00
1982 Butterflies Are Free	15,000	70.00
Christian Bell (Schumann)		
Preserving a Way of Life		
1980 Making Way for Cars	5,000	60.00
1980 Atop Hay Wagon	5,000	60.00
1980 Turning Sod	5,000	60.00
1980 Winter's Morning	5,000	60.00
1981 Sugarbush	10,000	70.00
1981 Fishing for Redfin	10,000	70.00
1981 Wheat Harvest	10,000	70.00
1981 Returning from Village	10,000	70.00
American Steam		
1982 Hiawatha	15,000	65.00
1983 Hittin' Diamond	15,000	65.00

	Edition Limit	Issue Price (US)
1983 Morning at Depot	15,000	$ 65.00
1984 Boston and Maine	15,000	65.00
Men of Rails		
1982 Engineer	30 Days	39.50
1983 Conductor	30 Days	39.50
1983 Pullman Porter	30 Days	39.50
1983 Night Operator	30 Days	39.50
1984 Brakeman	30 Days	39.50
Vanishing Africa		
1983 Sentinel	15,000	55.00
Wild North		
1983 Emperor of North	15,000	55.00
Men of Sea		
1984 Helmsman	NA	39.50
1984 Dorryman	NA	39.50
(Single issue)		
1984 Royal Hudson "2860"	25,000	75.00
Bengough		
Christmas		
1972 Charles Dickens Christmas Carol	490	125.00
Northwest Mounted Police		
1972 1898 Dress Uniform	1,000	140.00
1972 First Uniform	1,000	140.00
Royal Canadian Police		
1972 Order Dress	1,000	140.00
Goldcrown Ceramics		
Wild West		
1981 Horse and Rider	5,000	49.95
1982 Bucking Horse	5,000	49.95
1983 Cowboy	10,000	49.95
1983 Chuckwagon Race	10,000	49.95
1984 Bull Rider	10,000	49.95
Bush Pilot Planes		
1983 Fokker Universal	10,000	49.95
1983 DeHavilland DH80 Puss Moth	10,000	49.95
1984 Ford 6-AT-AS Tri-Motor	10,000	49.95
1984 Fairchild 71B	10,000	49.95

	Edition Limit	Issue Price (US)
Endangered American Wildlife		
1983 Bald Eagle	15,000	$ 59.95
Famous Fighter Aircraft of World War II		
1983 P-51 D Mustang	10,000	49.95
1983 Chance Vought F4U Corsair	10,000	49.95
1984 Lockheed P-38 Lightning	10,000	49.95
1984 Supermarine Spitfire	10,000	49.95
Royal Doulton		
Aged in Wood		
1984 Sugarbush	5,000	55.00
1984 Peggy's Cove	5,000	55.00
1985 Weathering Storm	5,000	55.00
1985 Thunder in Air	5,000	55.00
Captured Moments		
1984 Treasure Seekers	5,000	45.00
1984 Seascape	5,000	45.00
Encore		
1985 Gabriella	10,000	95.00
Sorrina		
Christmas		
1981 Gingerbread House	5,000	40.00
1982 Christmas Eve at Jesuit House	5,000	42.50
1983 Main Street, Barkerville	5,000	45.00
Country Friends		
1983 Meeting at Fence	10,000	65.00
Every Boy's Dream		
1983 Going to Rink	7,500	70.00
1984 Lacing Up	7,500	70.00
Waldenburg Porcelain		
Punkinhead Happy Little Bear		
1983 Punkinhead and His Friends	5,000	39.50
1983 Punkinhead and Santa Claus	5,000	39.50
1984 School's Out	5,000	39.50

CHINA (TAIWAN)

Royal Cornwall

	Edition Limit	Issue Price (US)
Five Perceptions of Weo Cho		
1979 Sense of Touch	19,500	$ 55.00
1979 Sense of Sight	19,500	55.00
1979 Sense of Taste	19,500	55.00
1979 Sense of Hearing	19,500	55.00
1979 Sense of Smell	19,500	55.00

CZECHOSLOVAKIA

Bohemia

	Edition Limit	Issue Price (US)
Mother's Day		
1974 Mother's Day	500	130.00
1975 Mother's Day	500	140.00
1976 Mother's Day	500	150.00

Koschevak Bros.

	Edition Limit	Issue Price (US)
Mary Gregory Christmas		
1973 Christmas	1,000	55.00
1974 Christmas	1,000	60.00
1975 Christmas	1,000	60.00
1976 Christmas	500	65.00
Mary Gregory Mother's Day		
1973 Mother's Day	500	55.00
1974 Mother's Day	300	60.00
1975 Mother's Day	300	60.00
1976 Mother's Day	500	65.00

Moser

	Edition Limit	Issue Price (US)
Christmas (Vanoce)		
1970 Hradcany Castle	400	75.00
1971 Karlstein Castle	1,365	75.00
1972 Old Town Hall	1,000	85.00
1973 Karlovy Vary Castle	500	90.00
Mother's Day (Den Matek)		
1971 Peacocks	350	75.00
1972 Butterflies	750	85.00
1973 Squirrels	200	90.00

DENMARK

Bing & Grøndahl

	Edition Limit	Issue Price (US)
Olympic Games		
1972 Olympiade–Munich	Year	20.00
1976 Olympic Montreal	Year	29.50
1980 Moscow by Night	Year	43.00
1984 Los Angeles	Year	45.00
Bicentennial		
1976 E. Pluribus Unum	Year	50.00
Heritage		
1976 Norseman	5,000	30.00
1977 Navigators	5,000	30.00
1978 Discovery	5,000	39.50
1979 Exploration	5,000	39.50
1980 Helmsman	NA	45.00
1981 Swordsman	NA	49.50
Carl Larsson (Sets of four)		
1977 Flowers on Windowsill		
1977 Breakfast under Big Birch		
1977 Yard & Warehouse		
1977 Kitchen	7,500	150.00
1978 First Born		
1978 Room for Mother and Children		
1978 Portrait of Inga-Maria Thiel		
1978 Iduna	7,500	170.00
1979 Forestry		
1979 Cutting Grass		
1979 Potato Harvest		
1979 Fishery	7,500	165.00
(Single issue)		
1977 Madonna	10,000	45.00
(Single issue)		
1978 Seagull	7,500	75.00
Classical Composers		
1979 Beethoven	Year	37.50
1980 Bach	Year	37.50
1981 Brahms	Year	37.50
1982 Chopin	Year	37.50
1983 Haydn	Year	37.50
1984 Grieg	Year	37.50
Windjammers		
1980 Danmark	10,000	95.00
1980 Eagle	10,000	95.00
1981 Gladan	10,000	95.00
1981 Gorch/Fock	10,000	95.00
1982 Amerigo Vespucci	10,000	95.00
1982 Christian Radich	10,000	95.00
Year of Viking (Single issue)		
1980 Viking	10,000	65.00
New Generation		
1982 Fledglings	10,000	$ 29.50
1982 Kittens	10,000	29.50
1982 Bunnies	10,000	29.50
1982 Fawns	10,000	29.50
Country Garden Calendar		
1984 September	12,500	55.00
1984 October	12,500	55.00
1984 November	12,500	55.00
1984 December	12,500	55.00
1984 January	12,500	55.00
1984 February	12,500	55.00
1984 March	12,500	55.00
1984 April	12,500	55.00
1984 May	12,500	55.00
1984 June	12,500	55.00
1984 July	12,500	55.00
1984 August	12,500	55.00
Seasons Remembered		
1984 Promise of Spring	7,500	35.00
1984 Wildflowers of Summer	7,500	35.00
Gentle Love		
1985 Joanna and Jon	9,500	45.00
1985 Alexandra and Amy	9,500	45.00
(Single issue)		
1985 Give Me Liberty	10,000	60.00

See also: Ghent Collection (U.S.A.)

Grande Copenhagen

	Edition Limit	Issue Price (US)
Bicentennial (Single issue)		
1976 Great Seal	Year	35.00

Grande Danica

	Edition Limit	Issue Price (US)
Mother's Day		
1977 Dog with Puppies	10,000	25.00
1978 Storks	10,000	25.00
1979 Badgers	10,000	25.00

Georg Jensen

	Edition Limit	Issue Price (US)
Christmas		
1972 Doves	Year	15.00
1973 Christmas Eve	Year	15.00
1974 Christmas Story	Year	17.50
1975 Winter Scene	Year	22.50
1976 Christmas in Country	Year	22.50
Chagall (Single issue)		
1972 Lovers	12,500	50.00
Mother's Day		
1973 Mother & Child	Year	15.00
1974 Sweet Dreams	Year	17.50
1975 Mother's World	Year	22.50

Svend Jensen

	Edition Limit	Issue Price (US)
Christmas		
1970 H.C. Andersen House	Year	14.50
1971 Little Match Girl	Year	15.00
1972 Mermaid of Copenhagen	Year	16.50
1973 Fir Tree	Year	22.00
1974 Chimney Sweep	Year	25.00
1975 Ugly Duckling	Year	27.50
1976 Snow Queen	Year	27.50
1977 Snowman	Year	29.50
1978 Last Dream of Old Oak	Year	32.00
1979 Old Street Lamp	Year	36.50
1980 Willie Winky	Year	42.50
1981 Uttermost Parts of Sea	Year	49.50
1982 Twelve by Mailcoach	Year	54.50
1983 Story of Year	Year	54.50
1984 Nightingale	Year	54.50
Mother's Day		
1970 Bouquet for Mother	Year	14.50
1971 Mother's Love	Year	15.00
1972 Good Night	Year	16.50
1973 Flowers for Mother	Year	20.00
1974 Daisies for Mother	Year	25.00
1975 Surprise for Mother	Year	27.50
1976 Complete Gardener	Year	27.50
1977 Little Friends	Year	29.50
1978 Dreams	Year	32.00
1979 Promenade	Year	36.50
1980 Nursery Scene	Year	42.50
1981 Daily Duties	Year	49.50
1982 My Best Friend	Year	54.50
1983 An Unexpected Meeting	Year	54.50
1984 Who Are You?	Year	54.50
Anniversary		
1980 Hans Christian Andersen's Home	NA	60.00

Kera

	Edition Limit	Issue Price (US)
Christmas		
1967 Kobenhavn	Year	6.00
1968 Forste	Year	6.00
1969 Andersen's House	Year	$ 6.00
1970 Langelinie	Year	6.00
1971 Lille Peter	Year	6.00
Moon		
1969 Apollo 11	Year	6.00
1970 Apollo 13	Year	6.00
Mother's Day		
1970 Mother's Day	Year	6.00
1971 Mother's Day	Year	6.00

Lund & Clausen

	Edition Limit	Issue Price (US)
Moon		
1969 Moon Landing–Apollo 11	Year	10.00
1971 Apollo 13	Year	15.00
Mother's Day		
1970 Rose	Year	10.00
1971 Forget-Me-Nots	Year	10.00
1972 Bluebell	Year	15.00
1973 Lily of Valley	Year	16.00
Christmas		
1971 Animal Garden	Year	13.50
1972 Stave Church	Year	13.50
1973 Christmas Scene	Year	13.50

Palisander

	Edition Limit	Issue Price (US)
Christmas		
1971 Red Robin on Holly	1,200	50.00
1972 Flying Geese	1,200	50.00
1973 Christmas	1,200	50.00
Presidential		
1971 George Washington	1,000	50.00
1972 Thomas Jefferson	1,000	50.00
1973 John Adams	1,000	50.00
(Single issue)		
1973 Bicentennial	250	50.00

Royal Copenhagen

	Edition Limit	Issue Price (US)
Historical		
1975 R. C. Bicentennial	Year	30.00
1976 U.S. Bicentennial	Year	35.00
1977 Electro-Magnetism	Year	35.00
1978 Capt. Cook	Year	37.50
1979 Adam Oehlenschlager	Year	42.50
1980 Amagertorv	Year	52.50
National Parks of America		
1978 Yellowstone	5,000	75.00
1979 Shenandoah	5,000	75.00
1980 Yosemite	5,000	75.00
1980 Mt. McKinley	5,000	75.00
1981 Everglades	5,000	75.00
1981 Grand Canyon	5,000	75.00
(Single issue)		
1980 Year of Viking	5,000	55.00
Hans Christian Andersen		
1983 Shepherdess and Chimney Sweep	Year	39.50
1984 Thumbelina	Year	39.50
1985 Little Mermaid	Year	39.50

FINLAND

Arabia

	Edition Limit	Issue Price (US)
Christmas 100 Years Ago		
1978 Inland Village Scene	Year	49.00
1979 Forest Village Scene	Year	72.00
1980 Seaside Village Scene	Year	79.00
1981 Farm Village Scene	Year	87.00
1982 Country Village Scene	Year	95.00
Pictures of Lapland		
1981 Laplander Village	7,000	175.00
(Single issue)		
1981 Rose	2,000	360.00

FRANCE

Bayel of France

	Edition Limit	Issue Price (US)
Flowers		
1972 Rose	300	50.00
1973 Lilies	300	50.00
1973 Orchid	300	50.00
Bicentennial		
1974 Liberty Bell	500	50.00
1975 Independence Hall	500	60.00
1976 Spread Eagle	500	60.00
Eagles		
1974 Eagle Head	300	50.00
1974 Eagle in Flight	300	50.00

Betourne Studios

	Edition Limit	Issue Price (US)
Jean-Paul Loup Christmas		
1971 Noel	300	125.00
1972 Noel	300	150.00
1973 Noel	300	175.00
1974 Noel	400	200.00
1975 Noel	250	$250.00
1976 Noel	150	300.00
Mother's Day (Champleve)		
1974 Mother & Child	500	250.00
Mother's Day (Enamel)		
1975 Mother's Day	400	285.00
1976 Mother & Child	250	300.00

Cartier

	Edition Limit	Issue Price (US)
Cathedral		
1972 Chartres Cathedral	12,500	50.00
1974 Chartres, Millous	500	130.00

Cristal D'Albret

	Edition Limit	Issue Price (US)
Four Seasons		
1972 Summer	1,000	75.00
1973 Autumn	648	75.00
1973 Spring	312	75.00
1974 Winter	1,000	88.00
(Single issue)		
1972 Bird of Peace	3,700	64.00

Daum

	Edition Limit	Issue Price (US)
Four Seasons		
1969 Autumn (Amethyst)	2,000	150.00
1970 Winter (Aquamarine)	2,000	150.00
1970 Spring (Emerald)	2,000	150.00
1970 Summer (Topaz)	2,000	150.00
Famous Musicians		
1970 Bach (Emerald)	2,000	60.00
1970 Beethoven (Amethyst)	2,000	60.00
1971 Mozart (Tourmaline)	2,000	60.00
1971 Wagner (Peridot)	2,000	60.00
1972 Debussy (Topaz)	2,000	60.00
1972 Gershwin (Sapphire)	2,000	60.00
Dali		
1971 Ceci N'est Pas Une Assiette	2,000	200.00
1971 Triomphale	2,000	200.00
Art Nouveau		
1979 Waterlilies	4,000	125.00
1980 Lily Pond	4,000	150.00
1981 Swan	4,000	170.00

Gourinat-Dolan

	Edition Limit	Issue Price (US)
(Single issue)		
1978 Doves of Peace	3,000	60.00

Haviland

	Edition Limit	Issue Price (US)
Historical		
1968 Martha Washington	2,500	35.00
1969 Lincoln	2,500	100.00
1970 Grant	3,000	100.00
1971 Hayes	2,500	110.00
Bicentennial		
1972 Burning of Gaspee	10,000	39.95
1973 Boston Tea Party	10,000	39.95
1974 First Continental Congress	10,000	39.95
1975 Ride of Paul Revere	10,000	40.00
1976 Declaration of Independence	10,000	48.00
French Collection		
1973 Breakfast	10,000	29.95
1974 Wash	10,000	29.95
1975 In Park	10,000	30.00
1976 To Market	10,000	38.00
1977 A Wash Before Dinner	10,000	38.00
1978 An Evening at Home	10,000	40.00
1979 Happy Mother's Day	10,000	45.00
Theatre Des Saisons		
1978 Spring	5,000	120.00
1978 Summer	5,000	120.00
1978 Autumn	5,000	120.00
1978 Winter	5,000	120.00
Mother's Day		
1980 Child and His Animals	Year	55.00
Visit from Saint Nicholas		
1980 Twas Night Before Christmas	Year	55.00
1981 Children Were Nestled	Year	60.00
1982 Tore Open Shutters	Year	60.00
1983 What to Wondering Eyes	Year	60.00
1984 Up Chimney	15,000	45.00
Fleurs et Rubens		
1980 Orchidée	7,500	120.00
1981 Hibiscus	7,500	120.00
1982 Poppy	7,500	120.00

Haviland & Parlon

	Edition Limit	Issue Price (US)
Nan Lee (Single issue)		
1973 Peaceable Kingdom	5,000	30.00

OVER-THE-COUNTER ISSUES

	Edition Limit	Issue Price (US)
Mother's Day		
1975 Laura and Child	15,000	$ 37.50
1976 Pinky and Baby	15,000	42.50
1977 Amy and Snoopy	10,000	45.00
King Tut (Single issue)		
1977 Scarab	2,500	80.00
Zodiac (Single issue)		
1977 Astrological Man	5,000	50.00
Enchanted Forest		
1982 Entrance to Forest	10,000	65.00
1983 Birds of Forest	10,000	65.00

See also: Kern Collectibles (U.S.A.)

Josair

	Edition Limit	Issue Price (US)
Bicentennial		
1972 American Eagle	400	250.00
1973 American Flag	400	250.00
1974 Abraham Lincoln	400	250.00
1975 George Washington	400	250.00
1976 Declaration of Independence	400	250.00

Poillerat

	Edition Limit	Issue Price (US)
Christmas		
1972 Three Kings	500	350.00
1973 Rose	250	350.00

Puiforcat

	Edition Limit	Issue Price (US)
Cartes a Jouer		
1972 (Set of five)	2,000	300.00
(Single issue)		
1973 Exodus (Silver)	2,000	200.00

Raynaud-Limoges

	Edition Limit	Issue Price (US)
Castles		
1979 Bodiam Castle	5,000	48.00
1979 Glamis Castle	5,000	48.00
1979 Tower of London	5,000	48.00
Wildlife Collection		
1978 Tiger Bouquet	Year	50.00

Royal Limoges

	Edition Limit	Issue Price (US)
Christmas		
1972 Nativity	5,000	25.00
1973 Three Wise Men	5,000	27.50

Sabino

	Edition Limit	Issue Price (US)
Annual Crystal		
1970 King Henry IV & Maria De Medici	1,500	65.00
1971 Milo & Beasts	1,500	65.00

GERMANY

Anna-Perenna

	Edition Limit	Issue Price (US)
Birds of Fancy		
1978 Firebird	5,000	110.00
Floral Fantasies		
1978 Empress Gold	5,000	110.00
Enchanted Gardens		
1978 June Dream	5,000	75.00
1979 Summer Day	5,000	95.00
Oriental Tranquility		
1978 Chun Li at Pond	5,000	100.00
1979 Ming Tao on Path of Faith	5,000	110.00
Joy of Motherhood		
1979 Gesa and Children	5,000	165.00
1980 Alexandra and Children	5,000	175.00
American Silhouettes I–Children		
1981 Fiddlers Two	5,000	75.00
1981 Mary with Lambs	5,000	75.00
1981 Waiting for Tom	5,000	75.00
1981 Ring Around Rosie	5,000	75.00
American Silhouettes II–Family		
1982 Family Outing	5,000	75.00
1982 John and Mary	5,000	75.00
1982 Homemakers A-Quilting	5,000	75.00
1982 Leisure Time	5,000	75.00
American Silhouettes III–Valley Life		
1983 Frosty Frolic	5,000	75.00
1983 Hayride	5,000	75.00
1983 Sunday Ride	5,000	75.00
1983 Market Day	5,000	75.00
Bashful Bunnies		
1981 Spring's Surprise	15,000	62.50
1981 Summer's Sunshine	15,000	62.50
1982 Fall's Frolic	15,000	62.50
1982 Winter's Wonder	15,000	62.50
Children of Mother Earth		
1982 Spring	2,500	250.00
1982 Summer	2,500	250.00
1982 Autumn	2,500	250.00
1982 Winter	2,500	250.00
Happy Village		
1982 Spring Picnic	5,000	$ 55.00
1982 Summer on Pond	5,000	55.00
1982 Autumn Harvest Dance	5,000	55.00
1982 Winter Snow Kids	5,000	55.00
Masquerade Fantasy		
1982 Masquerade Party	9,800	95.00
1982 Clowns and Unicorns	9,800	95.00
1982 Merry-Go-Round Ballet	9,800	95.00
Uncle Tad's Holiday Cats		
1982 Jingle Bells	9,800	75.00
1983 Pollyanna	9,800	75.00
1984 Pumpkins	9,800	75.00
1985 Perry, Buttercup and Black-Eyed Susan	9,800	75.00
Arctic Spring		
1983 Patience	9,500	75.00
1984 Proud Mother	9,500	75.00
Flowers of Count Bernadotte		
1983 Iris	17,800	75.00
1983 Carnation	17,800	75.00
1984 Freesia	17,800	75.00
1984 Lily	17,800	75.00
1984 Orchid	17,800	75.00
1984 Rose	17,800	75.00
1985 Tulip	17,800	75.00
1985 Chrysanthemum	17,800	75.00
Rhythm and Dance		
1983 Ballroom	5,000	29.50
1983 Two-Step	5,000	29.50
1983 Strut	5,000	29.50
1983 Swing	5,000	29.50
1983 Aerobics	5,000	29.50
1983 Jazz	5,000	29.50
1983 Charleston	5,000	29.50
1983 Cake-Walk	5,000	29.50
Moss Christmas		
1984 Noel, Noel	5,000	69.00
1985 Helping Hands	5,000	69.00
Reflections of Youth		
1984 Swimmers	9,500	69.00
1985 Daydreamer	9,500	69.00
Me and My Shadow		
1985 Jason and Ginger	7,500	75.00
Uncle Tad's Golden Oldies		
1985 My Merry Oldsmobile	NA	39.50
1985 Paddlin' Madelin' Home	NA	39.50
1985 Ramona	NA	39.50

Bareuther

	Edition Limit	Issue Price (US)
Mother's Day		
1969 Mother & Children	5,000	12.00
1970 Mother & Children	5,000	12.00
1971 Mother & Children	5,000	13.50
1972 Mother & Children	5,000	15.00
1973 Mother & Children	5,000	15.00
1974 Musical Children	5,000	19.00
1975 Spring Outing	5,000	21.50
1976 Rocking Cradle	5,000	23.00
1977 Noon Feeding	5,000	24.50
1978 Blind Man's Bluff	5,000	27.50
1979 Mother's Love	5,000	35.00
1980 First Cherries	5,000	37.50
1981 Playtime	5,000	39.50
1982 Suppertime	5,000	39.50
1983 On Farm	5,000	39.50
1984 Village Children	5,000	42.50
1985 Sunrise	5,000	42.50
Thanksgiving		
1971 First Thanksgiving	2,500	13.50
1972 Harvest	2,500	14.50
1973 Country Road in Autumn	2,500	15.00
1974 Old Mill	2,500	19.00
1975 Wild Deer in Forest	2,500	21.50
1976 Thanksgiving on Farm	2,500	23.50
1977 Horses	2,500	24.50
1978 Apple Harvest	2,500	27.50
1979 Noontime	2,500	35.00
1980 Longhorns	2,500	37.50
1981 Gathering Wheat	2,500	39.50
1982 Autumn	2,500	39.50

Barthmann

	Edition Limit	Issue Price (US)
Christmas		
1977 Mary with Child	300	236.00
1978 Adoration of Child	500	326.00
1979 Holy Mother of Kasanskaja	500	361.00
1980 Holy Mother by Kykos	500	385.00

Berlin Design

	Edition Limit	Issue Price (US)
Father's Day (Historical)		
1971 Brooklyn Bridge on Opening Day	12,000	$ 14.50
1972 Continent Spanned	3,000	15.00
1973 Landing of Columbus	2,000	18.00
1974 Adorn's Balloon	Year	25.00
1975 Washington Crossing Delaware	Year	30.00
1976 Tom Thumb	Year	32.00
1977 Zeppelin	Year	32.00
1978 Carl Benz	Year	36.00
1979 Johannes Gutenberg at Mainz	Year	47.50
Mother's Day		
1971 Grey Poodles	20,000	14.50
1972 Fledglings	10,000	15.00
1973 Duck Family	6,000	16.50
1974 Squirrels	6,000	22.50
1975 Cats	6,000	30.00
1976 Doe and Her Fawn	6,000	32.00
1977 Storks	6,000	32.00
1978 Mare with Foal	6,000	36.00
1979 Swans and Cygnets	6,000	47.50
1980 Goat Family	6,000	55.00
1981 Dachshund Family	6,000	55.00
1982 Partridge Family	6,000	55.00
1983 Swallow Family	6,000	55.00
1984 Care	6,000	55.00

Danish Church

	Edition Limit	Issue Price (US)
Church		
1968 Roskilde Cathedral	Year	12.00
1969 Ribe Cathedral	Year	13.00
1970 Marmor Church	Year	13.00
1971 Ejby Church	Year	13.00
1972 Kalundborg Church	Year	13.00
1973 Grundtvig Church	Year	15.00
1974 Broager Church	Year	15.00
1975 Sct. Knuds Church	Year	18.00
1976 Osterlars Church	Year	22.00
1977 Budolfi Church	Year	15.95
1978 Haderslev Cathedral	Year	19.95
1979 Holmens Church	Year	19.95
1980 Sct. Bendts Church	Year	24.00
1981 Vor Frue Church	Year	32.50
1982 Fjennesler Church	Year	33.00
1983 Udby Church	Year	39.50

Dresden

	Edition Limit	Issue Price (US)
Christmas		
1971 Shepherd Scene	3,500	14.50
1972 Niklas Church	6,000	18.00
1973 Schwanstein Church	6,000	18.00
1974 Village Scene	5,000	20.00
1975 Rothenberg Scene	5,000	24.00
1976 Bavarian Village Church	5,000	26.00
1977 Old Mill in Hexenloch	5,000	28.00
Mother's Day		
1972 Doe and Fawns	8,000	15.00
1973 Mare and Colt	6,000	16.00
1974 Tiger and Cub	5,000	20.00
1975 Dachshund Family	5,000	24.00
1976 Mother Owl and Young	5,000	26.00
1977 Chamois	5,000	28.00

Fürstenberg

	Edition Limit	Issue Price (US)
Easter		
1971 Sheep	3,500	15.00
1972 Chicks	4,000	15.00
1973 Bunnies	4,000	16.00
1974 Pussywillow	4,000	20.00
1975 Village Church	4,000	24.00
1976 Country Watermill	4,000	25.00
Christmas		
1971 Rabbits	7,500	14.00
1972 Snowy Village	6,000	15.00
1973 Christmas Eve	3,000	18.00
1974 Sparrows	4,000	20.00
1975 Deer Family	4,000	24.00
1976 Winter Birds	4,000	25.00
Deluxe Christmas		
1971 Three Wise Men	1,500	45.00
1972 Holy Family and Angel	2,000	45.00
1973 Christmas Eve	2,000	60.00
Mother's Day		
1972 Hummingbird	5,000	15.00
1973 Hedgehogs	5,000	16.00
1974 Doe with Fawn	4,000	20.00
1975 Swan Family	4,000	24.00
1976 Koala Bear	4,000	25.00
Olympic		
1972 Olympics–Munich	5,000	20.00
1976 Olympics–Montreal	5,000	37.50
New York City Landscape		
1981 City Hall	3,500	$ 75.00
1981 Central Park	3,500	75.00

Glaskunst/Schott-Zwiesel

	Edition Limit	Issue Price (US)
Christmas		
1977 Three Wise Man	NA	105.00
1978 Holy Family	NA	112.50
1979 Shepherd of Field	NA	115.00
1980 Annunciation of Maria	NA	118.00

Goebel

	Edition Limit	Issue Price (US)
Charlot Byj		
1973 Santa at Tree	Year	16.50
1974 Santa and Girl	Year	22.00
1975 Up and Away	Year	25.00
1976 Boy with Teddy Bear	Year	25.00
1977 Joy to World	Year	25.00
Wildlife		
1974 Robin	Year	45.00
1975 Blue Titmouse	Year	50.00
1976 Barn Owl	Year	50.00
1977 Bullfinch	Year	50.00
1978 Sea Gull	Year	55.00
1979 Mallard	10,000	90.00
1980 Cardinal	10,000	90.00
1981 Peregrine Falcon	10,000	90.00
Mothers		
1975 Rabbits	Year	45.00
1976 Cats	Year	45.00
1977 Panda Bears	Year	45.00
1978 Doe and Fawn	Year	50.00
1979 Long-Eared Owl	10,000	65.00
1980 Raccoon and Baby	10,000	75.00
1981 Ringed Seal	10,000	80.00
1982 Swan	10,000	80.00
1983 Walrus	10,000	80.00
Robson Christmas		
1975 Flight to Egypt (Porcelain)	Year	50.00
1975 Flight to Egypt (Pewter)	Year	45.00
Annual Crystal		
1978 Praying Girl	Year	45.00
1979 Praying Boy	Year	50.00
1980 Praying Angel	15,000	50.00
1981 Girl with Teddy Bear	10,000	50.00
Old Testament Themes		
1978 Twelve Tribes of Israel	10,000	125.00
1979 Ten Commandments	10,000	175.00
1980 Traditions	10,000	225.00
1981 Prophet	10,000	275.00
American Heritage		
1979 Freedom & Justice Soaring	15,000	100.00
1980 Wild & Free	10,000	120.00
1981 Where Buffalo Roam	5,000	125.00
Crystal Mother's Day		
1979 Butterfly	Year	50.00
1980 Sparrow	15,000	50.00
1981 Doves	5,000	50.00
(Single issue)		
1979 Christmas	200	500.00
Bratsoff		
1979 Star Steed	15,000	125.00
Bavarian Forest		
1980 Owls	7,500	150.00
1981 Deer	7,500	150.00
1982 Pheasants	7,500	150.00
North American Wildlife		
1980 Beaver	10,000	125.00
1981 Harp Seal	10,000	125.00
1982 Polar Bear	10,000	125.00
1983 Fox and Kits	10,000	125.00
1984 Lynx	10,000	75.00
Christmas in Kinderland		
1982 A Gift of Joy	10,000	49.50
1983 A Midnight Clear	10,000	49.50
1984 Three Wee Kings	10,000	49.50
Christmas Morning in Dingle Dell		
1982 Dolly Dingle	10,000	30.00
1983 Billy Bumps	10,000	30.00
Dolly Dingle World Traveler		
1982 Dolly Visits Germany	10,000	30.00
1982 Dolly Visits Italy	10,000	30.00
1982 Dolly Visits Holland	10,000	30.00
1982 Dolly Visits Spain	10,000	30.00
Native Companions		
1982 Rachel	10,000	49.50
1983 Hummingbird	10,000	49.50
1983 Rabbit Dancer	10,000	49.50
1984 Celebration	10,000	49.50

	Edition Limit	Issue Price (US)
Winged Fantasies		
1982 Strawberries	10,000	$ 49.50
1983 Bacchanalia	10,000	49.50
1983 Cerises	10,000	49.50
1983 Brambleberries	10,000	49.50
Blue-Button Twins Christmas		
1983 By Fireplace	10,000	30.00
1983 Down Stairs	10,000	30.00
English Countryside Cat		
1983 James	10,000	35.00
1983 Henry	10,000	35.00
1983 Lucy	10,000	35.00
(Single issue)		
1984 Skater's Waltz	10,000	33.00
Little Hugs		
1985 Dolly Dearest	7,500	34.50
Grafburg		
Christmas		
1975 Black-Capped Chickadee	5,000	20.00
1976 Squirrels	5,000	22.00
Heinrich		
UNICEF Children in World		
1977 Europe	Year	30.00
1978 Asia	Year	30.00
1979 Africa	Year	30.00
1980 America	Year	30.00
1981 Malaysia	Year	30.00
1982 India	Year	35.00
1983 Mexico	Year	35.00
(Single issue)		
1979 International Year of Child	Year	35.00
Flower Fairies Collection		
1979 Lavender Fairy	21 Days	35.00
1980 Sweet Pea Fairy	21 Days	35.00
1980 Candytuft Fairy	21 Days	35.00
1980 Heliotrope Fairy	21 Days	35.00
1981 Black Thorne Fairy	21 Days	35.00
1981 Apple Blossom Fairy	21 Days	35.00
Famous Sea Battles		
1981 Battle of Trafalgar	Year	42.00
1982 Battle/Flamborough Head	Year	42.00
1983 Battle of Lepanto	Year	42.00
Hibel Studio (Kaiser)		
Tribute to Classical Greek Beauty		
1980 Diana	3,000	350.00
World I Love		
1981 Leah's Family	17,500	85.00
1982 Kaylin	17,500	85.00
1983 Edna's Music	17,500	85.00
1984 O-Hana	17,500	85.00
A Tribute to All Children		
1984 Giselle	19,500	55.00
1985 Gerard	19,500	55.00
1985 Wendy	19,500	55.00
Flower Girl		
1985 Lily	15,000	79.00
Hibel Studio (Rosenthal)		
Famous Women and Children		
1980 Pharoah's Daughter and Moses	3,000	350.00
1981 Cornelia and Jewels	2,500	350.00
1982 Anna and Children	2,500	350.00
1983 Mozart and Maria	2,500	350.00
Hutschenreuther		
*Christmas**		
1972 On Way to Egypt	5,000	NA
1973 Adoration	5,000	NA
1974 Annunciation	5,000	NA
*Series not available in U.S.		
Gunther Granget Annual		
1972 Sparrows	5,000	50.00
1973 Killdeer	2,500	75.00
1973 Squirrel	2,500	75.00
1974 Partridge	2,500	75.00
1975 Rabbits	2,500	90.00
1976 Wrens	2,500	100.00
1976 Freedom in Flight	5,000	100.00
1977 Bears	2,500	100.00
1978 Foxes	1,000	125.00
Songbirds of America		
1972 Eastern Bluebird and Goldfinch (Pair)	5,000	100.00
1973 Mockingbird and Robin (Pair)	5,000	100.00
Canada Christmas		
1973 Parliament Building	Year	15.00
1974 Moose	Year	16.00

	Edition Limit	Issue Price (US)
1975 Basilica	Year	$ 21.00
1976 Winter on Prairies	Year	23.00
1977 Bluenose	Year	23.00
1978 Lost Lagoon	Year	27.00
1979 Yukon Highway Bridge	Year	33.00
1980 Covered Bridge	Year	38.00
1981 Saskatchewan Winter	Year	38.00
1982 Christmas to Celebrate	Year	38.00
1983 Province House	Year	38.00
1984 Christmas in Winnipeg	Year	38.00
Bicentennial		
1976 Freedom in Flight	5,000	100.00
1976 Freedom in Flight (Gold)	200	200.00
Plates of Month (Set of 12)		
1977 January–December	5,000	780.00
Mother and Child Annual		
1978 Mother and Child	Year	55.00
1979 Mother and Child	Year	65.00
1980 Mother and Child	Year	87.50
1981 Mother and Child	Year	87.50
Birthday Annual		
1978 Birthday Plate	10,000	165.00
Winter Christmas		
1978 Silent Night	Year	260.00
1979 Saint Lucia	Year	295.00
1980 Christmas Pavillion	Year	325.00
1981 Christmas Sleigh	Year	400.00
1982 Joy to World	Year	400.00
Friendship Annual		
1978 Friendship Plate	Year	80.00
Dolores Valenza Enchantment		
1979 Princess Snowflake	5,000	50.00
1979 Blossom Queen	5,000	62.50
1980 Princess Marina	5,000	87.50
1980 Princess Starbright	5,000	87.50
1981 Princess Aura	5,000	87.50
1981 Harvest Queen	5,000	87.50
Wedding Annual		
1978 Wedding Plate	10,000	210.00
Zodiac Collection (Set of 12)		
1978 Aries–Pisces	1,500	1500.00
Hans Achtziger Annual		
1979 Heading South	4,000	150.00
1980 Playful Flight	5,000	187.50
1981 Tropical Skies	5,000	245.00
1982 Carried by Wind	2,500	250.00
1983 Toward Sun	5,000	250.00
Arzberg Christmas		
1979 Christmas	2,500	60.00
(Single issue)		
1979 Celebration Plate	Year	67.50
(Single issue)		
1979 Anniversary Plate	Year	120.00
(Single issue)		
1977 Allegro Ensemble	7,500	120.00
Hibel Museum (Single issue)		
1977 Flower Girl of Provence	12,750	175.00
Floral Heirlooms		
1978 Zinnias in Sugar Bowl	5,000	65.00
1979 Pansies in Antique Tin	5,000	70.00
1981 Primroses in Staffordshire Pitcher	5,000	75.00
1982 Asters	5,000	75.00
Birds of Paradise		
1981 Bluebird of Paradise	10,000	175.00
1982 Raggis Great Bird of Paradise	10,000	175.00
Glory of Christmas		
1982 Nativity	25,000	80.00
1983 Angels	25,000	80.00
1984 Shepherds	25,000	80.00
Legendary Animals (Set of four)		
1982 Unicorn		
1982 Griffin		
1982 Dragon		
1982 Pegasus	12,500	175.00
Songbirds of North America		
1982 Eastern Bluebird	12,500	60.00
1982 Mockingbird	12,500	60.00
1982 American Goldfinch	12,500	60.00
1982 Rosebreasted Grosbeak	12,500	60.00
Early Memories		
1983 Do They Bite?	7,500	75.00
1983 Tug of War	7,500	75.00
1984 Explorers	7,500	75.00
1984 My Turn	7,500	75.00
Water Babies		
1983 Tom and Dragon-Fly	15 Days	45.00
1983 Fairies Take Care of Tom	15 Days	45.00

	Edition Limit	Issue Price (US)
1983 Tom and Mrs. Do-As-You-Would	15 Days	$ 45.00
1983 Tom and Mrs. Be-Done-By	15 Days	45.00
1984 Tom and Sweet Chest	15 Days	45.00
1984 Ellie Teaches Tom	15 Days	45.00
1984 Tom Takes Care of Baby	15 Days	45.00
1984 Tom and Ellie	15 Days	45.00
Unicorns in Dreamer's Garden (Set of five)		
1984 Sound of Melodies		
1984 Sight of Wonders		
1984 Smell of Roses		
1984 Taste of Sweetness		
1984 Touch of a Dream	12,500	197.50
Women of Four Seasons		
1984 Woman of Spring	7,500	70.00
Spring in World of Birds		
1985 Pheasants	2,500	325.00
See also:		
Hamilton Collection (U.S.A.)		
Kaiser		
(Single issue)		
1970 Oberammergau Passion Play	Year	25.00
(Single issue)		
1970 Royal Horse Show–Toronto	1,000	29.00
Great Yachts		
1971 Cetonia	1,000	50.00
1971 Westward	1,000	50.00
Anniversary		
1972 Love Birds	Year	16.50
1973 In Park	Year	18.00
1974 Canoeing Down River	7,000	22.00
1975 Tender Moment	7,000	25.00
1976 Serenade for Lovers	Year	25.00
1977 A Simple Gift	Year	25.00
1978 Viking Toast	Year	30.00
1979 Romantic Interlude	Year	32.00
1980 Love at Play	Year	40.00
1981 Rendezvous	Year	40.00
1982 Betrothal	Year	40.00
1983 Sunday Afternoon	Year	40.00
Feathered Friends		
1978 Blue Jays	10,000	70.00
1979 Cardinals	10,000	80.00
1980 Cedar Waxwings	10,000	80.00
1981 Goldfinches	10,000	80.00
King Tut		
1978 Golden Mask	15,000	65.00
People of the Midnight Sun		
1978 Northern Lullaby	15,000	65.00
1979 Ilaga, My Friend	15,000	75.00
1980 Motherhood	15,000	85.00
1981 Odark and Son Samik	15,000	90.00
1982 Anana with Little Nutak	15,000	90.00
1983 Hunter's Reward	15,000	90.00
Yesterday's World		
1978 Time for Dreaming	5,000	70.00
1979 Summer Is Forever	5,000	75.00
1980 Sunday Afternoon	5,000	80.00
1981 Breath of Spring	5,000	80.00
(Single issue)		
1980 Oberammergau Passion Play	Year	40.00
Little Men		
1980 Magical Moment	9,500	60.00
1983 A Day to Remember	9,500	60.00
Four Seasons (Set of four)		
1981 Spring		
1981 Summer		
1981 Fall		
1981 Winter	NA	200.00
Happy Days		
1981 Aeroplane	5,000	75.00
1982 Julie	5,000	75.00
1983 Winter Fun	5,000	75.00
1984 Lookouts	5,000	75.00
Little Clowns		
1981 Red Mask	9,500	35.00
1982 Pigtails and Puppies	9,500	35.00
1983 Concertina	9,500	35.00
Nativity		
1981 Old Country Christmas	Year	20.00
Romantic Portraits		
1981 Lilie	5,000	175.00
1982 Camelia	5,000	175.00
1983 Rose	5,000	175.00
1984 Daisy	5,000	175.00

	Edition Limit	Issue Price (US)
Children's Prayers		
1982 Now I Lay Me Down to Sleep	5,000	$ 29.50
1983 Saying Grace	10,000	25.00
Memories of Christmas		
1983 Wonder of Christmas	19,500	42.50
1984 Christmas Dreams	19,500	42.50
Famous Horses		
1983 Snow Knight	3,000	95.00
Traditional Fairy Tales		
1983 Cinderella	NA	39.50
1983 Jack and Beanstalk	NA	39.50
1984 Three Little Pigs	NA	39.50
1984 Tom Thumb	NA	39.50
Racing for Pride and Profit		
1984 Aging Victor	9,500	50.00
1985 Second Goes Hungry	9,500	50.00
Woodland Creatures		
1984 Springtime Frolic	10 Days	34.95
1984 Fishing Trip	10 Days	34.95
Bird Dogs		
1985 Cocker Spaniel	15,000	39.50
1985 Beagle	15,000	39.50
1985 English Setter	15,000	39.50
1985 Black Labrador	15,000	39.50
1985 German Pointer	15,000	39.50
1985 Golden Labrador	15,000	39.50
1985 English Pointer	15,000	39.50
1985 Irish Setter	15,000	39.50
Water Fowl		
1985 Mallard Ducks	15,000	55.00
1985 Canvas Back	15,000	55.00
1985 Wood Duck	15,000	55.00
1985 Pintail	15,000	55.00
See also:		
Ghent Collection (U.S.A.)		
Hibel Studio (Ger.)		
KPM–Royal Berlin		
Christmas		
1969 Christmas Star	5,000	28.00
1970 Three Kings	5,000	28.00
1971 Christmas Tree	5,000	28.00
1972 Christmas Angel	5,000	31.00
1973 Christchild on Sled	5,000	33.00
1974 Angel & Horn	5,000	35.00
1975 Shepherds	5,000	40.00
1976 Star of Bethlehem	5,000	43.00
1977 Mary at Crib	5,000	46.00
1978 Three Wise Men	5,000	49.00
1979 At Manger	5,000	55.00
1980 Shepherd	5,000	59.00
Lihs-Lindner		
Christmas		
1972 Little Drummer Boy	6,000	25.00
1973 Little Carolers	6,000	25.00
1974 Peace on Earth	6,000	25.00
1975 Christmas Cheer	6,000	30.00
1976 Joy of Christmas	6,000	30.00
1977 Holly-Jolly Christmas	6,000	30.00
Mother's Day		
1972 Mother and Child	1,000	25.00
1973 Mother and Child	2,000	25.00
1974 Bouquet for Mother	2,000	25.00
1975 We Wish You Happiness	2,000	28.00
Union Pacific Railroad		
1972 Union Pacific	1,500	22.00
1973 Union Pacific Big Boy	1,500	25.00
History		
1973 Tribute to Flag	3,000	60.00
1974 Golden Spike Centennial	1,500	40.00
Easter		
1973 Happy Easter	1,500	25.00
1974 Springtime	1,500	25.00
1975 With Love to You at Easter	1,500	28.00
America Beautiful		
1975 Independence Hall	1,500	42.00
1975 Statue of Liberty	1,500	42.00
1975 Niagara Falls	1,500	42.00
1975 Grand Canyon	1,500	42.00
1975 Golden State	1,500	42.00
1975 Capitol	1,500	42.00
Bicentennial		
1976 Freedom Train	1,500	45.00
1976 Spirit of America	3,500	45.00
Playmates		
1976 Timmy and His Pal	5,000	45.00
1977 Heidi and Playmate	5,000	45.00

OVER-THE-COUNTER ISSUES

	Edition Limit	Issue Price (US)
Golden Spike Centennial		
1977 Central Pacific Jupiter	1,500	$ 25.00
1977 Union Pacific 119	1,500	25.00
A Child's Christmas		
1978 Holy Night	5,000	40.00
Marmot		
Father's Day		
1970 Stag	3,500	12.00
1971 Horse	3,500	12.50
Christmas		
1970 Polar Bear	5,000	13.00
1971 Buffalo	5,000	14.00
1972 Boy & Grandfather	5,000	20.00
1973 Snowman	3,000	20.00
1974 Dancing Children	2,000	24.00
1975 Covey of Quail	2,000	30.00
1976 Windmill	2,000	30.00
Presidents		
1971 Washington	1,500	25.00
1972 Jefferson	1,500	25.00
1973 John Adams	1,500	25.00
Mother's Day		
1972 Seal	6,000	16.00
1973 Polar Bear	2,000	20.00
1974 Penguins	2,000	24.00
1975 Raccoons	2,000	30.00
1976 Ducks	2,000	40.00
Meissen		
Annual		
1973 Winter Countryside by Sleigh	5,000	71.00
1974 Sleeping Beauty	5,000	75.00
1975 Archway to Albrecht's Castle	5,500	92.00
1976 Doge's Palace in Venice	5,000	92.00
1977 Fra Holle	5,000	114.00
1978 Ice Crystal with Children	7,000	123.00
1979 Winter Fairy Tale	7,000	151.00
1980 Booted Cat	NA	155.00
Mueller		
Christmas		
1971 Christmas in Tyrol	Year	20.00
1972 Christmas Messenger	Year	15.00
1973 Bringing Home Tree	Year	20.00
1974 Trimming Tree	Year	25.00
1975 Family on Christmas Morning	Year	27.50
1976 Christmas Fire	Year	28.50
1977 Ice Skating	Year	28.50
Father's Day		
1973 Three Generations	NA	17.50
1974 Fishing	NA	20.00
1975 Hiking	NA	27.50
Porcelaine Ariel		
See: Hamilton Collection (U.S.A.)		
Rosenthal		
Annual (Porcelain)		
1971 Tapio Wirkkala	3,000	NA
1972 Natale Sapone	3,000	NA
1973 Otto Piene	3,000	NA
1974 Gunther Fruhtrunk	3,000	NA
1975 Srivastava Narendra	3,000	NA
1976 Salvador Dali	3,000	NA
1977 Victor Vasarely	3,000	NA
1978 E. Paolozzi	3,000	NA
1979 Arnold Leissler	3,000	NA
1980 O.H. Hajek	3,000	NA
*Artist Plates**		
1973 NR 1 Gunter Grass	5,000	NA
1974 NR 2 Jean Cocteau	5,000	NA
1974 NR 3 Eugen Gomringer	5,000	NA
1974 NR 4 Otto Piene	5,000	NA
1975 NR 5 Max Bill	5,000	NA
1975 NR 6 Hans-Werner Henze	5,000	NA
1975 NR 7 Bjørn Wiinblad	5,000	NA
1975 NR 8 Kriwet	5,000	NA
1976 NR 9 Hildegard Knef	5,000	NA
1977 NR10 Yehudi Menuhin	5,000	NA
1977 NR11 Emilio Pucci	5,000	NA
1978 NR12 Salvador Dali	5,000	NA
1978 NR13 Victor Vasarely	5,000	NA
1978 NR14 Almir Mazignier	5,000	NA
1979 NR15 Ivan Rapuzin	5,000	NA
1979 NR16 Ottmar Alt	5,000	NA
*Series not available in U.S.		
*Satire Plates**		
NR1 Konrad Adenauer	5,000	NA
NR2 Willy Brandt	5,000	NA

	Edition Limit	Issue Price (US)
NR3 Theodor Heuss	5,000	NA
NR4 Walter Scheel	5,000	NA
NR5 Helmut Schmidt	5,000	NA
NR6 Franz-Josef Strauss	5,000	NA
NR7 Helmut Kohl	5,000	NA
NR8 Heinz Ruhmann	5,000	NA
NR9 Herbert Von Karajan	5,000	NA
NR10 Marlene Dietrich	5,000	NA
NR11 Mao-Tse-Tung	5,000	NA
NR12 Bruno Kreisky	5,000	NA
*Series not available in U.S.		
Annual (Crystal)		
1974 Otto Piene (Clear)	3,000	$ 200.00
1974 Otto Piene (Gold Inlaid)	3,000	250.00
1974 Otto Piene (Platinum Inlaid)	3,000	250.00
1975 G. Uecker	3,000	200.00
1976 Bjørn Wiinblad	3,000	NA
1977 Gunter F. Ris	3,000	NA
1978 Ivan Rapuzin	3,000	600.00
1979 Salvador Dali	3,000	NA
1980 Ernst Fuchs	3,000	NA
Lorraine Trester		
1975 Once Upon a Summertime	5,000	60.00
1976 One Lovely Yesterday	5,000	70.00
Fantasies and Fables		
1976 Oriental Night Music	NA	50.00
1977 Mandolin Players	NA	55.00
Wiinblad Studio-Linie		
1976 Madonna	2,000	150.00
1977 Annunciation	2,000	195.00
1978 Three Kings	2,000	225.00
1979 Holy Family	2,000	230.00
1980 Appearance of Angels	2,000	240.00
1981 Adoration of Shepherds	2,000	295.00
Aladdin		
1979 Aladdin and Lamp	NA	65.00
1979 Aladdin and Street Urchins	NA	65.00
1980 Aladdin and Magician	NA	65.00
1980 Aladdin in Garden	NA	65.00
1981 Aladdin and Spirit	NA	85.00
1981 Aladdin and Princess	NA	85.00
1982 Aladdin's Mother and Genie	NA	85.00
1982 Aladdin's Mother and Sultan	NA	85.00
1983 Aladdin Rides to Palace	NA	85.00
1983 Genie Builds Palace	NA	85.00
Christmas Carols		
1983 Silent Night	NA	195.00
1984 Jingle Bells	NA	195.00
See also:		
Hibel Studio (Ger.)		
Kern Collectibles (U.S.A.)		
Royal Bayreuth		
See: Kern Collectibles (U.S.A.)		
Royal Tettau		
Papal Plates		
1971 Pope Paul VI	5,000	100.00
1972 Pope John XXIII	5,000	100.00
1973 Pope Pius XII	5,000	100.00
Christmas (Single issue)		
1972 Carriage in Village	NA	12.50
Royale		
Christmas		
1969 Christmas Fair in Ebeltoft	6,000	12.00
1970 Kalundborg Church	10,000	13.00
1971 Christmas Night	8,000	16.00
1972 Elks	8,000	16.00
1973 Christmas	6,000	20.00
1974 Village at Christmas	5,000	22.00
1975 Feeding Time	5,000	26.00
1976 Christmas at Seaport	5,000	27.50
1977 Sledding	5,000	30.00
Mother's Day		
1970 Swan and Brood	6,000	12.00
1971 Doe and Fawn	9,000	13.00
1972 Rabbit Family	9,000	16.00
1973 Owl Family	6,000	18.00
1974 Duck Family	5,000	22.00
1975 Lynx Family	5,000	26.00
1976 Woodcock and Young	5,000	27.50
1977 Koala Bear	5,000	30.00

	Edition Limit	Issue Price (US)
Father's Day		
1970 U.S. Frigate Constitution	5,000	$ 13.00
1971 Man Fishing	5,000	13.00
1972 Mountain Climber	6,000	16.00
1973 Camping	4,000	18.00
1974 Eagle	2,500	22.00
1975 Regatta	2,500	26.00
1976 Hunting Scene	2,500	27.50
1977 Fishing	5,000	30.00
Game		
1972 Setters Pointing Quail	500	180.00
1973 Fox	500	200.00
1974 Osprey	250	250.00
1975 California Quail	250	265.00
Royale Germania		
Annual		
1970 Orchid (Blue)	600	200.00
1971 Cyclamen (Red)	1,000	200.00
1972 Silver Thistle (Green)	1,000	250.00
1973 Tulips (Lilac)	600	275.00
1974 Sunflowers (Topaz)	500	300.00
1975 Snowdrops (Amber)	350	450.00
1976 Flaming Heart (Red)	350	450.00
Mother's Day		
1971 Roses (Red)	250	135.00
1972 Elephant (Green)	750	180.00
1973 Koala Bear (Lilac)	600	200.00
1974 Squirrels (Topaz)	500	240.00
1975 Swan Family (Amber)	350	250.00
Schmid		
Bavarian Christmas		
1971 Family Portrait	5,000	25.50
1972 On Horseback	5,000	26.50
1973 Bringing Home Tree	5,000	26.50
1974 Decorating Tree	5,000	26.50
1975 Opening Presents	5,000	26.50
1976 By Fireside	5,000	26.50
1977 Skating	5,000	28.50
1978 Family Picking Tree	5,000	36.00
1979 Breakfast by Tree	5,000	45.00
1980 Feeding Animals	5,000	55.00
Ferrandiz Christmas		
1972 Christ in Manger	Year	30.00
1973 Christmas	Year	30.00
Golden Moments		
1978 Tranquility	15,000	250.00
Christmas (Pewter)		
1977 Santa	5,000	30.00
1978 Beautiful Snow	5,000	45.00
1979 I Hear America Singing	6,000	50.00
Ferrandiz Mother and Child		
1977 Orchard Mother	10,000	65.00
1978 Pastoral Mother	10,000	75.00
1979 Floral Mother	10,000	95.00
1980 Avian Mother	10,000	100.00
Beatrix Potter (Pewter)		
1978 Peter Rabbit	5,000	50.00
1979 Jemima-Puddle Duck	5,000	50.00
Reflections of Life		
1980 Quiet Reflections	10,000	85.00
1981 Tree of Life	10,000	85.00
Country Pride		
1981 Surprise in Cellar	7,500	35.00
1981 Plum Tuckered Out	7,500	35.00
1981 Duke's Mixture	7,500	35.00
1982 Bustin with Pride	7,500	35.00
Music Makers		
1981 Flutist	10,000	25.00
1982 Entertainer	10,000	25.00
1982 Magical Medley	10,000	25.00
1982 Sweet Serenade	10,000	25.00
My Name Is Star		
1981 Star's Spring	10,000	30.00
1981 Star's Summer	10,000	30.00
1982 Star's Autumn	10,000	30.00
1982 Star's Winter	10,000	30.00
Beautiful Bounty		
1982 Summer's Golden Harvest	10,000	40.00
1982 Autumn's Blessing	10,000	40.00
1983 A Mid-Winter's Dream	10,000	40.00
1983 Spring Blossoms	10,000	40.00
Cat Tales		
1982 Right Church, Wrong Pew	12,500	37.50
1982 Company's Coming	12,500	37.50
1983 Flew Coop	12,500	37.50
1983 On Move	12,500	37.50
Prairie Women		
1982 Maiden	12,500	35.00
1982 Courtship Blanket	12,500	35.00

	Edition Limit	Issue Price (US)
1983 Mother Now	12,500	$ 35.00
1983 Passing of Moons	12,500	35.00
Carousel Fantasies		
1983 A Fairy Tale Princess	7,500	50.00
Lowell Davis Christmas		
1983 Country Christmas	7,500	45.00
1984 Country Christmas	7,500	45.00
1985 Christmas at Foxfire	7,500	45.00
(Single issue)		
1983 Critics	12,500	45.00
Gift of Happiness		
1984 Lilies of Field	7,500	125.00
1984 Morning Glories	7,500	125.00
Good Ol' Days (Set of two)		
1984 Waiting for Master		
1984 Minutes Like Hours	5,000	60.00
Nature's Treasures		
1984 Rose Haven/Sparrow	5,000	45.00
1984 Tulip Nest/Robin	5,000	45.00
1984 Leafy Bower/Oriole	5,000	45.00
1984 Nesting/Mockingbird	5,000	45.00
Prime Time		
1984 Love Boat	NA	30.00
1984 Dynasty	NA	30.00
1984 Dallas	NA	30.00
Statuette		
1984 Hark Herald	Year	40.00
See also: Addams Family (U.S.A.)		
Schumann		
Composers		
1970 Beethoven	NA	8.00
1972 Mozart	NA	13.00
Christmas		
1971 Snow Scene	10,000	12.00
1972 Deer in Snow	15,000	12.00
1973 Weihnachten	5,000	12.00
1974 Church in Snow	5,000	12.00
1975 Fountain	5,000	12.00
See also:		
Christian Bell (Can.)		
Calhoun's Collector's Society (U.S.A.)		
Stumar		
Christmas		
1970 Angel	10,000	8.00
1971 Old Canal	10,000	8.00
1972 Countryside	10,000	8.00
1973 Friendship	10,000	10.00
1974 Making Fancy	10,000	10.00
1975 Preparation	10,000	10.00
1976 Drummer Boy	10,000	10.00
1977 Joyful Expectations	10,000	15.00
1978 Christmas	10,000	19.50
Mother's Day		
1971 Amish Mother & Daughter	10,000	8.00
1972 Children	10,000	8.00
1973 Mother Sewing	10,000	10.00
1974 Mother Cradle	10,000	10.00
1975 Baking	10,000	10.00
1976 Reading to Children	10,000	15.00
1977 Comforting Child	10,000	15.00
1978 Tranquility	10,000	19.50
Egyptian		
1977 Ancient Egyptian Trilogy	5,000	45.00
1978 Charioteer	5,000	54.00
Tirschenreuth		
Christmas		
1969 Homestead	3,500	12.00
1970 Church	3,500	12.00
1971 Star of Bethlehem	3,500	12.00
1972 Elk Silhouette	2,000	13.00
1973 Christmas	Year	14.00
Villeroy & Boch		
Christmas		
1977 Holy Family	10,000	175.00
1978 Three Holy Kings	20,000	175.00
1979 Mary with Child	10,000	198.00
1980 Madonna in Glory	10,000	200.00
1981 Mary Glorious	10,000	210.00
World Wildlife		
1983 Panda Bear	Year	38.00
1983 Tiger	Year	38.00
1984 Otter	Year	38.00
1984 Orangutan	Year	38.00
1985 Seal	Year	38.00
Enchanted Fairyland Lovers		
1982 Prince	NA	39.00
1982 Ivan and Horse	NA	39.00
1982 Princess and Stag	NA	39.00
1983 Goose Girl	NA	39.00

	Edition Limit	Issue Price (US)
1983 Cinderella	NA	$ 39.00
1983 Prince Ahmed and Peri	NA	39.00
1984 Ta-Khai and Bird Feng	NA	39.00
1984 Fisherman and Dragon King's Daughter	NA	39.00
Flower Fairies		
1983 Columbine	21 Days	39.00
1983 Cornflower	21 Days	39.00
1984 Mallow	21 Days	39.00
1984 Black Medick	21 Days	39.00
1985 Canterbury Bell	21 Days	39.00
1985 Fuschia	21 Days	39.00
French Fairy Tales		
1983 Fortunata and Hen	19,750	70.00
1983 King of Peacocks	19,750	70.00
1983 King and Puss in Boots	19,750	70.00
1984 In Search of Phoenix	19,750	70.00
1984 Princess Radiant and Phoenix	19,750	70.00
1985 Monkeys in Garden	19,750	70.00
1985 Florina and Fairy Pie	19,750	70.00
Exotic Birds		
1984 Fiery Parakeet	15,000	70.00
1984 Long-Billed Cockatoo	15,000	70.00
(Single issue)		
1985 Golden Lady	1,000	150.00
WMF Geislingen		
Annual		
1978 Rose-Motif I	2,500	117.50
1979 Rose-Motif-II	2,500	120.00
1980 Rose-Motif III	2,500	120.00
Christmas		
1978 Birth of Christ	2,500	117.50
1979 Praising King	2,500	120.00
1980 Praising Shepherd	2,500	120.00

GREAT BRITAIN

	Edition Limit	Issue Price (US)
Aynsley		
A Christmas Carol		
1979 Mr. Fezziwig's Ball	Year	30.00
1980 Marley's Ghost	Year	36.00
1981 Cratchit Family	Year	41.00
1982 Christmas Day	Year	41.00
Belleek		
Irish Countryside Christmas		
1984 Irish White Beam	10,000	95.00
1985 Sprig of Heather	10,000	95.00
St. Patrick's Day Annual		
1985 Slemish Mountain	NA	75.00
Boehm Studios		
European Bird Plates		
1973 Swallow	5,000	48.75
1973 Chaffinch	5,000	48.75
1973 Coal Tit	5,000	48.75
1973 Tree Sparrow	5,000	48.75
1973 King Fisher	5,000	48.75
1973 Gold Crest	5,000	48.75
1973 Blue Tit	5,000	48.75
1973 Linnet	5,000	48.75
Honor America		
1974 American Bald Eagle	12,000	85.00
Butterfly		
1975 Blue Mountain Swallowtails	100	450.00
1975 Jezabels	100	450.00
1976 Comma with Loops	100	450.00
1976 African Butterflies	100	450.00
1976 Solandras Maxima	100	450.00
Hard Fruit		
1975 Plums	100	450.00
1975 Pears	100	450.00
1976 Peaches	100	450.00
1976 Apples	100	450.00
Oriental Birds		
1975 Bluebacked Fairy Bluebirds	100	400.00
1975 Azure-Winged Magpies	100	400.00
1976 Golden-Fronted Leafbird	100	400.00
1976 Golden-Throated Barbet	100	400.00
Seashell		
1975 Violet Spider Conch	100	450.00
1975 Rooster Tail Conch	100	450.00
1976 Orange Spider Conch	100	450.00
1976 Cheragra Spider Conch	100	450.00
Soft Fruit		
1975 Loganberries	100	450.00
1975 Cherries	100	450.00

	Edition Limit	Issue Price (US)
1976 Strawberries	100	$450.00
1976 Grapes	100	450.00
Butterflies of World		
1978 Monarch and Daisy	5,000	62.00
1978 Red Admiral and Thistle	5,000	62.00
Flower		
1975 Lilies	100	450.00
1975 Passion Flowers	100	450.00
1976 Double Clematis	100	450.00
Favorite Floral		
1978 Clematis	2,500	58.00
1978 Rhododendron	2,500	58.00
1979 Boehm Orchid	2,500	58.00
1979 Yellow Rose	2,500	58.00
1980 Spider Orchid	2,500	58.00
1980 Dahlia	2,500	58.00
Musical Maidens of Imperial Dynasties		
1984 Balloon Guitar	15,000	65.00
1984 Three-Stringed Guitar	15,000	65.00
1984 Harp	15,000	65.00
1984 Gong	15,000	65.00
1984 Reen Organ	15,000	65.00
1984 Ceremonial Flute	15,000	65.00
1984 Lute	15,000	65.00
1984 Common Flute	15,000	65.00
See also: Hamilton Collection (U.S.A.)		
Caithness Glass		
America's Favorite Birds		
1979 Crystal Wren	5,000	79.50
Coalport		
Christmas		
1976 Christmas Eve	Year	12.00
1977 Dangerous Skating	Year	16.00
1978 Alas! Poor Bruin	Year	18.00
1979 Christmas Morning	Year	22.00
1980 Blind Man's Bluff	Year	27.00
1981 Skating	Year	32.50
1982 Snapdragon	Year	35.00
1983 Trafalgar Square	Year	35.00
Mother's Day		
1978 Clematis	Year	16.00
1979 Orchid	Year	21.00
1980 Peony	Year	27.00
1981 Rose	Year	30.00
(Single issue)		
1972 Indy 500	2,000	49.95
Crown Staffordshire		
Wildlife in Winter		
1982 Tranquility	10,000	55.00
1983 Winter's Orphan	10,000	55.00
1983 Early Awakening	10,000	55.00
1984 Vigilance	10,000	55.00
Hornsea		
Christmas		
1979 "C"–Nativity	10,000	21.00
1980 "H"–Mary and Child	10,000	25.00
1981 "R"–Three Wise Men	10,000	30.00
1982 "I" –At Inn	10,000	32.50
1983 "S"–Shepherds	10,000	35.00
Mason		
Christmas		
1975 Windsor Castle	Year	75.00
1976 Holyrood House	Year	75.00
1977 Buckingham Palace	Year	75.00
1978 Balmoral Castle	Year	75.00
1979 Hampton Court	Year	75.00
1980 Sandringham House	Year	75.00
Poole Pottery		
Medieval Calendar		
1972 Drinking Wine by Fire (January)	1,000	100.00
1972 Chopping Wood (February)	1,000	100.00
1973 Digging in Fields and Setting Seeds (March)	1,000	125.00
1973 Carrying Flowering Branch (April)	1,000	125.00
1974 Hawking (May)	1,000	125.00
1974 Mowing Hay (June)	1,000	125.00
1975 Cutting Corn with Sickle (July)	1,000	125.00
1975 Threshing with Flail (August)	1,000	125.00
1976 Picking Grapes (September)	1,000	125.00
1976 Sowing Winter Corn (October)	1,000	125.00

	Edition Limit	Issue Price (US)
1977 Gathering Acorns to Feed Pigs (November)	1,000	$125.00
1977 Pig Killing (December)	1,000	125.00
Cathedral		
1973 Christ on Cross	11,000	125.00
Christmas		
1973 Adoration of Magi	1,000	125.00
1973 Flight into Egypt	1,000	125.00
Home at Christmas		
1978 Santa's Helpers	10,000	37.50
1979 Three Wisemen	10,000	37.50
Birds of North America		
1979 Great Horned Owl	10,000	37.50
Mother's Day		
1979 Tenderness	10,000	37.50
Rhea Silva		
Feline Favourites		
1982 Long Haired Ladies	10,000	47.00
1983 Siamese & Apple Blossoms	10,000	47.00
1984 Abyssinian Playmates	10,000	47.00
1985 Tom in Garden	10,000	47.00
Child's Garden of Verses		
1983 Land of Counterpane	17,500	39.00
Portraits of Countryside		
1983 Autumn Wayside	5,000	79.00
Endangered Birds		
1984 Whooping Crane	5,000	60.00
Royal Doulton		
Flower Garden		
1975 Spring Harmony	15,000	60.00
1976 Dreaming Lotus	15,000	65.00
1977 Poet's Garden	15,000	70.00
1978 Country Bouquet	15,000	70.00
1980 From My Mother's Garden	15,000	85.00
Ports of Call		
1975 San Francisco	15,000	60.00
1976 New Orleans	15,000	65.00
1977 Venice	15,000	70.00
1978 Montmartre	15,000	70.00
Reflections on China		
1976 Garden of Tranquility	15,000	70.00
1977 Imperial Palace	15,000	70.00
1978 Temple of Heaven	15,000	75.00
1980 Lake of Mists	15,000	85.00
I Remember America		
1977 Pennsylvania Pastorale	15,000	70.00
1978 Lovejoy Bridge	15,000	70.00
1979 Four Corners	15,000	75.00
1980 Marshlands	15,000	95.00
Victorian Christmas		
1977 Skater	Year	25.00
1978 Victorian Girl	Year	27.50
1979 Sleigh Ride	Year	29.95
1980 Victorian Christmas	Year	32.50
1981 Carolers	Year	37.50
1982 Santa Claus	Year	37.50
All God's Children		
1978 Brighter Day	10,000	60.00
1980 Village Children	10,000	65.00
1981 Noble Heritage	10,000	85.00
1982 Buddies	10,000	85.00
1983 Little Brother	10,000	95.00
1985 Sisterly Love	10,000	95.00
American Tapestries		
1978 Sleigh Bells	10,000	70.00
1979 Pumpkin Patch	10,000	70.00
1980 General Store	10,000	95.00
1981 Fourth of July	10,000	95.00
Jungle Fantasy		
1979 Ark	10,000	75.00
1980 Compassion	10,000	95.00
1981 Patience	10,000	95.00
1982 Refuge	10,000	95.00
(Single issue)		
1980 Winning Colors	15,000	80.00
Behind Painted Masque		
1982 Painted Feelings	10,000	95.00
1983 Make Me Laugh	10,000	95.00
1983 Minstrel Serenade	10,000	95.00
1984 Pleasing Performance	10,000	95.00
Celebration of Faith		
1982 Rosh Hashanah	7,500	250.00
1982 Passover	7,500	250.00
1983 Yom Kippur	7,500	250.00
1983 Chanukah	7,500	250.00
Children of Pueblo		
1983 Apple Flower	10,000	60.00
1983 Morning Star	10,000	60.00

	Edition Limit	Issue Price (US)
Christmas Carol		
1983 Silent Night	NA	$ 39.95
1984 While Shepherds Watched	NA	39.95
Festival Children of World		
1983 Mariani (Bali)	15,000	65.00
1983 Magdalena (Mexico)	15,000	65.00
1984 Michiko (Japan)	15,000	65.00
1984 Monika (Poland)	15,000	65.00
1985 Maureen	15,000	65.00
1985 Marijke	15,000	65.00
Grandest Gift		
1984 Reunion	10,000	75.00
1985 Storytime	10,000	75.00
Royal Grafton		
Twelve Days of Christmas		
1976 Partridge in Pear Tree	3,000	17.50
1977 Two Turtle Doves	3,000	17.50
1978 Three French Hens	3,000	21.50
1979 Four Colly Birds	3,000	26.50
1980 Five Gold Rings	3,000	35.00
1981 Six Geese A'Laying	3,000	38.50
1982 Seven Swans A'Swimming	3,000	40.00
1983 Eight Maids A'Milking	3,000	41.00
Royal Worcester		
Doughty Bird		
1972 Redstarts and Beech	2,750	125.00
1973 Myrtle Warbler/Cherry	3,000	175.00
1974 Blue-Grey Gnatcatchers	3,000	195.00
1975 Blackburnian Warbler	3,000	195.00
1976 Blue-Winged Sivas	3,000	195.00
1977 Paradise Wydah	3,000	195.00
1978 Bluetits/Witch Hazel	3,000	195.00
1979 Mountain Bluebird	3,000	195.00
1980 Cerulean Warblers	3,000	315.00
1981 Willow Warbler	3,000	330.00
1982 Ruby-Crowned Kinglets	3,000	330.00
1983 Bewick's Wren	3,000	330.00
Bicentennial		
1976 Independence	10,000	150.00
Fabulous Birds		
1976 Peacocks I	10,000	65.00
1977 Peacocks II	10,000	65.00
Audubon Birds		
1977 Warbler & Jay	5,000	150.00
1978 Kingbird & Sparrow	10,000	150.00
Chinoiserie		
1977 Bishop Summer	Year	65.00
English Christmas		
1979 Christmas Eve	Year	60.00
1980 Christmas Morning	Year	65.00
1981 Christmas Day	Year	70.00
1982 Christmas Evening	Year	70.00
Kitten Classics		
1985 Cat Nap	14 Days	29.50
Spode		
Ray Harm Birds (Set of 12)		
1970 Rufus-Sided Towhee		
1970 Winter Wren		
1971 Eastern Bluebird		
1971 Stellar's Jay		
1971 Eastern Mockingbird		
1971 Barn Swallow		
1971 Rose-Breasted Grosbeak		
1971 Cardinal		
1972 Western Tanager		
1972 Woodpecker		
1972 Chickadee		
1972 American Goldfinch	5,000	300.00
Maritime Plates (Set of six)		
1980 USS United States and HMS Macedonian		
1980 USS President and HMS Little Belt		
1980 HMS Shannon and USS Chesapeake		
1980 USS Constitution and HMS Guerriere		
1980 USS Constitution and HMN Java		
1980 HMS Pelican and USS Argus	2,000	300.00
Christmas Pastimes		
1982 Sleigh Ride	Year	75.00
Wedgwood		
Calendar		
1971 Victorian Almanac	Year	12.00
1972 Animal Carnival	Year	12.95

OVER-THE-COUNTER ISSUES

	Edition Limit	Issue Price (US)
1973 Bountiful Butterfly	Year	$ 12.95
1974 Camelot	Year	15.00
1975 Children's Games	Year	15.00
1976 Robin	Year	25.00
1977 Tonatiuh Warriors	Year	30.00
1978 Samurai	Year	30.00
1979 Sacred Scarab	Year	35.00
1980 Safari	Year	36.00
1981 Horses	Year	37.50
1982 Wild West	Year	40.00
1983 Age of Reptiles	Year	54.00
1984 Pets	Year	54.00
1985 Cats	Year	54.00
Children's Story		
1971 Sandman	Year	7.95
1972 Tinder Box	Year	9.00
1973 Emperor's New Clothes	Year	9.00
1974 Ugly Duckling	Year	10.00
1975 Little Mermaid	Year	12.00
1976 Hansel & Gretel	Year	12.00
1977 Rumpelstiltskin	Year	15.00
1978 Frog Prince	Year	15.00
1979 Golden Goose	Year	15.00
1980 Rapunzel	Year	16.00
1981 Tom Thumb	Year	18.00
1982 Lady and Lion	Year	20.00
1983 Elves and Shoemaker	Year	20.00
1984 King Roughbeard	Year	20.00
1985 Little Tailor	Year	20.00
(Single issue)		
1978 Tri-Color Decade Christmas	10,000	325.00
(Single issue)		
1978 Anniversary Christmas	Year	130.00
Trophy		
1978 Tutankhamun	500	1000.00
1978 Ankhesenamum	500	1000.00
Child's Christmas		
1979 Snowman	Year	35.00
1980 Bringing Home Tree	Year	35.00
1981 Tobogganing	Year	35.00
1982 Skaters	Year	35.00
1983 Carolers	Year	35.00
1984 Christmas Baking	Year	35.00
Queen's Ware Christmas		
1980 Windsor Castle	Year	24.95
1981 Trafalgar Square	Year	29.95
1982 Piccadilly Circus	Year	32.50
1983 St. Paul's Cathedral	Year	32.50
1984 Tower of London	Year	32.50
Remarkable World of Charles Dickens		
1980 Oliver Twist and Fagin	19,500	60.00
1980 Scrooge and Marley's Ghost	19,500	60.00
1980 Bob Cratchit	19,500	60.00
1980 David Copperfield	19,500	60.00
1981 Micawber/Uriah Heep	19,500	60.00
1981 Little Nell	19,500	60.00
1981 Madame Defarge	19,500	60.00
1981 Mr. Pickwick	19,500	60.00
Valentine's Day		
1982 Lilac on White	Year	55.00
1983 White on Pink	Year	55.00
1984 White on Teal	Year	55.00
Eyes of Child		
1983 Little Lady Love	15,000	65.00
1984 My Best Friend	15,000	65.00
1985 I Wish Upon a Star	15,000	65.00
1985 In a Child's Thoughts	15,000	65.00
(Single issue)		
1983 200 Years of Ballooning	Year	35.00

INDIA

	Edition Limit	Issue Price (US)
Sarna		
Christmas		
1975 Holy Family	4,000	17.50

ITALY

	Edition Limit	Issue Price (US)
Anri		
Mother's Day		
1972 Alpine Mother & Children	5,000	35.00
1973 Alpine Mother & Children	5,000	40.00
1974 Alpine Mother & Children	5,000	50.00
1975 Alpine Stroll	5,000	60.00
1976 Knitting	5,000	60.00
Father's Day		
1972 Alpine Father & Children	5,000	$ 35.00
1973 Alpine Father & Children	5,000	40.00
1974 Cliff Gazing	5,000	50.00
1975 Sailing	5,000	60.00
Ferrandiz Birthday		
1972 Birthday Girl	Year	15.00
1972 Birthday Boy	Year	15.00
1973 Birthday	Year	20.00
1974 Birthday Girl	Year	22.00
1974 Birthday Boy	Year	22.00
1975 Birthday Girl	Year	35.00
Ferrandiz Mother's Day		
1972 Mother Sewing	2,500	35.00
1973 Mother and Child	1,500	40.00
1974 Mother and Child	1,500	50.00
1975 Mother Holding Dove	1,500	60.00
1976 Mother and Child	1,500	60.00
1977 Girl with Flowers	1,500	65.00
1978 Beginning	3,000	77.50
1979 All Hearts	3,000	120.00
1980 Spring Arrivals	3,000	150.00
1981 Harmony	3,000	150.00
1982 With Love	3,000	150.00
Ferrandiz Christmas		
1972 Christ in Manger	Year	30.00
1973 Boy with Lamb	Year	30.00
1974 Nativity	Year	50.00
1975 Flight into Egypt	Year	60.00
1976 Mary and Joseph Pray	Year	60.00
1977 Girl with Tree	4,000	65.00
1978 Leading Way	4,000	77.50
1979 Drummer Boy	4,000	120.00
1980 Rejoice	4,000	150.00
1981 Spreading Word	4,000	150.00
1982 Shepherd Family	4,000	150.00
1983 Peace Attend Thee	4,000	150.00
Ferrandiz Wedding Day		
1972 Wedding	Year	40.00
1973 Wedding	Year	40.00
1974 Wedding	Year	48.00
1975 Wedding	Year	60.00
1976 Wedding	Year	60.00
(Single issue)		
1982 Riding Thru Rain	2,500	550.00
Ferrandiz Annual		
1984 Pastoral Journey	2,000	180.00
1985 Tender Touch	2,000	170.00
Sarah Kay Annual		
1984 A Time for Secrets	2,500	120.00
1985 Carousel Magic	2,500	120.00
Capo Di Monte		
Christmas		
1972 Cherubs	500	55.00
1973 Bells & Holly	500	55.00
1974 Christmas	1,000	60.00
1975 Christmas	1,000	60.00
1976 Christmas	250	65.00
Mother's Day		
1973 Mother's Day	500	55.00
1974 Mother's Day	500	60.00
1975 Mother's Day	500	60.00
1976 Mother's Day	500	65.00
Carlo Monti		
Mother's Day		
1973 Madonna & Child	2,000	35.00
Count Agazzi		
Famous Personalities		
1968 Famous Personalities	600	8.00
1970 Famous Personalities	1,000	12.50
1973 Famous Personalities	600	15.00
(Single issue)		
1969 Apollo II	1,000	17.00
Children's Hour		
1970 Owl	2,000	12.50
1971 Cat	2,000	12.50
1972 Pony	2,000	12.50
1973 Panda	2,000	12.50
Easter		
1971 Playing Violin	600	12.50
1972 At Prayer	600	12.50
1973 Winged Cherub	600	12.50
Mother's Day		
1972 Mother's Day	144	35.00
1973 Mother's Day	720	19.50
Father's Day		
1972 Father's Day	144	35.00
1973 Father's Day	288	19.50
Christmas		
1973 Christmas	1,000	$ 19.50
(Single issue)		
1973 Peace	720	12.50
Kings		
Mother's Day		
1973 Dancing Girl	1,500	100.00
1974 Dancing Boy	1,500	115.00
1975 Motherly Love	1,500	140.00
1976 Maiden	1,500	180.00
Christmas		
1973 Adoration	1,500	150.00
1974 Madonna	1,500	150.00
1975 Heavenly Choir	1,500	160.00
1976 Girl and Brother	1,500	200.00
Veneto Flair		
Christmas		
1971 Three Kings	1,500	45.00
1972 Shepherds	2,000	45.00
1973 Christ Child	2,000	55.00
1974 Angel	2,000	55.00
Wildlife		
1971 Deer	500	37.50
1972 Elephant	1,000	37.50
1973 Puma	2,000	37.50
1974 Tiger	2,000	40.00
Birds		
1972 Owl	2,000	37.50
1973 Falcon	2,000	37.50
1974 Mallard Duck	2,000	45.00
Dogs		
1972 German Shepherd	2,000	37.50
1973 Poodle	2,000	37.50
1974 Doberman	2,000	37.50
1975 Collie	2,000	40.00
1976 Dachshund	2,000	45.00
Mother's Day		
1972 Madonna and Child	2,000	55.00
1973 Madonna and Child	2,000	55.00
1974 Mother and Son	2,000	55.00
1975 Daughter and Doll	2,000	45.00
1976 Son and Daughter	2,000	55.00
1977 Mother and Child	2,000	50.00
Easter		
1973 Rabbits	2,000	50.00
1974 Chicks	2,000	50.00
1975 Lamb	2,000	50.00
1976 Composite	2,000	55.00
Goddess		
1973 Pomona	1,500	75.00
1974 Diana	1,500	75.00
Mosaic		
1973 Justinian	500	50.00
1974 Pelican	1,000	50.00
1977 Theodora	500	50.00
Cats		
1974 Persian	2,000	40.00
1975 Siamese	2,000	45.00
1976 Tabby	2,000	45.00
Christmas Card		
1975 Christmas Eve	5,000	45.00
1976 Old North Church	5,000	50.00
1977 Log Cabin Christmas	5,000	50.00
1978 Dutch Christmas	5,000	50.00
Valentine's Day		
1977 Valentine Boy	3,000	45.00
1978 Valentine Girl	3,000	45.00
1979 Hansel	3,000	60.00
1980 Gretel	3,000	67.50
Flower Children		
1978 Rose	3,000	45.00
1979 Orchid	3,000	60.00
1980 Camillia	3,000	65.00
La Belle Femme		
1978 Lily	9,500	70.00
1978 Gigi	9,500	76.50
1980 Dominique	9,500	76.50
1980 Gabrielle	9,500	76.50
American Landscape		
1979 Hudson Valley	7,500	75.00
1980 Northwest Cascade	7,500	75.00
Children's Christmas		
1979 Carolers	7,500	60.00
1980 Heading Home	7,500	70.00
1981 Night Before	7,500	95.00
1982 A Visit to Santa	7,500	80.00
Mother and Child		
1981 Buffalos	5,000	95.00
1981 Elephants	5,000	95.00
1981 Koalas	5,000	95.00
1981 Lions	5,000	95.00
1981 Loons	5,000	$ 95.00
1981 Polar Bears	5,000	95.00
Lamincia Annual		
1981 Young Love	5,000	95.00

JAPAN

	Edition Limit	Issue Price (US)
Manjundo		
Chinese Lunar Calendar		
1972 Year of Rat	5,000	15.00
1973 Year of Ox	5,000	15.00
Noritake		
Christmas		
1975 Madonna with Child	3,000	42.00
1976 Gratia Hoso Kawa	3,000	54.00
1977 Julia Otaa	3,000	83.00
1978 Amakusa Shiro	3,000	109.00
1979 Munzio Ito	3,000	124.00
1980 Furst Takayama	3,000	125.00
Annual		
1977 Paradise Birds	3,000	380.00
1978 Chrysanthemums	3,000	494.00
1979 Cranes	3,000	556.00
1980 Water Lilies and Butterflies	3,000	575.00
Sango		
Christmas		
1976 Undesired Slumber	7,500	25.00
1977 Togetherness	7,500	25.00
Mother's Day		
1976 Spring Delight	7,500	20.00
1977 Broken Wing	5,000	22.50
See also: Kern Collectibles (U.S.A.)		
Schmid		
Raggedy Ann Christmas		
1975 Gifts of Love	Year	12.50
1976 Raggedy Ann Skates	Year	13.00
1977 Decorating Tree	Year	13.00
1978 Checking List	Year	15.00
1979 Little Helper	15,000	17.50
Bicentennial		
1976 Peanuts	NA	13.00
1976 Disney	NA	13.00
1976 Raggedy Ann	NA	13.00
Raggedy Ann Mother's Day		
1976 Motherhood	Year	13.00
1977 Bouquet of Love	Year	13.00
1978 Hello Mom	Year	15.00
1979 High Spirits	10,000	17.50
Raggedy Ann Valentine's Day		
1978 As Time Goes By	Year	13.00
1979 Daisies Do Tell	Year	17.50
Disney Valentine's Day		
1979 Hands and Hearts	Year	17.50
1980 Mickey's I Love You	Year	17.50
1981 Be Mine	Year	17.50
1982 Picnic for Two	Year	17.50
A Year with Paddington Bear		
1979 Pyramid Presents	25,000	12.50
1980 Springtime	25,000	12.50
1981 Sandcastles	25,000	12.50
1981 School Days	25,000	12.50
Peanuts 30th Anniversary (Single issue)		
1980 Happy Anniversary	15,000	27.50
Alice in Wonderland Anniversary (Single issue)		
1981 Alice in Wonderland	7,500	17.50
Disney Anniversary (Single issue)		
1981 Pluto's 50th Birthday	7,500	17.50
Four Seasons of Love		
1982 Tickets on 50 Yard Line	10,000	17.50
1982 Let it Snow	10,000	17.50
1983 Spring Bouquet	10,000	17.50
1983 Shades of Summer	10,000	17.50
A Musician's Dream		
1982 Beat Goes On	10,000	17.50
1982 Knowing Score	10,000	17.50
1983 Perfect Harmony	10,000	17.50
1983 Tickling Ivory	10,000	17.50
World's Greatest Athlete		
1982 Go Deep	10,000	17.50
1982 Puck Stops Here	10,000	17.50
1983 Way You Play Game	10,000	17.50
1983 Crowd Went Wild	10,000	17.50
Disney Annual		
1983 Sneak Preview	20,000	22.50
1984 Command Performance	20,000	22.50
Paddington Bear Annual		
1983 Bear's Noel	10,000	22.50
1984 How Sweet It Is	10,000	22.50

	Edition Limit	Issue Price (US)
Peanuts Annual		
1983 Peanuts in Concert	20,000	$ 22.50
1984 Snoopy/Beaglescouts	20,000	22.50
I Love Plate Collecting		
1984 A Great Beginning	20,000	22.50

See also: Addams Family (U.S.A.)

MEXICO

Bonita Silver

	Edition Limit	Issue Price (US)
Mother's Day		
1972 Mother and Baby	4,000	125.00

Roman Ceramica Excelsis

	Edition Limit	Issue Price (US)
Masterpiece Collection		
1979 Adoration	5,000	65.00
1980 Madonna with Grapes	5,000	87.50
1981 Holy Family	5,000	95.00
1982 Madonna of Streets	5,000	85.00
Ceramica Excelsis Collection		
1980 Little Children, Come to Me	15,000	45.00

NETHERLANDS

Blue Delft (Schoonhaven)

	Edition Limit	Issue Price (US)
Christmas		
1970 Drawbridge Near Binnehof	Year	12.00
1971 St. Lauren's Church	Year	12.00
1972 Church at Bierkade	Year	12.00
1973 St. Jan's Church	Year	12.00
1974 Dongeradeel	Year	13.00
1975 Maassluis	Year	15.00
1976 Montelbaanstower	Year	15.00
1977 Harbour Tower of Hoorn	Year	19.50
1978 Binnenpoort Gate	Year	21.00
Mother's Day		
1971 Mother & Daughter of 1600s	Year	12.00
1972 Mother & Daughter of Isle of Urk	Year	12.00
1973 Rembrandt's Mother	Year	12.00
Father's Day		
1971 Francisco Lana's Airship	Year	12.00
1972 Dr. Jonathon's Balloon	Year	12.00

Crown Delft

	Edition Limit	Issue Price (US)
Christmas		
1969 Man by Tree	Year	10.00
1970 Two Sleigh Riders	Year	10.00
1971 Christmas Tree on Market Square	Year	10.00
1972 Baking for Christmas	Year	10.00
Mother's Day		
1970 Sheep	Year	10.00
1971 Stork	Year	10.00
1972 Ducks	Year	10.00
1973 Mother's Day	1,000	10.00
Father's Day		
1970 Father's Day	Year	10.00
1971 Father's Day	Year	10.00
1972 Father's Day	1,000	10.00
1973 Father's Day	1,000	10.00

Kurz (Shuler International)

	Edition Limit	Issue Price (US)
Christmas		
1972 Christmas	500	60.00
1973 Christmas	500	70.00
1974 Christmas	500	65.00
Mother's Day		
1973 Mother's Day	500	65.00

Metawa

	Edition Limit	Issue Price (US)
Christmas		
1972 Skaters	3,000	30.00
1973 One-Horse Sleigh	1,500	30.00
1974 Sailboat	Year	35.00

Royal Delft

	Edition Limit	Issue Price (US)
Christmas		
1915 Glory to God, Christmas Bells (10″)	Year	NA
1915 Christmas Star (7″)	Year	NA
1916 Star–Floral Design (10″)	Year	NA
1916 Cradle of Child (10″)	Year	NA
1917 Shepherd with Sheep in Stable (10″)	Year	NA
1917 Christmas Star (10″)	Year	NA
1918 Shepherd with Sheep in Stable (10″)	Year	NA
1918 Christmas Star–Peace on Earth (10″)	Year	NA
1919 Church (10″)	Year	NA
1919 Christmas Star (10″)	Year	NA
1920 Holly Wreath (10″)	Year	NA
1920 Church Tower (10″)	Year	NA
1921 Canal Boatman (10″)	Year	NA
1921 Christmas Star (10″)	Year	NA
1922 Landscape (10″)	Year	NA
1922 Christmas Wreath (10″)	Year	NA
1923 Shepherd (10″)	Year	NA
1923 Christmas Star (10″)	Year	NA
1924 Christmas Star (10″)	Year	NA
1924 Town Gate with Shepherd (10″)	Year	NA
1925 Towngate in Delft (10″)	Year	NA
1925 Christmas Star (10″)	Year	NA
1926 Christmas Star (10″)	Year	NA
1926 Bell Tower (7″)	Year	NA
1926 Windmill Landscape (10″)	Year	NA
1927 Christmas Star (10″)	Year	NA
1927 Sailing Boat (10″)	Year	NA
1927 Church Tower (7″)	Year	NA
1928 Christmas Poinsettia (10″)	Year	NA
1928 Mill Christmas (7″)	Year	NA
1928 Lighthouse Christmas (10″)	Year	NA
1929 Christmas Bell (10″)	Year	NA
1929 Church Spire (7″)	Year	NA
1929 Small Dutch Town (10″)	Year	NA
1930 Church Entrance, Delft (10″)	Year	NA
1930 Christmas Rose (10″)	Year	NA
1930 Sailing Boat (7″)	Year	NA
1931 Christmas Star (10″)	Year	NA
1931 Snow Landscape (10″)	Year	NA
1931 Church Tower (7″)	Year	NA
1932 Bell Tower (7″)	Year	NA
1932 Fireplace (10″)	Year	NA
1932 Christmas Star (10″)	Year	NA
1933 Interior Scene with Exterior View (10″)	Year	NA
1934 Interior Scene (10″)	Year	NA
1934 Snowy Stable (10″)	Year	NA
1935 Interior Scene with Exterior View (10″)	Year	NA
1936 Interior Scene with Exterior View (10″)	Year	NA
1937 Interior Scene with Exterior View (10″)	Year	NA
1938 Interior Scene with Exterior View (10″)	Year	NA
1939 Interior Scene with Well-Staircase (10″)	Year	NA
1940 Interior with Christmas Tree (10″)	Year	NA
1941 Interior Scene Fireplace & Tree (10″)	Year	NA
1955 Christmas Star (9″)	Year	NA
1955 Church Tower (10″)	200	$ 20.00
1956 Two Christmas Bells in Floral (9″)	Year	NA
1956 Landscape (10″)	200	20.00
1956 Flower Design (9″)	Year	NA
1957 Christmas Star (9″)	Year	NA
1957 Landscape (10″)	225	22.00
1958 Christmas Star (9″)	Year	NA
1958 View of Village at Riverside (10″)	225	25.00
1959 View of Village at Riverside (10″)	250	25.00
1959 Landscape with Mill (7″)	400	10.00
1960 Landscape (7″)	400	10.00
1960 Street in Delft (10″)	250	25.00
1961 Snow Landscape (7″)	500	10.00
1961 Village Scene with Church Town (10″)	260	30.00
1962 Town View (7″)	500	10.00
1962 Tower in Leeuwarden (10″)	275	30.00
1963 Mill in Zeddam (7″)	500	15.00
1963 Tower in Enkhuisen (10″)	275	35.00
1964 Tower in Hoorn (10″)	300	35.00
1964 Mill in Poelenburg (7″)	600	15.00
1965 Towngate in Kampen (7″)	600	15.00
1965 Corn-Mill in Rhoon (10″)	300	35.00
1966 Towngate in Medemblik (7″)	600	20.00
1966 Snuff Mill in Rotterdam (10″)	325	40.00
1967 Mill in Hazerswoude (7″)	700	$ 20.00
1967 Tower in Amsterdam (10″)	350	45.00
1968 Mill in Schiedam (7″)	700	25.00
1968 Tower in Amsterdam "Schreierstoren" (10″)	350	60.00
1969 Mill Near Gorkum (7″)	800	35.00
1969 Church in Utrecht (10″)	400	60.00
1970 Mill Near Haarlem (7″)	1,500	25.00
1970 Cathedral in Veere (10″)	500	60.00
1971 Towngate at Zierikzee (7″)	3,500	25.00
1971 "Dom" Tower in Utrecht (10″)	550	60.00
1972 Towngate at Elburg (7″)	3,500	40.00
1972 Church in Edam (10″)	1,500	70.00
1973 Towngate at Amersfoort (7″)	4,500	50.00
1973 DeWaag in Alkmaar (10″)	1,500	75.00
1974 Watergate at Sneek (7″)	4,500	80.00
1974 Kitchen in Hindeloopen (10″)	1,500	160.00
1975 Towngate at Amsterdam (7″)	1,000	140.00
1975 Farmer in Laren (10″)	1,500	250.00
1976 Towngate in Gorinehem (7″)	4,500	115.00
1976 Farmer's Wife in Staphorst (10″)	1,500	220.00
1977 Dromedaris Tower (7″)	4,500	140.00
1977 Farm Family in Spakenburg (10″)	1,500	277.00
1978 Winter Skating Scene (10″)	1,000	277.00
1978 Christmas Fisherman (7″)	1,500	140.00
1978 Christmas Angels (7″)	1,500	140.00
Mother's Day		
1971 Mother & Daughter (Volendam)	2,500	50.00
1972 Mother & Daughter (Hindeloopen)	2,500	40.00
1973 Mother & Daughter (Marken)	3,000	50.00
1974 Mother & Daughter (Zuid-Beveland)	Year	80.00
1975 Mother & Daughter (Spakenburg)	Year	100.00
1976 Mother & Daughter (Scheveningen)	Year	115.00
Father's Day		
1972 Father & Son (Volendam)	1,500	40.00
1973 Father & Son (Hindeloopen)	2,000	40.00
1974 Father & Son (Marken)	1,000	80.00
1975 Father & Son (Zuid-Beveland)	Year	80.00
1976 Father & Son (Spakenburg)	Year	140.00
Easter		
1973 Dutch Easter Palm (7″)	3,500	75.00
1973 Dutch Easter Palm (10″)	3,500	NA
1974 Dutch Easter Palm	1,000	110.00
1975 Dutch Easter Palm	1,000	125.00
1976 Dutch Easter Palm	1,000	175.00
Valentine		
1973 Enduring Beauty	1,500	75.00
1974 Valentine	1,000	125.00
1975 Valentine	1,000	125.00
1976 Valentine	1,000	175.00
Special Bicentenary		
1976 George Washington	2,500	350.00
1976 Eagle Plate	5,000	150.00

Schoonhaven

See: Blue Delft (Neth.)

Shuler International

See: Kurz (Neth.)

Zenith Delftware

	Edition Limit	Issue Price (US)
Hans Brinker		
1972 Skating	500	60.00
1973 Gretel Tending Geese	750	60.00
Anniversary		
1973 Autumn	500	45.00
1973 Spring	500	45.00
1973 Summer	500	$ 45.00
1973 Winter	500	45.00
Birthday Boy		
1973 Monday's Child	3,000	15.00
1973 Tuesday's Child	3,000	15.00
1973 Wednesday's Child	3,000	15.00
1973 Thursday's Child	3,000	15.00
1973 Friday's Child	3,000	15.00
1973 Saturday's Child	3,000	15.00
1973 Sunday's Child	3,000	15.00
Birthday Girl		
1973 Monday's Child	3,000	15.00
1973 Tuesday's Child	3,000	15.00
1973 Wednesday's Child	3,000	15.00
1973 Thursday's Child	3,000	15.00
1973 Friday's Child	3,000	15.00
1973 Saturday's Child	3,000	15.00
1973 Sunday's Child	3,000	15.00

NORWAY

Porsgrund

	Edition Limit	Issue Price (US)
(Single issue)		
1909 Christmas Flowers	Year	NA
Father's Day		
1971 Fishing	Year	10.00
1972 Cookout	Year	10.00
1973 Sledding	Year	10.00
1974 Father and Son	Year	10.00
1975 Skating	Year	12.50
1976 Skiing	Year	15.00
1977 Soccer	Year	16.50
1978 Canoeing	Year	17.50
1979 Father and Daughter	Year	19.50
1980 Sailing	Year	21.50
1981 Building a Ship	Year	24.00
1982 Father and Daughter	Year	26.00
1983 Father's Day	Year	26.00
1984 Tree Planting	Year	25.00
Easter		
1972 Ducks	Year	7.00
1973 Birds	Year	10.00
1974 Rabbits	Year	11.00
1975 Chicks	Year	16.00
1976 Sheep in Field	Year	18.00
1977 Butterflies	Year	23.00
Christmas		
1983 Christmas Night	Year	42.00
1984 Christmas Sheaf	Year	40.00

SPAIN

Lladro

	Edition Limit	Issue Price (US)
Christmas		
1971 Caroling	Year	27.50
1972 Carolers	Year	35.00
1973 Boy and Girl	Year	45.00
1974 Carolers	Year	55.00
1975 Cherubs	Year	60.00
1976 Christ Child	Year	60.00
1977 Nativity Scene	Year	80.00
1978 Caroling Child	Year	80.00
1979 Snow Dance	Year	90.00

Santa Clara

	Edition Limit	Issue Price (US)
Christmas		
1970 Christmas Message	10,000	18.00
1971 Three Wise Men	10,000	18.00
1972 Children in Woods	10,000	20.00
1973 Archangel	5,000	25.00
1974 Spirit of Christmas	10,000	25.00
1975 Christmas Eve in Country	10,000	27.50
1976 Madonna and Child	10,000	25.00
1977 Mother and Child	10,000	27.50
1978 Angel with Flowers	10,000	32.00
1979 Madonna and Angels	10,000	34.50
Mother's Day		
1971 Mother and Child	10,000	15.00
1972 Mother and Children	12,000	15.00

SWEDEN

Kosta

	Edition Limit	Issue Price (US)
Annual		
1971 Madonna & Child	Year	30.00
1972 St. George & Dragon	Year	30.00
1973 Viking Ship	Year	40.00
1974 Annual	Year	40.00

Orrefors

	Edition Limit	Issue Price (US)
Mother's Day		
1971 Flowers for Mother	2,500	45.00
1972 Mother and Children	2,500	45.00
1973 Mother and Child	2,500	50.00
1974 Mother and Child	5,000	50.00

		Edition Limit	Issue Price (US)
1975	Mother and Child	2,500	$ 60.00
1976	Children and Puppy	2,500	75.00
1977	Child and Dove	1,500	85.00
1978	Mother and Child	1,500	90.00

Rörstrand

Christmas

1904	Christmas Night in Stockholm	Year	.27
1905	Porridge Dish for Tomten	Year	.27
1906	Star Boys Singing to Lucia	Year	.27
1907	Christmas Eve in Lapland	Year	.27
1908	Christmas Eve with Christmas Roses	Year	.27
1909	Christmas Star over Jerusalem	Year	.27
1910	Christmas Tree	Year	.27
1911	Christmas Bells and Angel	Year	.56
1912	Christmas Service	Year	.56
1913	Christmas Day Early Service Trip	Year	.56
1914	Returning Home	Year	.56
1915	On Way to Church	Year	.56
1916	Kneeling Shepherd	Year	.56
1917	Three Kings Following Star	Year	.56
1918	Sleigh-ride in Dalecarlia	Year	.87
1919	Christmas on Snow Mountain	Year	.87
1920	Mary and Child Jesus	Year	.87
1921	Knight Offering Prayers	Year	.87
1922	Christmas Bells on Gotland	Year	.87
1923	Christmas Sheaf	Year	.87
1924	Tomtefar Bearing Gifts	Year	.87
1925	Christmas Star and Angels	Year	.87

Mother's Day

1971	Mother & Child	Year	15.00
1972	Shelling Peas	Year	15.00
1973	Old Fashioned Picnic	Year	16.00
1974	Candle Lighting	Year	18.00
1975	Pontius on Floor	Year	20.00
1976	Apple Picking	Year	20.00
1977	Kitchen	Year	27.50
1978	Azalea	Year	27.50
1979	Studio Idyll	Year	31.50
1980	Lisbeth	Year	31.50
1981	Karin with Brita	Year	42.50
1982	Mother's Day	Year	36.00
1983	Little Girl	Year	42.50
1984	Mother and Crafts	Year	42.50

Father's Day

1971	Father & Child	Year	15.00
1972	Meal at Home	Year	15.00
1973	Tilling Fields	Year	16.00
1974	Fishing	Year	18.00
1975	Painting	Year	20.00
1976	Plowing	Year	20.00
1977	Sawing	Year	27.50
1978	Self Portrait	Year	27.50
1979	Bridge	Year	31.50
1980	My Etch-Nook	Year	31.50
1981	Esbjorn with Playmate	Year	42.50
1982	Father's Day	Year	36.00
1983	Man Painting	Year	42.50
1984	Farm Life	Year	42.50

Christmas Poetry

1979	Silent Night, Holy Night	NA	173.00
1980	Three Holy Kings	NA	180.00
1981	O Holy Night	NA	280.00
1982	Shepherds in Bethlehem	NA	280.00

UNITED STATES

Abbey Press (Viletta)

Mother's Day

1979	Special Mothers Are God's Creation	6,000	37.50

Christmas

1979	Christmas Is a Gentle Season	6,000	37.50

Accent on Art

Mother Goose

1978	Jack & Jill	5,000	59.50

		Edition Limit	Issue Price (US)
Nobility of Plains			
1978	Commanche	12,500	$ 80.00
1979	Moving Day	3,500	80.00

Addams Family (Schmid)

Mother's Day

1972	On Tracks	Year	10.00

Christmas

1972	Christmas Dinner	Year	10.00

Allison

Nature's Beauty

1981	Winter's Peace	7,500	70.00
1982	Summer's Joy	7,500	70.00

Late to Party

1982	Piece of Cake	12,500	35.00
1983	Cheese Please	12,500	35.00
1983	Toast to a Mouse	12,500	35.00

American Archives (International Silver)

(Single issue)

1972	Christmas Rose	2,500	100.00

American Artists

Famous Stallions

1983	Black Stallion	19,500	49.50
1983	Andalusian	19,500	49.50

Feathered Friends

1983	Parakeets	19,500	29.50

Mother and Child Cats

1983	Kitty Love	19,500	29.50

Noble Tribes

1983	Algonquin	19,500	49.50
1984	Sioux	19,500	49.50

Saturday Evening Post Covers

1983	Santa's Computer	15 Days	29.50

Sport of Kings

1984	Man O' War	9,500	65.00
1984	Secretariat	9,500	65.00
1985	John Henry	9,500	65.00

Zoë's Cats

1984	Sniffer	12,500	29.50
1985	Waiting	12,500	29.50
1985	Sunshine	12,500	29.50
1985	Tarzan	12,500	29.50

Flower Fantasies

1985	Spring Blossoms	15 Days	24.50

Mare and Foal

1985	Water Trough	12,500	49.50

American Arts Services (Viletta)

Children

1979	Last of Ninth	5,000	45.00

American Commemorative (Gorham)

Southern Landmark

1973	Monticello	9,800	35.00
1973	Williamsburg	9,800	40.00
1974	Beauvoir	9,800	40.00
1974	Cabildo	9,800	40.00
1975	Hermitage	9,800	40.00
1975	Oak Hill	9,800	40.00
1976	Governor Tryon's Palace	9,800	40.00
1976	Montpelier	9,800	40.00
1977	Elmscourt	9,800	40.00
1977	Ashland	9,800	40.00
1978	Mt. Vernon	9,800	40.00
1978	White House	9,800	40.00
1979	Custis Lee	9,800	40.00
1979	Drayton Hall	9,800	40.00
1980	Fort Hall	9,800	40.00
1980	Liberty Hall	9,800	40.00

American Express (Gorham)

Four Freedoms

1976	Freedom to Worship	Year	37.50
1976	Freedom from Want	Year	37.50
1976	Freedom from Fear	Year	37.50
1976	Freedom of Speech	Year	37.50

Birds of North America

1978	Saw Whet Owls	9,800	38.00
1978	Bobwhite Quail	9,800	38.00
1978	October Cardinals	9,800	38.00
1978	Long-Eared Owl	9,800	38.00
1978	Eastern Bluebirds	9,800	38.00
1978	American Woodcock	9,800	38.00
1978	Ruffed Grouse	9,800	38.00
1978	House Wren	9,800	38.00

American Express (Lenox)

American Trees of Christmas

1976	Douglas Fir	Year	60.00
1977	Scotch Pine	Year	60.00

		Edition Limit	Issue Price (US)
American Heritage Art (Crown Parian)			
Battle Wagon			
1982	General Quarters	15,000	$ 39.50
1983	Last Cruise	11,103	39.50
1984	Delaware	10,000	39.50
1984	Kentucky	10,000	39.50
Celebrity Clowns			
1982	Emmett	12,500	50.00
1982	Judy	12,500	50.00
1982	Jimmy	12,500	50.00
1982	Shark	12,500	50.00
Early American Sail			
1982	Squall	5,000	39.50
1983	Young America	5,000	39.50
1984	Ironsides	5,000	39.50
1984	Charles W. Morgan	5,000	39.50
Lil Critters			
1982	Inquisitive	10,000	39.50
1982	Sassy	10,000	39.50
1983	Vigilance	10,000	39.50
1983	Chatty	10,000	39.50
Vanishing West			
1982	Hell Bent	5,000	60.00
1983	Cold Trail	5,000	60.00
1983	Horse Stick Medicine	5,000	60.00
1984	Letting 'em Blow	5,000	60.00
1984	Eyeing Back Trail	5,000	60.00
Africa's Beauties			
1983	Elephant Family	5,000	65.00
1983	Zebra Family	5,000	65.00
America's Heritage of Flight			
1983	Kitty Hawk	5,000	39.50
1983	Jenny	5,000	39.50
1984	Race	5,000	39.50
1984	Corsair	5,000	39.50
Craftsman Heritage			
1983	Decoy Maker	5,000	39.50
1983	Sailmaker	5,000	39.50
1983	Farmer	5,000	39.50
1984	Platemaker	5,000	39.50
1984	Blacksmith	5,000	39.50
1984	Spinning Wheel	5,000	39.50
1985	Gunsmith	5,000	39.50
Equestrian Love			
1983	Arabian Destiny	5,000	39.50
1983	Quarterhorse Wrangler	5,000	39.50
1984	Arab Destiny	5,000	39.50
Sawdust Antics			
1983	Emmett's 8 Ball	5,000	50.00
1983	Emmett with a Bang	5,000	50.00
1984	Emmett at Races	5,000	50.00
1984	Emmett at Plate	5,000	50.00
Clown Antics			
1984	Comedy	10,000	19.50
1984	Tragedy	10,000	19.50
Endangered			
1984	Sidney	10,000	19.50
1984	Chein	10,000	19.50
Homer's Antics			
1984	Homer at Races	10,000	39.50
1984	Homer on Wall Street	10,000	39.50
Indian Greats			
1984	Two Moons	10,000	19.50
1984	Chief Joseph	10,000	19.50
Kitty Kats			
1984	Pansy and Sammy	10,000	19.50
Whimsical Moments			
1984	Three's Company	NA	29.50

American Historial Plates (Castleton China)

Aviation

1972	Amelia Earhart	3,500	40.00
1972	Charles Lindberg	3,500	40.00

American Preservation Guild (Gorham)

Catesby Collection

1977	Cardinal	9,900	39.00

American Rose Society (Gorham)

All-American Rose

1975	Oregold	9,800	39.00
1975	Arizona	9,800	39.00
1975	Rose Parade	9,800	39.00
1976	America	9,800	39.00
1976	Cathedral	9,800	39.00
1976	Seashell	9,800	39.00
1977	Yankee Doodle	9,800	39.00
1977	Double Delight	9,800	39.00
1977	Prominent	9,800	39.00
1978	First Edition	9,800	39.00
1978	Color Magic	9,800	39.00
1978	Charisma	9,800	39.00
1979	Paradise	9,800	39.00
1979	Sundowner	9,800	39.00

		Edition Limit	Issue Price (US)
1979	Friendship	9,800	$ 39.00
1980	Love	9,800	39.00
1980	Honor	9,800	39.00
1980	Cherish	9,800	39.00
1981	Bing Crosby	9,800	49.00
1981	White Lightnin'	9,800	49.00
1981	Marina	9,800	49.00
1982	Shreveport	9,800	49.00
1982	French Lace	9,800	49.00
1982	Brandy	9,800	49.00
1983	Mon Cheri	9,800	49.00
1983	Sun Flare	9,800	49.00
1983	Sweet Surrender	9,800	49.00
1984	Olympiad	9,800	49.00
1984	Impatient	9,800	49.00
1984	Intrigue	9,800	49.00

Antique Trader

Currier & Ives

1969	Baseball	2,000	9.00
1969	Franklin Experiment	2,000	9.00
1969	Haying Time	2,000	9.00
1969	Winter in Country	2,000	9.00

Easter

1971	Child and Lamb	1,500	10.95
1972	Shepherd with Lamb	1,000	10.95

Mother's Day

1971	Madonna and Child	1,500	10.95
1972	Mother Cat and Kittens	1,000	10.95

Father's Day

1971	Pilgrim Father	1,500	10.95
1972	Deer Family	1,000	10.95

Thanksgiving

1971	Pilgrims	1,500	10.95
1972	First Thanksgiving	1,000	10.95

Christmas

1971	Christ Child	1,500	10.95
1972	Flight into Egypt	1,000	10.95

C. M. Russell

1971	Bad One	2,000	11.95
1971	Discovery of Last Chance Gulch	2,000	11.95
1971	Doubtful Visitor	2,000	11.95
1971	Innocent Allies	2,000	11.95
1971	Medicine Man	2,000	11.95

Bible

1973	David & Goliath	2,000	10.75
1973	Moses & Golden Idol	2,000	10.75
1973	Noah's Ark	2,000	10.75
1973	Samson	2,000	10.75

Arizona Artisan

Christmas

1974	Mexican Christmas	Year	20.00
1975	Navajo Christmas	Year	20.00

Thanksgiving

1975	Navajo Thanksgiving Feast	Year	15.00

Arlington Mint

Christmas

1972	Hands in Prayer	Year	125.00

Armstrong's

(Single issue)

1983	Seventy Years Young	15,000	85.00

Lovable Kittens

1984	Cat's Meow	10,000	29.50
1984	Purr-Swayed	10,000	29.50

Three Graces

1984	Thalia	10,000	49.50

(Single issue)

1984	Freddie Torchbearer	15,000	62.50

Reflections of Innocence

1985	Me and My Friend	10,000	37.50
1985	My RainBeau	10,000	37.50

Huggable Puppies

1984	Take Me Home	10,000	29.50
1985	Oh How Cute	10,000	29.50

Statue of Liberty

1985	Dedication	10,000	39.50

Artists of the World

Ruffin Annual

1976	Navajo Lullaby	10,000	40.00
1977	Through Years	5,000	45.00
1978	Child of Pueblo	5,000	50.00
1979	Colima Madonna	5,000	50.00
1980	Sun Kachina	5,000	50.00
1981	Inner Peace	5,000	55.00
1982	Madonna of Cross	5,000	60.00
1983	Navajo Princess	5,000	60.00
1984	Americans All	7,500	60.00

World of Game Birds

	Edition Limit	Issue Price (US)
1977 Mallards	5,000	$ 45.00
1978 Gambel Quail	5,000	45.00
1979 American Autumn Ring-necked Pheasant	5,000	50.00
1980 November Journey-Canada Geese	5,000	50.00

Don Ruffin Self-Portrait

1979 Clown Also Cries	7,500	65.00

Children of Don Ruffin

1980 Flowers for Mother	7,500	50.00
1981 Little Eagle	7,500	55.00
1982 Lost Moccasins	7,500	60.00
1983 Security	7,500	60.00
1984 Americans All	7,500	60.00

Prowlers of Clouds

1981 Great Horned Owl	5,000	55.00
1981 Screech Owl	5,000	55.00
1982 Bald Eagle	5,000	60.00
1982 Golden Eagle	5,000	60.00

Anthony Sidoni

1982 Little Yankee	15,000	35.00
1983 Little Satchmo	15,000	40.00

Vel Miller

1982 Mama's Rose	15,000	35.00
1983 Papa's Boy	15,000	40.00

Woodland Friends

1983 Whitetail Deer	5,000	60.00
1984 Black Bear	5,000	60.00
1984 No Rest for Night Shift	5,000	60.00
1985 No Peace in Paradise	5,000	60.00

(Single issue)

1983 DeGrazia and His Mountain	15,000	65.00

Sweet-Hearts

1984 We Believe	10,000	40.00

(Single issue)

1984 Girl Paints DeGrazia	12,500	65.00

Audubon Crystal

Endangered Birds

1976 Kirtland's Warbler	5,000	195.00
1976 American Eagle	5,000	195.00
1977 Peregrine Falcon	5,000	200.00

Avondale

Cameos of Childhood

1978 Melissa	28,050	65.00
1979 First Born	12,000	70.00
1980 Melissa's Brother	Year	70.00
1981 Daddy and I	Year	75.00

Myths of Sea

1979 Poseidon	15,000	70.00
1980 Maiden of Sea	15,000	75.00

Tribute to Ageless Art

1979 Court Jesters	10,000	70.00

World of Dance

1979 Prima Ballerina	15,000	70.00

Christmas

1981 And Heavens Rejoiced	6,500	90.00
1982 And There Came Wise Men	6,500	90.00
1983 Shepherd	6,500	90.00

Growing Up

1982 Ribbon for Her Hair	6,500	75.00
1983 Just Like Mother	6,500	75.00

See also: Judaic Heritage Society (U.S.A.)

B & J Art Designs

Old Fashioned Christmas

1983 Carol	15,000	45.00
1984 Chris	15,000	45.00
1985 Noel	15,000	45.00

Country

1984 Cristina	20,000	39.00
1985 Laurel	20,000	42.50

Brantwood Collection

Marian Carlsen Mother's Day

1978 Jennifer and Jenny Fur	Year	45.00
1979 Football Brothers	5,000	45.00

Howe Christmas

1978 Visit from Santa	Year	45.00

(Single issue)

1978 Tribute to Rockwell	Year	35.00

John Falter Christmas

1979 Christmas Morning	5,000	24.50

Rockwell Mother's Day

1979 Homecoming	20,000	39.50

Little Clown

1979 Going to Circus	5,000	29.50

Braymer Hall

Childhood Sonatas

	Edition Limit	Issue Price (US)
1981 Serenade	15,000	$ 28.50
1982 Prelude	15,000	28.50
1982 Caprice	15,000	28.50

American Folk

1982 Spring Celebration	10,000	24.50
1982 Summer Bounty	10,000	24.50

Yesterday's Dreams

1983 Swing Quartet	5,000	50.00
1983 Sleigh Belles	5,000	50.00

Brentwood Fine Arts (Fairmont)

Nostalgic Memories

1982 Amy	12,500	39.50

Briarcrest

Good Ole Summertime

1982 Watermelon Eater	10 Days	42.00

This Ole Bear

1982 Chauncey James	5,000	45.00

(Single issue)

1982 Carousel	10,000	35.00

John Brindle Fine Arts

Fantasy in Motion

1978 Little Blue Horse	3,000	75.00
1979 Horse of a Different Color	3,000	75.00
1980 Horse with Golden Horn	3,000	75.00

Moods of Orient

1978 Softly, Sun Sets	4,000	75.00
1980 Tranquil Morn	4,000	75.00

Expressions

1979 Quiet Eyes	3,000	60.00

(Single issue)

1980 Homage	2,500	125.00

Those Precious Years

1980 Little Curt and Friend	3,000	60.00

Cabochon

Nancy Doyle's Candy Girls

1983 Rebecca	15,000	50.00
1984 Shantelle	15,000	50.00
1984 Kelly Ann	15,000	50.00

Calhoun's Collectors Society

Crystal Maidens

1979 Spring-Strawberry Season	2,500	49.50
1979 Summer-Sunshine Season	2,500	49.50
1979 Autumn-Scenic Season	2,500	49.50
1979 Winter-Snowflake Season	2,500	49.50

Calhoun's Collectors Society (Schumann)

Imperial Christmas

1979 Liebling	10,000	65.00
1980 Hallelujah	10,000	65.00
1981 Stille Nacht	10,000	65.00
1982 Winter Melodie	10,000	75.00

California Porcelain and Bronze

Best of Sascha

1979 Flower Bouquet	7,500	65.00

Vanishing Animals

1979 Asian Monarchs	7,500	40.00
1979 Snow Leopards	7,500	45.00
1980 Pandas	7,500	45.00
1981 Polar Bears	7,500	50.00

(Single issue)

1983 Koala	5,000	29.95

Now Is Moment

1984 Be Still	12,500	35.00

Seed of People

1984 Keenah	10,000	29.95

Carmel Collection

Famous Parades

1983 Thanksgiving Day Parade	Year	39.50

First Performances

1983 Darling Diana	19,500	39.50

Joys of Christmas

1983 Christmas Delight	19,500	39.50

Memories of Heart

1984 Petals	15,000	28.50

Carson Mint (Viletta)

Yesterday's Children

1978 Lisa and Jumeau Doll	5,000	60.00
1979 Adrianne and Bye-Lo Baby	5,000	60.00

	Edition Limit	Issue Price (US)
1980 Lydia and Shirley Temple Doll	5,000	$ 60.00
1981 Melanie and Scarlett O'Hara Doll	5,000	60.00

Hollywood Squares

1979 Peter Marshall	100 Days	28.50
1980 George Gobel	100 Days	28.50

Moment in Time

1979 Freedom Flight	5,000	55.00

Old Fashioned Mother's Day

1979 Daisies from Mary-Beth	20 Days	37.50
1980 Daisies from Jimmy	20 Days	37.50
1981 Daisies from Meg	20 Days	37.50
1982 Daisies for Mommie	20 Days	37.50

America Has Heart

1980 My Heart's Desire	Year	24.50
1981 Hearts and Flowers	Year	24.50
1982 Hearty Sailer	Year	28.50
1983 Shannon's Sweetheart	Year	28.50

Magic Afternoon

1980 Enchanted Garden	5,000	39.50
1981 Delightful Tea Party	5,000	39.50

Big Top

1981 White Face	60 Days	28.50
1982 Tramp	60 Days	28.50

Littlest Christmas

1982 Littlest Stocking	12,500	29.50
1983 Littlest Santa	12,500	29.50

Nature's Children

1982 Candice	12,500	29.50
1983 Cory	12,500	29.50
1984 Ryan's Retreat	12,500	29.50

Bear Feats

1983 Teddy Bear Picnic	15,000	37.50
1984 On Beach	15,000	37.50

To Mom with Love

1983 A Basket of Love	15,000	37.50

Castleton China

Natural History

1973 Painted Lady	1,500	40.00
1973 Roseate Spoonbill	1,500	40.00

(Single issue)

1976 Gen. Douglas MacArthur	1,000	30.00

Castleton China (Shenango)

Bicentennial

1972 New Dawn	7,600	60.00
1972 Turning Point	7,600	60.00
1973 Valley Forge	7,600	60.00
1973 Declaration	7,600	60.00
1973 Star Spangled Banner	7,600	60.00
1973 U.S.S. Constitution	7,600	60.00
1974 One Nation	7,600	60.00
1974 Westward Ho	7,600	60.00

See also: American Historical Plates (U.S.A.)

Caverswall

See: Ghent Collection (U.S.A.)

Certified Rarities

Indian Dancer

1978 Eagle Dancer	2,500	300.00
1979 Hoop Dancer	2,500	300.00

Postal Artists

1978 Colias Eurydice	15,000	60.00
1979 Euphydryas Phaeton	7,500	60.00

Renaissance Masters

1978 Alba Madonna	15,000	55.00
1979 Pieta	5,000	55.00

Chilmark

Family Christmas

1978 Trimming Tree	10,000	65.00

In Appreciation

1979 Flowers of Field	10,000	65.00

Holy Night

1979 Wisemen	10,000	65.00

Twelve Days of Christmas

1979 Partridge in Pear Tree	10,000	89.50

Cleveland Mint

Da Vinci

1972 Last Supper	5,000	125.00

Collector Creations (Reed & Barton)

Thomas Nast Christmas

1973 Christmas	750	100.00

(Single issue)

1973 Alice in Wonderland	750	100.00

Collector's Heirlooms (Fairmont)

Children at Play

1979 Maple Leaf Noses	7,500	60.00

	Edition Limit	Issue Price (US)
Passing of Plains Indians		
1979 Cheyenne Chieftain	5,000	$ 65.00

Collector's Heirlooms (Viletta)

Childhood Memories

1978 Jennifer by Candlelight	5,000	60.00
1979 Brian's Birthday	5,000	60.00

Joys of Motherhood

1978 Crystal's Joy	7,500	60.00

Collectors Weekly

American

1971 Miss Liberty	500	12.50
1972 Miss Liberty	900	12.50
1973 Eagle	900	9.75

Continental Mint

Tom Sawyer

1976 Taking His Medicine	5,000	60.00
1977 Painting Fence	5,000	60.00
1978 Lost in Cave	5,000	60.00
1979 Smoking Pipe	5,000	60.00

(Single issue)

1979 Butter Girl	7,000	60.00

Creative World

Pearl Buck (Single issue)

1972 Good Earth	10,000	NA

Four Seasons

1972 Fall (Silverplate)	2,000	75.00
1972 Fall (Sterling)	2,000	125.00
1973 Winter (Silverplate)	2,000	75.00
1973 Winter (Sterling)	250	125.00
1973 Spring (Silverplate)	300	75.00
1973 Spring (Sterling)	750	125.00
1974 Summer (Silverplate)	300	75.00
1974 Summer (Sterling)	750	125.00

Brown's Rockwells

1977 Looking Out to Sea	15,000	50.00
1978 Yankee Doodle	15,000	50.00
1979 Girl at Mirror	15,000	55.00

Immortals of Early American Literature

1978 Village Smithy	15,000	50.00
1979 Rip Van Winkle	15,000	55.00

Aesop's Fables

1979 Fox & Grapes	9,750	85.00

Living Dolls

1982 Eriko and Noriko	9,500	49.50
1983 Ingrid and Ingemar	9,500	49.50

Prize

1982 Family Cares	12,500	45.00
1983 Wind in a Frolic	12,500	45.00

Wags to Riches

1982 Benji Movie Star	100 Days	29.50
1982 Benji and Tiffany	100 Days	29.50
1983 Merry Christmas Benji	19,500	35.00
1984 Benji's Barbershop Blues	19,500	35.00

Help My Friends

1983 Corky's Dream	100 Days	35.00

Crown Parian

Rosemary Calder

1978 Affection	7,500	60.00

James Daly

1978 Sweet Dreams	7,500	55.00

Beautiful Cats of World

1979 Sheena	5,000	60.00
1979 Sheena and Sheena's Cubs	5,000	60.00
1980 Elisheba	5,000	60.00
1980 Elisheba's Cubs	5,000	60.00
1981 Atarah	5,000	60.00
1981 Atarah's Cubs	5,000	60.00
1982 Tamar	5,000	60.00
1982 Tamar's Cubs	5,000	60.00

Penni Anne Cross

1979 Crow Baby	7,500	55.00
1981 Paiute Pals	7,500	55.00
1982 Big Sister's Buckskins	7,500	55.00
1984 Navajo Nanny	7,500	55.00

Julian Ritter

1979 Reve de Ballet	7,500	55.00

Western

1979 Under Surveillance	10,000	65.00
1979 Promised Land	10,000	65.00
1979 Winter Song	10,000	65.00
1979 Boomtown and Wildcatters	10,000	65.00

Sporting Dogs

1980 Decoy	5,000	55.00
1981 Dusty	5,000	55.00
1982 Rummy	5,000	55.00
1983 Scarlet	5,000	55.00

OVER-THE-COUNTER ISSUES

	Edition Limit	Issue Price (US)
Happy Art		
1981 Woody's Triple Self-Portrait	10,000	$ 39.50
1982 Gothic Woody	10,000	39.50
1984 Blue Boy Woody	10,000	39.50
Portraits of Childhood		
1981 Miss Murray	7,500	65.00
1984 Master Lambton	10,000	65.00
Children to Love		
1982 Wendy	10,000	60.00
1983 Jake	10,000	60.00
1984 Katy	10,000	60.00
Owl Family		
1982 Saw-Whet Owl Family	5,000	55.00
1982 Great Horned Owl Family	5,000	55.00
1983 Snowy Owl Family	5,000	55.00
1983 Barred Owl Family	5,000	55.00
Reflections of Seasons		
1982 Winter's Dream	7,500	39.50
(Single issue)		
1982 Buon Natale	1,000	300.00
Special Heart		
1983 Reaching Together	40,000	35.00
1983 Love in Your Heart	40,000	35.00
Holidays Around the World		
1984 Elysa's Christmas	12,500	39.50
See also: American Heritage Art (U.S.A.)		
Curator Collection		
Masterpieces of Impressionism		
1980 Woman with a Parasol	17,500	35.00
1981 Young Mother Sewing	17,500	35.00
1982 Sara in Green Bonnet	17,500	35.00
1983 Margot in Blue	17,500	35.00
Masterpieces of West		
1980 Texas Night Herder	17,500	35.00
1981 Indian Trapper	17,500	35.00
1982 Cowboy Style		
1982 Indian Style (Set of two)	17,500	70.00
Masterpieces of Rockwell		
1980 After Prom	17,500	35.00
1981 Challenger	17,500	42.50
1981 Girl at Mirror	17,500	50.00
1982 Missing Tooth	17,500	50.00
Jesse's World		
1981 This Simple Faith	17,500	39.95
Magical Moments		
1981 Happy Dreams	NA	29.95
1981 Harmony	NA	29.95
1982 His Majesty	NA	29.95
1982 Waiting for Daddy	NA	29.95
1983 Thank You, God	NA	29.95
1983 Lullaby	NA	29.95
Rockwell Americana		
1981 Shuffleton's Barbershop	17,500	75.00
1982 Breaking Home Ties	17,500	75.00
1983 Walking to Church	17,500	75.00
Special Occasions		
1981 Bubbles	NA	29.95
1982 Butterflies	NA	29.95
Stockbridge Trilogy		
1981 Stockbridge in Winter, Part I	NA	45.00
1982 Stockbridge in Winter, Part II	NA	45.00
1983 Stockbridge in Winter, Part III	NA	45.00
Classic Circus		
1982 Favorite Clown	17,500	39.95
Playful Pets		
1982 Curiosity	10,000	45.00
1982 Master's Hat	10,000	45.00
Tribute		
1982 I Want You	NA	29.95
1982 Gee! I Wish I Were a Man	NA	29.95
1983 Soldier's Farewell	NA	29.95
Becker Babies		
1983 Snowpuff	NA	29.95
1984 Smiling Through	NA	29.95
1984 Pals	NA	29.95
Nursery		
1983 In Slumberland	NA	35.00
1983 Awakening	NA	35.00
Mother's Love		
1984 Contentment	7,500	35.00
On Road		
1984 Pride of Stockbridge	NA	35.00
1985 City Pride	NA	35.00
1985 Country Pride	NA	35.00

	Edition Limit	Issue Price (US)
Simpler Times		
1984 Lazy Daze	7,500	$ 35.00
Triple Play		
1984 Chums	NA	29.95
1984 Nitey-Nite	NA	29.95
1984 Oh, Oh! A Bunny	NA	29.95
Great Trains		
1985 Santa Fe	7,500	35.00
1985 Twentieth Century Ltd.	7,500	35.00
Danbury Mint		
Currier & Ives (Silver)		
1972 Road Winter	7,500	125.00
1973 Central Park Winter	7,500	125.00
1974 Winter in Country	7,500	125.00
1975 American Homestead	7,500	125.00
1976 American Winter-Evening	7,500	135.00
1977 Winter Morning	7,500	135.00
Christmas		
1975 Silent Night	NA	24.50
1976 Joy to World	NA	27.50
1977 Away in Manger	NA	27.50
1978 First Noel	NA	29.50
Bicentennial (Silver)		
1973 Boston Tea Party	7,500	125.00
1974 First Continental Congress	7,500	125.00
1975 Paul Revere's Ride	7,500	125.00
1976 Declaration of Independence	7,500	125.00
1977 Washington at Valley Forge	7,500	125.00
1978 Molly Pitcher	7,500	125.00
1979 Bon Homme Richard	7,500	125.00
Michelangelo (Silver)		
1973 Creation of Adam	7,500	125.00
1973 Pieta	7,500	125.00
1973 Moses	7,500	125.00
1973 Holy Family	7,500	125.00
Great Art Masterpieces (Silver)		
1975 Mona Lisa	7,500	125.00
1975 Last Supper	7,500	125.00
1976 Sunflower	7,500	125.00
1976 Blue Boy	7,500	125.00
Derby Collection		
Mischief Makers		
1985 Puddles	10,000	39.95
Wild Innocence		
1985 My Buddy	5,000	29.95
Designers Collection		
Faerie Seasons		
1984 Meadow Nymph	10,000	29.00
1984 Flower Nymph	10,000	29.00
1984 Arbor Nymph	10,000	29.00
1984 Woodland Nymph	10,000	29.00
Stuart Devlin Silver		
Americana		
1972 Gaspee Incident	1,000	130.00
Walt Disney Productions		
Enchantment of Snow White		
1984 At Wishing Well	15,000	26.50
1984 Dance	15,000	26.50
1984 Witch and Apple	15,000	26.50
1984 Happily Ever After	15,000	26.50
1984 Enchantment of Snow White	15,000	26.50
Ebeling & Reuss		
Christmas		
1981 Waiting for Christmas	7,000	15.00
1982 Time of Song and Caroling	7,500	15.00
(Single issue)		
1983 Love One Another	12,500	17.50
Enesco		
Christmas		
1981 Come Let Us Adore Him	15,000	40.00
1982 Heaven and Nature Sing	15,000	40.00
1983 We Three Kings	15,000	40.00
Inspired Thoughts		
1981 Love One Another	15,000	40.00
1981 Make a Joyful Noise	15,000	40.00
1982 I Believe in Miracles	15,000	40.00
Mother's Love		
1981 Mother Sew Dear	15,000	40.00
1982 Purr-fect Grandma	15,000	40.00
1983 Hand That Rocks Future	15,000	40.00

	Edition Limit	Issue Price (US)
Little Bible Friends		
1981 Nativity	25,000	$ 40.00
1982 Flight into Egypt	25,000	40.00
1982 Last Supper	25,000	40.00
Joy of Christmas		
1982 Play My Drum for Him	Year	40.00
1983 Christmas Time	Year	40.00
1984 Wonder of Christmas	Year	40.00
1985 Tell Me Story of Jesus	Year	40.00
Four Seasons		
1985 Voice of Spring	Year	40.00
1985 Summer's Joy	Year	40.00
R.J. Ernst Enterprises (Viletta)		
Performance		
1979 Act I	5,000	65.00
Women of West		
1979 Expectation	10,000	39.50
1979 Silver Dollar Sal	10,000	39.50
1980 School Marm	10,000	39.50
1980 Dolly	10,000	39.50
Love Is		
1980 Rufus and Roxanne	19,000	14.95
A Beautiful World		
1981 Tahitian Dreamer	27,500	27.50
1982 Flirtation	27,500	27.50
1983 Elke of Oslo	27,500	27.50
Hollywood Greats		
1980 John Wayne	27,500	29.95
1981 Gary Cooper	27,500	29.95
1982 Clark Gable	27,500	29.95
1983 Alan Ladd	27,500	29.95
Classy Cars		
1981 '26 T	20 Days	24.50
1982 Model A	20 Days	24.50
1982 Model A Pickup	20 Days	24.50
1983 Panel Van	20 Days	24.50
Commemoratives		
1981 John Lennon	30 Days	39.50
1981 Elvis Presley	30 Days	39.50
1982 Marilyn Monroe	30 Days	39.50
1983 Judy Garland	30 Days	39.50
A Love Story		
1981 Chapter One	20 Days	24.50
Pinups		
1981 Stars and Stripes Forever	20 Days	24.50
So Young, So Sweet		
1981 Girl with Straw Hat	10 Days	39.50
1982 My Favorite Necklace	10 Days	39.50
1983 Breakfast Time	10 Days	39.50
Turn of Century		
1981 Riverboat Honeymoon	10 Days	35.00
1982 Children's Carousel	10 Days	35.00
1982 Flower Market	10 Days	35.00
1983 Ballroom Race	10 Days	35.00
Little Misses Young and Fair		
1982 Heart of a Child	29,000	60.00
1983 Where Wild Flowers Grow	29,000	60.00
1984 Whispered Memories	29,000	60.00
1985 Final Touch	29,000	60.00
Mommie and Me		
1982 First Tea	10 Days	35.00
1983 Baby's Sleeping	10 Days	35.00
My Fair Ladies		
1982 Lady Sabrina	29,000	50.00
1983 Lady Victoria	29,000	50.00
(Single issue)		
1982 Henry Fonda	100 Days	45.00
Fondest Memories		
1983 A Touching Moment	NA	60.00
1984 Mother's Pearls	NA	60.00
Liebchen		
1983 Winter Liebchen	30 Days	19.50
1983 Spring Liebchen	30 Days	19.50
1984 Summer Liebchen	30 Days	19.50
1984 Autumn Liebchen	30 Days	19.50
Narrow Gauge		
1983 Halfway to Alamosa	10 Days	29.50
1984 Down from Rico	10 Days	29.50
Star Trek		
1983 Mr. Spock	90 Days	29.50
1983 Dr. McCoy	90 Days	29.50
1984 Sulu	90 Days	29.50
1984 Scotty	90 Days	29.50
1984 Uhura	90 Days	29.50
1984 Chekov	90 Days	29.50
1985 Captain Kirk	90 Days	29.50
Yesterdays		
1983 Amber	10 Days	24.50
1983 Elmer	10 Days	24.50

	Edition Limit	Issue Price (US)
Americana		
1984 Somewhere in Autumn	20 Days	$ 29.50
Childhood Memories		
1984 Sometimes an Angel	20 Days	24.50
Children of Past		
1984 Buttercup Test	NA	29.50
1984 Minuet	NA	29.50
Days Ago		
1984 Blue Belle	20 Days	24.50
Fishing Boats		
1984 Sunset at Monterey	10 Days	24.50
1984 Blue Sea	10 Days	24.50
Friends		
1984 I Love You Orville	20 Days	24.50
Romantic Memories		
1984 Sunday Afternoon	14,400	60.00
Bare Innocence		
1985 Singing in Rain	10 Days	24.50
Shades of Time		
1985 Morning Glo	5,000	45.00
This Land Is Our Land		
1985 Oak Creek Canyon	5,000	29.50
Fairmont		
Carousel Horses		
1977 (Set of two)	3,000	80.00
Spencer Annual		
1977 Patient Ones	10,000	42.50
1978 Yesterday, Today and Tomorrow	10,000	47.50
Irene Spencer's Special Requests		
1978 Hug Me	10,000	55.00
1978 Sleep Little Baby	10,000	65.00
Olaf Wieghorst		
1978 Sioux Warrior	5,000	65.00
1979 Indian Scout	5,000	65.00
Rural America		
1978 Fence	5,000	45.00
Timeless Moments		
1978 Tenderness	5,000	45.00
1979 Renaissance	5,000	50.00
1980 Coming in Glory	5,000	39.95
Children of America		
1979 Eskimo Girl	3,000	48.00
Lords of Plains		
1979 Sitting Bull	5,000	60.00
Rockwell Early Works		
1979 Old Man Winter	15,000	19.95
1980 Inventor	15,000	19.95
1980 Ready for School	15,000	19.95
1980 Music Master	15,000	19.95
1981 Tinkerer	15,000	19.95
Gnome Holiday		
1980 Gnome Bliss	5,000	24.50
1981 Gift of Love	5,000	29.95
Gnomes Four Seasons		
1980 Little Swinger (Spring)	15,000	29.50
1980 Gnome de Bloom (Summer)	15,000	29.50
1980 Lookouts (Fall)	15,000	29.50
1980 First Skater (Winter)	15,000	29.50
1981 Spring Sharing (Spring)	15,000	29.95
1981 Fun and Games (Summer)	15,000	29.95
1981 Up Up and Away (Fall)	15,000	29.95
1981 First Skier (Winter)	15,000	29.95
1982 Gnome Knowledge (Spring)	15,000	29.95
1982 Summer Harvest (Summer)	15,000	29.95
1982 Gnome Family Tailors (Fall)	15,000	29.95
1982 Keep Gnome Fires Burning (Winter)	15,000	29.95
American's Most Beloved (Single issue)		
1980 John Wayne	5,000	13.95
Long Road West		
1981 Trailblazers	20,000	40.00
1981 Prairie Schooner	20,000	40.00
1981 Pony Express	20,000	40.00
1981 Peacemakers	20,000	40.00
1981 Cowboys of West	20,000	40.00
1981 Lawmen of West	20,000	40.00
When I Grow Up		
1981 I'll Be Loved	7,500	29.95
1981 I'll Be Like Mommy	7,500	29.95
1982 I'll Be First Lady	7,500	29.95
1982 I'll Be a Star	7,500	29.95
Jansen's International Beauties		
1982 Lisa	7,500	55.00
1983 Ingrid	7,500	55.00

	Edition Limit	Issue Price (US)
Vanishing Americana		
1983 American Eagle	15,000	$ 13.50
1984 Country Doctor	15,000	13.50
(Single issue)		
1983 I Love Teddy Bears	NA	39.50
(Single issue)		
1983 My Little Sheltie	5,000	39.95
(Single issue)		
1983 Organ Grinder	5,000	19.95
Legends of Gnomes		
1984 Gnome Home	15,000	29.95
Dreams Do Come True		
1985 Little Ballerina	5,000	29.95
See also:		
Brentwood Fine Arts (U.S.A.)		
Collector's Heirlooms (U.S.A.)		
Ghent Collection (U.S.A.)		
Mistwood Designs (U.S.A.)		
Fenton Glass		
American Craftsman		
1970 Glassmaker	Year	10.00
1971 Printer	Year	10.00
1972 Blacksmith	Year	10.00
1973 Shoemaker	Year	10.00
1974 Cooper	Year	11.00
1975 Silversmith	Year	13.50
1976 Gunsmith	Year	13.50
1977 Potter	Year	15.00
1978 Wheelwright	Year	15.00
1979 Cabinetmaker	Year	15.00
1980 Tanner	Year	16.50
1981 Housewright	Year	17.50
Christmas in America		
1970 Little Brown Church (Blue Satin)	Year	12.50
1970 Little Brown Church (Carnival)	Year	12.50
1970 Little Brown Church (Brown)	Year	17.50
1971 Old Brick Church (Blue Satin)	Year	12.50
1971 Old Brick Church (Brown)	Year	17.50
1971 Old Brick Church (Carnival)	Year	12.50
1971 Old Brick Church (White Satin)	Year	12.50
1972 Two Horned Church (Blue Satin)	Year	12.50
1972 Two Horned Church (Brown)	Year	17.50
1972 Two Horned Church (Carnival)	Year	12.50
1972 Two Horned Church (White Satin)	Year	12.50
1973 St. Mary's (Blue Satin)	Year	12.50
1973 St. Mary's (Carnival)	Year	12.50
1973 St. Mary's (White Satin)	Year	12.50
1973 St. Mary's (Brown)	Year	17.50
1974 Nation's Church (Blue Satin)	Year	13.50
1974 Nation's Church (Carnival)	Year	13.50
1974 Nation's Church (White Satin)	Year	13.50
1974 Nation's Church (Brown)	Year	18.50
1975 Birthplace of Liberty (Blue Satin)	Year	13.50
1975 Birthplace of Liberty (Carnival)	Year	13.50
1975 Birthplace of Liberty (White Satin)	Year	13.50
1975 Birthplace of Liberty (Brown)	Year	20.00
1976 Old North Church (Blue Satin)	Year	15.00
1976 Old North Church (Carnival)	Year	15.00
1976 Old North Church (White Satin)	Year	15.00
1976 Old North Church (Brown)	Year	25.00
1977 San Carlos (Blue Satin)	Year	15.00
1977 San Carlos (Carnival)	Year	15.00
1977 San Carlos (White Satin)	Year	15.00
1978 Church of Holy Trinity (Blue Satin)	Year	15.00
1978 Church of Holy Trinity (Carnival)	Year	15.00
1978 Church of Holy Trinity (White Satin)	Year	15.00

	Edition Limit	Issue Price (US)
1979 San Jose y Miguel de Aguayo (Blue Satin)	Year	$ 15.00
1979 San Jose y Miguel de Aguayo (Carnival)	Year	15.00
1979 San Jose y Miguel de Aguayo (White Satin)	Year	15.00
1980 Christ Church (Blue Satin)	Year	16.50
1980 Christ Church (Carnival)	Year	16.50
1980 Christ Church (White Satin)	Year	16.50
1981 Mission of San Xavier del Bac (Blue Satin)	Year	18.50
1981 Mission of San Xavier del Bac (Carnival)	Year	18.50
1981 Mission of San Xavier del Bac (White Satin)	Year	18.50
Mother's Day		
1971 Madonna, Sleeping Child (Blue Satin)	Year	12.50
1971 Madonna, Sleeping Child (Carnival)	Year	12.50
1972 Madonna of Goldfinch (Blue Satin)	Year	12.50
1972 Madonna of Goldfinch (Carnival)	Year	12.50
1972 Madonna of Goldfinch (White Satin)	Year	12.50
1973 Cowper Madonna (Blue Satin)	Year	12.50
1973 Cowper Madonna (Carnival)	Year	12.50
1973 Cowper Madonna (White Satin)	Year	12.50
1974 Madonna of Grotto (Blue Satin)	Year	12.50
1974 Madonna of Grotto (Carnival)	Year	12.50
1974 Madonna of Grotto (White Satin)	Year	12.50
1975 Taddei Madonna (Blue Satin)	Year	13.50
1975 Taddei Madonna (Carnival)	Year	13.50
1975 Taddei Madonna (White Satin)	Year	13.50
1976 Holy Night (Blue Satin)	Year	13.50
1976 Holy Night (Carnival)	Year	13.50
1976 Holy Night (White Satin)	Year	13.50
1977 Madonna & Child (Blue Satin)	Year	15.00
1977 Madonna & Child (Carnival)	Year	15.00
1977 Madonna & Child (White Satin)	Year	15.00
1978 Madonnina (Blue Satin)	Year	15.00
1978 Madonnina (Carnival)	Year	15.00
1978 Madonnina (White Satin)	Year	15.00
1979 Madonna of Rose Hedge (Blue Satin)	Year	15.00
1979 Madonna of Rose Hedge (Carnival)	Year	15.00
1979 Madonna of Rose Hedge (White Satin)	Year	15.00
Valentine's Day		
1972 Romeo and Juliet (Blue Satin)	Year	15.00
1972 Romeo and Juliet (Carnival)	Year	15.00
Bicentennial		
1974 Eagle (Blue Satin)	Year	15.00
1975 Eagle (Red Satin)	Year	15.00
1976 Eagle (Chocolate)	Year	17.50
1976 Eagle (White Satin)	Year	15.00
Alliance		
1975 Lafayette and Washington (Blue Satin)	Year	15.00
1975 Lafayette and Washington (Red Satin)	Year	17.50
1975 Lafayette and Washington (White Satin)	Year	15.00
1976 Lafayette and Washington (Blue Satin)	Year	15.00

	Edition Limit	Issue Price (US)
1976 Lafayette and Washington (Chocolate)	Year	$ 17.50
1976 Lafayette and Washington (White Satin)	Year	15.00
Christmas Classics		
1978 Christmas Morn	Year	25.00
1979 Nature's Christmas	Year	30.00
1980 Going Home	Year	38.50
1981 All Is Calm	Year	42.50
1982 Country Christmas	Year	42.50
Currier & Ives		
1980 Old Grist Mill	Year	25.00
1981 Harvest	Year	25.00
1982 Old Homestead in Winter	Year	25.00
1983 Winter Pastime	Year	25.00
Mother's Day Classics		
1980 New Born	Year	28.50
1981 Gentle Fawn	Year	32.50
1982 Nature's Awakening	Year	35.00
1983 Where's Mom?	Year	35.00
1984 Precious Panda	Year	35.00
Artists		
1982 After Snow	15,000	14.50
1983 Winter Chapel	15,000	15.00
Childhood Treasures		
1983 Teddy Bear	15,000	15.00
1984 Hobby Horse	15,000	15.00
Christmas Fantasy		
1983 Anticipation	7,500	45.00
1984 Expectation	7,500	50.00
Designer		
1983 Down Home	1,000	65.00
1983 Lighthouse Point	1,000	65.00
Firehouse		
This Ole Bear		
1982 Emma Louise	5,000	39.50
1983 Buster and Sam	5,000	39.50
1984 Matilda Jane	5,000	39.50
Fleetwood Collection (Gorham)		
Birds and Flowers of Meadow and Garden		
1980 Robin and Crab Apple Blossom	*	39.00
1980 Goldfinch and Bull Thistle	*	39.00
1980 Cardinal and Wild Lupine	*	39.00
1980 Chickadee and New England Aster	*	39.00
1980 Baltimore Oriole and Morning Glory	*	39.00
1980 Blue Bird and Black-Eyed Susan	*	39.00
1980 Painted Bunting and Blackberry	*	39.00
1980 Golden-Crowned Kinglet and Downey Phlox	*	39.00
1980 Red-Breasted Nuthatch and Japanese Honeysuckle	*	39.00
1980 Magnolia Warbler and Day Lily	*	39.00
1980 Ruby-Throated Hummingbird and Fire Pink	*	39.00
1980 Scarlet Tanager and Blue Columbine	*	39.00
*Subscription period		
Christmas		
1980 Magi	7,500	49.50
1981 Holy Child	7,500	49.50
1982 Shepherds	7,500	49.50
Mother's Day		
1980 Cottontails	5,000	45.00
1981 Raccoons	5,000	45.00
1982 Whitetail Deer	5,000	50.00
1983 Canada Geese	5,000	50.00
Blossoms of China		
1981 Azalea	7,500	49.50
1981 Camelia	7,500	49.50
1981 Herbaceous Peony	7,500	49.50
1981 Chrysanthemum	7,500	49.50
1981 Lotus	7,500	49.50
1981 Magnolia	7,500	49.50
1981 Narcissus	7,500	49.50
1981 Orchid	7,500	49.50
1981 Peony	7,500	49.50
1981 Plum Blossom	7,500	49.50
1981 Rose	7,500	49.50
1981 Winter Jasmine	7,500	49.50

	Edition Limit	Issue Price (US)
Tsarevich's Bride		
1981 Arrow in Air	7,500	$ 50.00
1982 Boyar's Courtyard	7,500	50.00
1982 Rich Merchant's Yard	7,500	50.00
1983 Mouth of Frog	7,500	50.00
Golden Age of Sail		
1982 Flying Cloud	5,000	39.00
1982 New World	5,000	39.00
1982 Young America	5,000	39.00
1982 Courier	5,000	39.00
1982 Sea Witch	5,000	39.00
1982 Great Republic	5,000	39.00
(Single issue)		
1983 Mom's Apple Pie	NA	29.00
(Single issue)		
1985 Presidential Inaugural	9,500	50.00
Fostoria		
American Milestones		
1971 Betsy Ross Flag	5,000	12.50
1972 National Anthem	8,000	12.50
1973 Washington Crossing Delaware	Year	12.50
1974 Spirit of '76	Year	13.00
1975 Mount Rushmore	Year	16.00
State Plates		
1971 California	6,000	12.50
1971 New York	12,000	12.50
1971 Ohio	3,000	12.50
1972 Florida	Year	12.50
1972 Hawaii	Year	12.50
1972 Pennsylvania	Year	12.50
1972 Massachusetts	Year	13.00
1972 Texas	Year	13.00
1973 Michigan	Year	13.50
Franklin Crystal		
Historical		
1976 Liberty Tree	10,927	120.00
Seven Seas		
1976 Atlantic Ocean	2,799	120.00
1976 Caribbean	2,799	120.00
1976 Indian Ocean	2,799	120.00
1976 Mediterranean	2,799	120.00
1976 Pacific	2,799	120.00
1976 South China Sea	2,799	120.00
1976 Arctic	2,799	120.00
Annual		
1977 Snowflake	3,428	185.00
1978 Snowbird	798	185.00
Rockwell's American Sweethearts		
1977 Youngsters at Play	1,004	120.00
1977 Teenagers Together	1,004	120.00
1978 Bride and Groom	1,004	120.00
1978 Proud Parents	1,004	120.00
1978 Graduation Day	1,004	120.00
1978 Retirement Kiss	1,004	120.00
Franklin Mint		
American West		
1972 Horizon's West (Silver)	5,860	150.00
1972 Horizon's West (Gold)	67	2200.00
1973 Mountain Man (Silver)	5,860	150.00
1973 Mountain Man (Gold)	67	2200.00
1973 Prospector (Silver)	5,860	150.00
1973 Prospector (Gold)	67	2200.00
1973 Plains Hunter (Silver)	5,860	150.00
1973 Plains Hunter (Gold)	67	2200.00
Audubon Society		
1972 Goldfinch	10,193	125.00
1972 Wood Duck	10,193	125.00
1973 Cardinal	10,193	125.00
1973 Ruffed Grouse	10,193	125.00
Mother's Day		
1972 Mother and Child	21,987	125.00
1973 Mother and Child	6,154	125.00
1974 Mother and Child	5,116	150.00
1975 Mother and Child	2,704	175.00
1976 Mother and Child	1,858	180.00
Presidential		
1972 George Washington	10,304	150.00
1972 John Adams	4,859	150.00
1972 Thomas Jefferson	4,933	150.00
1972 James Madison	3,058	150.00
1972 James Monroe	2,722	150.00
1972 John Quincy Adams	2,501	150.00
1972 Andrew Jackson	2,408	150.00
1973 Martin Van Buren	2,291	150.00
1973 William H. Harrison	2,182	150.00
1973 John Tyler	2,144	150.00
1973 James Polk	2,083	150.00
1973 Zachary Taylor	2,023	150.00
1973 Millard Fillmore	1,967	150.00
1974 Franklin Pierce	1,907	150.00
1974 James Buchanan	1,841	150.00

OVER-THE-COUNTER ISSUES

	Edition Limit	Issue Price (US)
1974 Abraham Lincoln	2,955	$150.00
1974 Andrew Johnson	1,777	150.00
1974 Ulysses S. Grant	1,754	150.00
1975 Rutherford B. Hayes	1,705	150.00
1975 James A. Garfield	1,675	150.00
1975 Chester A. Arthur	1,604	150.00
1975 Grover Cleveland	1,644	150.00
1976 Benjamin Harrison	1,619	150.00
1976 William McKinley	1,571	150.00
1976 Theodore Roosevelt	1,555	150.00
1976 William H. Taft	1,592	150.00
1976 Woodrow Wilson	1,563	150.00
1977 Warren G. Harding	1,544	150.00
1977 Calvin Coolidge	1,527	150.00
1977 Herbert Hoover	1,520	150.00
1977 Franklin D. Roosevelt	1,770	150.00
1977 Harry S. Truman	1,493	150.00
1978 Dwight D. Eisenhower	1,494	150.00
1978 John F. Kennedy	1,494	150.00
1978 Lyndon B. Johnson	1,483	150.00
1978 Richard M. Nixon	1,475	150.00
1978 Gerald R. Ford	NA	150.00
1978 Jimmy Carter	NA	150.00
Thanksgiving—by Dohanos		
1972 First Thanksgiving	10,142	125.00
1973 American Wild Turkey	3,547	125.00
1974 Thanksgiving Prayer	5,150	150.00
1975 Family Thanksgiving	3,025	175.00
1976 Home from Hunt	3,474	175.00
James Wyeth		
1972 Along Brandywine	19,670	125.00
1973 Winter Fox	10,394	125.00
1974 Riding to Hunt	10,751	150.00
1975 Skating on Brandywine	8,058	175.00
1976 Brandywine Battlefield	6,968	180.00
Younger's Bird		
1972 Cardinal	13,939	125.00
1972 Bobwhite	13,939	125.00
1972 Mallards	13,939	125.00
1972 American Bald Eagle	13,939	125.00
John James Audubon		
1973 Wood Thrush	5,273	150.00
1973 Bald Eagle	3,040	150.00
1974 Night Heron	3,005	150.00
1974 Audubon's Warbler	3,034	150.00
Bernard Buffet		
1973 Gazelle	570	150.00
1974 Panda	408	150.00
1975 Giraffe	333	150.00
1976 Lion	263	150.00
1977 Rhinoceros	200	150.00
Bicentennial		
1973 Jefferson Drafting Declaration of Independence	8,556	175.00
1974 John Adams Champions Cause of Independence	8,442	175.00
1975 Caesar Rodney Decides Vote on Independence	8,319	175.00
1976 John Hancock Signs Declaration of Independence	10,166	175.00
Easter		
1973 Resurrection	7,116	175.00
1974 He Is Risen	3,719	185.00
1975 Last Supper	2,004	200.00
1976 Crucifixion	3,904	250.00
1977 Resurrection	1,206	250.00
Presidential Inaugural		
1973 Nixon/Agnew	10,483	150.00
1974 Ford (Silver)	1,141	200.00
1974 Ford (Gold)	11	3500.00
1977 Carter	928	225.00
Roberts' Zodiac		
1973 Aries	NA	150.00
1973 Taurus	NA	150.00
1973 Gemini	NA	150.00
1973 Cancer	NA	150.00
1973 Leo	NA	150.00
1973 Virgo	NA	150.00
1973 Libra	NA	150.00
1973 Scorpio	NA	150.00
1973 Sagittarius	NA	150.00
1973 Capricorn	NA	150.00
1973 Aquarius	NA	150.00
1973 Pisces	NA	150.00
Four Seasons		
1975 Spring Blossoms	2,648	240.00
1975 Summer Bouquet	2,648	240.00
1976 Autumn Garland	2,648	240.00
1976 Winter Spray	2,648	240.00

	Edition Limit	Issue Price (US)
American Revolution Bicentennial		
1976 Boston Tea Party	3,596	$ 75.00
1976 Patrick Henry Urges Armed Resistance	3,596	75.00
1976 Paul Revere's Ride	3,596	75.00
1976 Battle of Concord Bridge	3,596	75.00
1976 Capture of Fort Ticonderoga	3,596	75.00
1976 Battle of Bunker Hill	3,596	75.00
1977 Signing of Declaration	3,596	75.00
1977 Washington Crosses Delaware	3,596	75.00
1977 Burgoyne Defeated at Saratoga	3,596	75.00
1977 Winter at Valley Forge	3,596	75.00
1977 Alliance with France	3,596	75.00
1977 Bonhomme Richard Defeats Serapis	3,596	75.00
1977 Victory at Yorktown	3,596	75.00
Annual		
1977 Tribute to Arts	1,901	280.00
1978 Tribute to Nature	435	280.00
Belskie		
1977 Mother's Day	290	210.00
Currier and Ives		
1977 Winter Pastime	1,836	39.50
1977 Preparing for Market	1,836	39.50
1977 Winter in Country	1,836	39.50
1977 American Homestead—Winter	1,836	39.50
1977 American Forest Scene	1,836	39.50
1977 American Homestead—Summer	1,836	39.50
1977 American Homestead—Autumn	1,836	39.50
1977 Haying Time—Last Load	1,836	39.50
1977 American Express Train	1,836	39.50
1977 Haying Time—First Load	1,836	39.50
1977 Catching a Trout	1,836	39.50
1977 Yosemite Valley	1,836	39.50
Freedom		
1977 Lafayette Joins Washington	546	275.00
Rockwell Thanksgiving		
1977 Old Fashioned Thanksgiving	2,361	85.00
Christmas		
1977 Skating Party	908	55.00
Franklin Porcelain		
Hans Christian Andersen		
1976 Princess and Pea	16,875	38.00
1976 Ugly Duckling	16,875	38.00
1976 Little Mermaid	16,875	38.00
1976 Emperor's New Clothes	16,875	38.00
1976 Steadfast Tin Soldier	16,875	38.00
1976 Little Match Girl	16,875	38.00
1977 Snow Queen	16,875	38.00
1977 Red Shoes	16,875	38.00
1977 Tinder Box	16,875	38.00
1977 Nightingale	16,875	38.00
1977 Thumbelina	16,875	38.00
1977 Shepherdess & Chimney Sweep	16,875	38.00
Christmas Annual		
1976 Silent Night	19,286	65.00
1977 Deck Halls	9,185	65.00
1978 We Three Kings	Year	75.00
1979 Hark, Herald Angels Sing	Year	75.00
1980 Joy to World	Year	125.00
1981 O, Holy Night	Year	125.00
Flowers of Year		
1976 January	27,394	50.00
1976 February	27,394	50.00
1977 March	27,394	50.00
1977 April	27,394	50.00
1977 May	27,394	50.00
1978 June	27,394	50.00
1978 July	27,394	50.00
1978 August	27,394	50.00
1978 September	27,394	50.00
1979 October	27,394	50.00
1979 November	27,394	50.00
1979 December	27,394	50.00

	Edition Limit	Issue Price (US)
Mother's Day		
1977 A Mother's Love	Year	$ 65.00
1978 A Mother's Joy	Year	65.00
1979 A Mother's Gift	Year	75.00
Songbirds of World		
1977 Baltimore Oriole	20,225	55.00
1977 Bohemian Waxwing	20,225	55.00
1977 Magnolia Warbler	20,225	55.00
1977 Bobolink	20,225	55.00
1977 Western Bluebird	20,225	55.00
1977 Cardinal	20,225	55.00
1977 European Goldfinch	20,225	55.00
1977 Wood Thrush	20,225	55.00
1977 Scarlet Tanager	20,225	55.00
1977 Barn Swallow	20,225	55.00
1977 Bluethroat	20,225	55.00
1977 Turquoise Wren	20,225	55.00
Mark Twain		
1977 Whitewashing Fence	2,645	38.00
1977 Stealing a Kiss	2,645	38.00
1977 Traveling River	2,645	38.00
1977 Trading Lives	2,645	38.00
1977 Rafting Down River	2,645	38.00
1978 Riding Bronc	2,645	38.00
1978 Jumping Frog Race	2,645	38.00
1978 Facing Charging Knight	2,645	38.00
1978 Disguising Huck	2,645	38.00
1978 Living Along River	2,645	38.00
1978 Learning to Smoke	2,645	38.00
1978 Finger Printing Pays Off	2,645	38.00
Flowers of American Wilderness		
1978 New England	8,759	39.00
1978 Alaska	8,759	39.00
1978 Everglades of Florida	8,759	39.00
1978 Mississippi Delta	8,759	39.00
1978 California	8,759	39.00
1978 Rocky Mountains	8,759	39.00
1978 Cape Cod	8,759	39.00
1978 Northwest	8,759	39.00
1978 Southwest	8,759	39.00
1978 Appalachian Mountains	8,759	39.00
1978 Prairies	8,759	39.00
1978 Great Lakes	8,759	39.00
Game Birds of World		
1978 Chinese Pheasant	76,294	55.00
1978 Red-Legged Partridge	76,294	55.00
1978 Common Snipe	76,294	55.00
1978 Common Partridge	76,294	55.00
1978 Rock Ptarmigan	76,294	55.00
1978 Woodcock	76,294	55.00
1978 Common Pheasant	76,294	55.00
1978 Hazel Grouse	76,294	55.00
1978 Red Grouse	76,294	55.00
1978 Black Grouse	76,294	55.00
1978 Capercaillie	76,294	55.00
1978 Common Quail	76,294	55.00
Grimm's Fairy Tales		
1978 Sleeping Beauty	27,006	42.00
1978 Twelve Dancing Princesses	27,006	42.00
1978 Brementown Musicians	27,006	42.00
1979 Golden Goose	27,006	42.00
1979 Hansel and Gretel	27,006	42.00
1979 Rapunzel	27,006	42.00
1980 Snow White/Seven Dwarfs	27,006	42.00
1980 Frog Prince	27,006	42.00
1980 Red Riding Hood	27,006	42.00
1981 Rumpelstilskin	27,006	42.00
1981 Cinderella	27,006	42.00
1981 Shoemaker and Elves	27,006	42.00
Days of Week		
1979 Monday's Child	1,890	39.00
1979 Tuesday's Child	1,890	39.00
1979 Wednesday's Child	1,890	39.00
1979 Thursday's Child	1,890	39.00
1979 Friday's Child	1,890	39.00
1979 Saturday's Child	1,890	39.00
1979 Sunday's Child	1,890	39.00
Hometown Memories		
1979 Country Fair	Year	29.00
1980 Little Red School House	Year	29.00
1981 Sunday Picnic	Year	29.00
1982 Skating Party	Year	29.00
Country Year		
1980 Woodlands in April	89,173	55.00
1980 Country Path in May	89,173	55.00
1980 June in Country Garden	89,173	55.00
1980 July Beside River	89,173	55.00

	Edition Limit	Issue Price (US)
1980 Wheatfields in August	89,173	$ 55.00
1980 September on Moors	89,173	55.00
1980 Colors of Autumn in October	89,173	55.00
1980 Country Lane in December	89,173	55.00
1980 January—Lambing Season	89,173	55.00
1980 Country Church in March	89,173	55.00
1980 Secluded Stream in November	89,173	55.00
International Gallery of Flowers		
1980 Wheat	4,294	55.00
1980 Orchid	4,294	55.00
1980 Irises	4,294	55.00
1980 Camelias	4,294	55.00
1980 Cherry Blossoms	4,294	55.00
1980 English Wild Flowers	4,294	55.00
Woodland Birds of World		
1980 Blue Jay	5,507	65.00
1980 White-Winged Crossbill	5,507	65.00
1980 Painted Redstart	5,507	65.00
1980 Rivoli's Hummingbird	5,507	65.00
1980 Chaffinch	5,507	65.00
1980 Collared Trogon	5,507	65.00
Calendar		
1981 Turn-of-Century Scenes	Year	55.00
1982 Turn-of-Century Children	Year	58.00
Clipper Ships		
1982 Red Jacket	NA	55.00
1982 Sea Witch	NA	55.00
1982 Cutty Sark	NA	55.00
1982 Thermoplyae	NA	55.00
1982 Ariel	NA	55.00
1982 Patriarch	NA	55.00
1982 Nightingale	NA	55.00
1982 Flying Cloud	NA	55.00
1982 Marco Polo	NA	55.00
Cobblestone Kids		
1982 Making Friends	NA	65.00
1982 Extra, Extra	NA	65.00
1982 Just Ducky	NA	65.00
1982 Feeding Raccoon	NA	65.00
1982 A Stitch in Time	NA	65.00
1982 Testing Wind	NA	65.00
Frankoma		
Christmas		
1965 Goodwill Toward Man	Year	5.00
1966 Bethlehem Shepherds	Year	5.00
1967 Gifts for Christ Child	Year	5.00
1968 Flight into Egypt	Year	5.00
1969 Laid in a Manger	Year	5.00
1970 King of Kings	Year	5.00
1971 No Room in Inn	Year	5.00
1972 Seeking Christ Child	Year	5.00
1973 Annunciation	Year	5.00
1974 She Loved & Cared	Year	5.00
1975 Peace on Earth	Year	5.00
1976 Gift of Love	Year	6.00
1977 Birth of Eternal Life	Year	6.00
1978 All Nature Rejoiced	Year	6.00
1979 Stay of Hope	Year	6.00
1980 Unto Us a Child Is Born	Year	10.00
1981 O Come Let Us Adore Him	Year	12.00
1982 Wise Men Rejoice	Year	12.00
1983 Wise Men Bring Gifts	Year	12.00
Bicentennial		
1972 Provocations	Year	6.00
1973 Patriots & Leaders	Year	6.00
1974 Battles, Independence	Year	5.00
1975 Victories for Independence	Year	6.00
1976 Symbols of Freedom	Year	6.00
Teenagers of Bible		
1973 Jesus, Carpenter	Year	5.00
1974 David, Musician	Year	5.00
1975 Jonathan, Archer	Year	5.00
1976 Dorcas, Seamstress	Year	5.00
1977 Peter, Fisherman	Year	5.00
1978 Martha, Homemaker	Year	7.50
1979 Daniel, Courageous	Year	7.50
1980 Ruth, Devoted	Year	8.00
1981 Joseph, Dreamer	Year	8.00
1982 Mary, Mother	Year	8.00
Madonnas		
1977 Grace Madonna	Year	12.50
1978 Madonna of Love	Year	12.50

	Edition Limit	Issue Price (US)
Ghent Collection		
Christmas Wildlife		
1974 Cardinals in Snow	10,135	$ 20.00
1975 We Three Kings	12,750	29.00
1976 Partridge and Pear Tree	12,750	32.00
1977 Foxes and Evergreen	12,750	32.00
1978 Snowy Owls	12,750	32.00
Mother's Day		
1975 Cotton Tail	12,750	22.00
1976 Mallard Family	12,750	29.00
1977 Chipmunks & Trillium	12,750	32.00
1978 Raccoon Family	12,750	32.00
1979 Maytime	12,750	32.00
American Bicentennial Wildlife		
1976 American Bald Eagle	2,500	95.00
1976 American White-Tailed Deer	2,500	95.00
1976 American Bison	2,500	95.00
1976 American Wild Turkey	2,500	95.00
Fausett Mural (Single issue)		
1976 From Sea to Shining Sea	1,976	76.00
(Single issue)		
1978 Pilgrim of Peace	15 Days	29.50
Lands of Fable		
1981 Xanadu	17,500	55.00
1982 Atlantis	17,500	55.00
Man's Dream of Flight		
1981 Flight of Icarus	19,500	37.50
1981 Vision of Leonardo	19,500	37.50
1981 First Lighter-than-Air Flight	19,500	37.50
1981 Wright Brothers	19,500	37.50
1981 Lindbergh Flies Atlantic	19,500	37.50
1981 Barnstormers	19,500	37.50
1981 Jet Age	19,500	37.50
1981 Giant Leap for Mankind	19,500	37.50
Hans Brinker Delft		
1982 Hero of Haarlem	17,500	29.50
1982 Race	17,500	29.50
1982 Thousand Guilders	17,500	29.50
1982 On Canal	17,500	29.50
1982 Shadows in Home	17,500	29.50
1982 Mysterious Watch	17,500	29.50
Ghent Collection (Bing & Grøndahl)		
Hans Christian Andersen		
1979 Thumbelina	7,500	42.50
1979 Princess and Pea	7,500	42.50
1979 Wild Swans	7,500	42.50
1979 Emperor's New Clothes	7,500	42.50
1980 Little Mermaid	7,500	42.50
1980 Nightingale	7,500	42.50
Ghent Collection (Caverswall)		
Christmas Annual		
1979 Good King Wenceslaus	2,500	350.00
Country Diary of an Edwardian Lady		
1979 April	10,000	80.00
1979 June	10,000	80.00
1980 September	10,000	80.00
1980 December	10,000	80.00
1981 July	10,000	80.00
1981 October	10,000	80.00
1982 January	10,000	80.00
1982 May	10,000	80.00
1983 February	10,000	80.00
1983 March	10,000	80.00
1984 August	10,000	80.00
1984 November	10,000	80.00
Ghent Collection (Fairmont)		
Legends of Christmas		
1979 Bringing in Tree	5,000	65.00
Memory Annual		
1978 1977 Memory Plate	1,977	77.00
1979 1978 Memory Plate	1,978	78.00
1980 1979 Memory Plate	1,979	79.00
Israeli Commemorative (Single issue)		
1978 Promised Land	5,738	79.00
Spirit of America		
1978 Making of a Nation	1,978	78.00
1979 Growing Years	1,978	78.00
Ghent Collection (Gorham)		
April Fool Annual		
1978 April Fool's Day	10,000	35.00
1979 April Fool's Day	10,000	35.00
1980 April Fool's Day	10,000	37.50

	Edition Limit	Issue Price (US)
Ghent Collection (Kaiser)		
Treasures of Tutankhamun		
1978 Golden Mask	3,247	$ 90.00
1978 Golden Throne	3,247	90.00
1978 Horus Falcon	3,247	90.00
1978 Ivory Chest	3,247	90.00
Ghent Collection (Viletta)		
Olympics		
1980 1980 Winter Olympics	13 Days	24.50
1980 1980 Summer Olympics	13 Days	29.50
Gnomes United		
Gnomes		
1979 Gnome on Range	10,000	23.00
Gnome Patrol		
1979 Dr. Kwik	5,000	45.00
Golf Digest		
Second Hole (Single issue)		
1973 Dorado Beach Club	2,000	45.00
Twelfth Hole (Single issue)		
1973 Spyglass Hill	2,000	45.00
Gorham		
(Single issue)		
1970 American Family Tree	5,000	17.00
Lionel Barrymore		
1971 Quiet Waters	15,000	25.00
1972 San Pedro Harbor	15,000	25.00
1972 Little Boatyard (Silver)	1,000	100.00
1972 Nantucket (Silver)	1,000	100.00
Bicentennial		
1971 Burning of Gaspee (Pewter)	5,000	35.00
1972 Burning of Gaspee (Silver)	750	550.00
1972 1776 (China)	18,500	17.50
1972 1776 (Vermeil)	500	500.00
1972 1776 (Silver)	750	250.00
1972 Boston Tea Party (Pewter)	5,000	35.00
1973 Boston Tea Party (Silver)	750	550.00
Gallery of Masters		
1971 Man in Gilt Helmet	10,000	50.00
1972 Self-Portrait Rembrandt, with Saskia	10,000	50.00
1973 Honorable Mrs. Graham	7,500	50.00
Moppets Mother's Day		
1973 Flowers for Mother	20,000	10.00
1974 Mother's Hat	20,000	12.00
1975 In Mother's Clothes	20,000	13.00
1976 Flowers	20,000	13.00
1977 Gift for Mother	18,500	13.00
1978 Moppet's Mother's Day	18,500	10.00
Moppets Christmas		
1973 Christmas March	20,000	10.00
1974 Trimming Tree	20,000	12.00
1975 Carrying Tree	20,000	13.00
1976 Asleep under Tree	18,500	13.00
1977 Star for Treetop	18,500	13.00
1978 Presents	18,500	10.00
1979 Moppet's Christmas	18,500	12.00
1980 Happy Merry Christmas Tree	Year	12.00
1981 Happy Merry Christmas Tree	Year	12.00
1982 Happy Merry Christmas Tree	Year	12.00
Remington Western		
1973 Aiding a Comrade	Year	25.00
1973 New Year on Cimarron	Year	25.00
1973 Fight for Waterhole	Year	25.00
1973 Flight	Year	25.00
1974 Old Ramond	Year	20.00
1974 Breed	Year	20.00
1975 Cavalry Officer	5,000	37.50
1975 Trapper	5,000	37.50
Irene Spencer Annual		
1974 Dear Child	10,000	37.50
1975 Promises to Keep	10,000	40.00
(Single issue)		
1974 Streakers	Year	19.50
(Single issue)		
1974 Golden Rule	Year	19.50
(Single issue)		
1974 Big Three	10,000	17.50
(Single issue)		
1974 Weigh-In	10,000	17.50
(Single issue)		
1975 Benjamin Franklin	18,500	19.50

	Edition Limit	Issue Price (US)
Boy Scouts of America		
1975 Our Heritage	18,500	$ 19.50
1976 Scout Is Loyal	18,500	19.50
1977 Scoutmaster	18,500	19.50
1977 Good Sign	18,500	19.50
1978 Pointing Way	18,500	19.50
1978 Campfire Story	18,500	19.50
American Artists		
1976 Apache Mother & Child	9,800	25.00
1976 Black Regiment	7,500	25.00
America's Cup Plates (Set of five)		
1976 America, 1861		
1976 Puritan		
1976 Reliance		
1976 Ranger		
1976 Courageous	1,000	200.00
Omnibus Muralis		
1976 200 Years with Old Glory	5,000	60.00
1977 Life of Christ	5,000	65.00
First Lady		
1977 Amy and Rosalynn	Year	24.95
Presidential		
1977 John F. Kennedy	9,800	30.00
1977 Eisenhower	9,800	30.00
Julian Ritter Christmas		
1977 Christmas Visit	9,800	24.50
Ritter's Four Seasons Clowns		
1977 Falling in Love (Set of four)	5,000	100.00
1978 To Love a Clown (Set of four)	5,000	120.00
Santa Fe Railway		
1977 Navajo Silversmith	7,500	37.50
1978 Turquoise Bead Maker	7,500	37.50
1979 Basketweaver	7,500	42.50
1980 Arrow Maker	7,500	45.00
Borsato Masterpiece		
1977 Serenity	5,000	75.00
1978 Titian Madonna	5,000	75.00
1979 Ballerina	5,000	75.00
Little Men		
1977 Come Ride with Me	9,500	50.00
1978 Julian Ritter Valentine	7,500	45.00
Moppets Anniversary		
1979 Moppet Couple	20,000	13.00
(Single issue)		
1978 Triple Self-Portrait	Year	37.50
Wild West		
1980 Bronc to Breakfast	9,800	38.00
1981 In Without Knocking	9,800	38.00
1982 Cowboy Life	9,800	45.00
1983 Ignorance Is Bliss	9,800	45.00
Four Seasons Landscape		
1980 Summer Respite	15,000	45.00
1980 Autumn Reflections	15,000	45.00
1981 Winter Delights	15,000	45.00
1981 Spring Recess	15,000	45.00
Rockwell Four Seasons		
1981 Old Timers (Set of four)	Year	100.00
1982 Life with Father (Set of four)	Year	100.00
1983 Old Buddies (Set of four)	Year	115.00
1984 Traveling Salesman (Set of four)	Year	115.00
(Single issue—Set of two)		
1981 Day in Life of Boy		
1981 Day in Life of Girl	Year	50.00
Four Ages of Love		
1981 Sweet Song So Young	10,000	100.00
1982 Flowers in Tender Bloom	10,000	100.00
Masterpieces of Rockwell		
1981 Girl at Mirror	17,500	50.00
Young Love		
1981 Beguiling Buttercup	17,500	62.50
1982 Flying High	17,500	62.50
Encounters, Survival and Celebrations		
1982 A Fine Welcome	7,500	50.00
1983 Winter Trails	7,500	50.00
1984 Alouette	7,500	62.50
1984 Trader	7,500	62.50
1985 Winter Camp	7,500	62.50
1985 Trapper Takes a Wife	7,500	62.50
Pastoral Symphony		
1982 When I Was a Child	7,500	42.50
1983 Gather Children	7,500	42.50
1984 Sugar and Spice	7,500	42.50
1985 He Loves Me	7,500	42.50

	Edition Limit	Issue Price (US)
A Merry Mouse		
1983 A Merry Mouse Christmas	5,000	$ 15.00
Museum Doll		
1983 Lydia	5,000	29.00
1984 Belton Bebe	5,000	29.00
1984 Lucille	5,000	29.00
1985 Bebe Jumeau	5,000	29.00
Heaven Mother's Day		
1984 Mother Is Love	5,000	24.95
See also:		
American Commemorative (U.S.A.)		
American Express (U.S.A.)		
American Preservation Guild (U.S.A.)		
American Rose Society (U.S.A.)		
Fleetwood Collection (U.S.A.)		
Ghent Collection (U.S.A.)		
Lincoln Mint (U.S.A.)		
Volair (U.S.A.)		
Greentree Potteries		
Grant Wood		
1971 Studio	2,000	10.00
1972 Antioch School	2,000	10.00
1973 At Stone City	2,000	10.00
1974 Adolescence	2,000	10.00
1975 Birthplace	2,000	10.00
1976 American Gothic	2,000	10.00
Kennedy		
1972 Center for Performing Arts	2,000	20.00
1973 Birthplace, Brookline, Mass.	2,000	12.00
Motorcar		
1972 1929 Packard Dietrich Convertible	2,000	20.00
1973 Model "A" Ford	2,000	20.00
Mississippi River		
1973 Delta Queen	2,000	10.00
1973 Tri-Centennial	2,000	10.00
Dave Grossman Designs		
Margaret Keane		
1976 Balloon Girl	5,000	25.00
1977 My Kitty	5,000	25.00
1978 Bedtime	5,000	25.00
Tom Sawyer		
1975 Whitewashing Fence	10,000	24.00
1976 First Smoke	10,000	24.00
1977 Take Your Medicine	10,000	24.00
1978 Lost in Cave	10,000	25.00
Looney Tunes Mother's Day		
1976 Bugs Bunny	10,000	13.00
Looney Tunes Christmas		
1977 Christmas	10,000	13.00
1978 Christmas	5,000	14.00
Children of Week		
1978 Monday's Child	5,000	30.00
1979 Tuesday's Child	5,000	30.00
1979 Wednesday's Child	5,000	30.00
1980 Thursday's Child	5,000	30.00
1980 Friday's Child	5,000	30.00
1981 Saturday's Child	5,000	30.00
1981 Sunday's Child	5,000	30.00
Annual Fall		
1978 Peace	5,000	55.00
1979 Santa	5,000	55.00
Annual		
1979 Leapfrog	Year	50.00
1980 Lovers	Year	60.00
1981 Dreams of Long Ago	Year	60.00
Rockwell		
1979 Butter Boy	5,000	40.00
Huckleberry Finn		
1979 Secret	10,000	40.00
1980 Listening	10,000	40.00
1981 No Kings Nor Dukes	10,000	40.00
1982 Snake Escapes	10,000	40.00
(Single issue)		
1980 Norman Rockwell Back to School	10,000	24.00
Rockwell Christmas		
1980 Christmas Trio	Year	75.00
1981 Santa's Good Boys	Year	75.00
1982 Faces of Christmas	Year	75.00
Rockwell Boy Scout Annual		
1981 Can't Wait	10,000	30.00
1982 A Guiding Hand	10,000	30.00
1983 Tomorrow's Leader	10,000	30.00
Magic People		
1982 Music for a Queen	9,500	65.00
1982 Fantasy Festival	10,000	65.00

OVER-THE-COUNTER ISSUES

	Edition Limit	Issue Price (US)
1983 Bubble Chariot	10,000	$ 65.00
1983 Kite Carriage	10,000	65.00
Milk Glass		
1983 Dreamboats	15,000	24.00
(Single issue)		
1984 Secret	10,000	39.50
Hackett American Collectors		
Corita Kent Annual		
1979 I Love You Very	30,000	21.95
1980 You Bring Spring	10,000	21.95
1981 Love	10,000	30.00
1982 Cheers	10,000	32.50
Endangered Species		
1980 California Sea Otters	7,500	35.00
1981 Asian Pandas	7,500	37.50
1982 Australian Koala Bears	7,500	39.50
1982 River Otters	7,500	39.50
Ocean Moods		
1980 Sunset Tide	5,000	50.00
1981 Moonlight Flight	5,000	50.00
1982 Morning Surf	5,000	50.00
1983 Afternoon Surf	5,000	50.00
Save Whales		
1980 Trust and Love	10,000	30.00
Snow Babies		
1980 Canadian Harp Seals	7,500	39.50
1981 Polar Bear Cubs	7,500	39.50
1982 Snow Leopards	7,500	42.50
Friends of Forest		
1981 Forest Alert	7,500	50.00
1982 Brookside Protection	7,500	50.00
1982 Mountain Guardian	7,500	50.00
1983 Lookouts	7,500	50.00
Horses in Action		
1981 Challenge	10,000	39.50
1982 Country Days	10,000	50.00
1983 Family Portrait	10,000	50.00
1983 All Grown Up	10,000	50.00
Parkhurst Christmas		
1981 Christmas Tear	7,500	39.50
1982 Christmas Morning	7,500	39.50
1983 Night Before Christmas	7,500	39.50
Wonderful World of Clowns		
1981 Kiss for a Clown	7,500	39.50
1981 Rainbow's End	7,500	39.50
1982 Happy Days	7,500	42.50
1982 Filling Pop's Shoes	7,500	42.50
Wonderous Years		
1981 After Rains	5,000	39.50
1982 I Got One	5,000	42.50
1982 Fascination	5,000	42.50
(Single issue)		
1981 John Lennon	90 Days	25.00
Crazy Cats		
1982 Primping Time	10,000	42.50
Daisy Cats		
1982 Daisy Kitten	10,000	42.50
1982 Daisy Cat	10,000	42.50
Days Remembered		
1982 First Birthday	19,500	29.50
1983 First Haircut	19,5000	35.00
Early Discoveries		
1982 Let's Play	10,000	42.50
Escalera Christmas		
1982 Special Delivery	19,500	32.50
1983 Especially for You	19,500	35.00
Everyone's Friends		
1982 Springtime	10,000	42.50
1982 Autumn Bandit	10,000	42.50
1983 Snowtime Bunnies	10,000	42.50
1983 Summer Bandits	10,000	42.50
Family Portraits		
1982 Mother's Joy	7,500	85.00
Fashions by Irene		
1982 Elegant Lady	15,000	45.00
Escalera Father's Day		
1982 Daddy's Rose	10,000	42.50
1983 Daddy's Wish	10,000	42.50
Impressions by Joanne Mix		
1982 Windy Day	10,000	42.50
1982 Sunny Day	10,000	42.50
1983 Summer's Day	10,000	42.50
Joanne Mix Christmas		
1982 Christmas Love	10,000	39.50
Kelly's Stable		
1982 My Champion	15,000	42.50
1983 Glory Bound	15,000	42.50
1983 Arabian Spring	15,000	42.50
1984 Summer Days	15,000	42.50

	Edition Limit	Issue Price (US)
Landfalls		
1982 San Francisco Bay	7,500	$ 39.50
1983 Newport Harbor	7,500	39.50
1983 Miami Beach	7,500	39.50
Little Orphans		
1982 Surprise Package	19,500	29.50
1983 Castaway	19,500	32.50
1984 Furry Surprise	19,500	35.00
Mother and Child		
1982 Mother's Love	10,000	42.50
1982 Tenderness	10,000	42.50
1983 Serenity	10,000	42.50
1984 Navajo Madonna	10,000	42.50
Parkhurst Mother's Day		
1982 Daisies for Mother	10,000	42.50
Ocean Stars		
1982 Sea Horses	10,000	42.50
1982 Dolphins	10,000	42.50
1983 Whales	10,000	42.50
Parkhurst Diamond		
1982 Chance Encounter	1,500	300.00
Peaceful Retreat		
1982 Refuge	19,500	29.50
1983 Solitude	19,500	32.50
1983 Tranquility	19,500	35.00
1984 Seclusion	19,500	35.00
Prairie Children		
1982 Young Pioneers	19,500	32.50
1983 Adam	19,500	35.00
Side by Side		
1982 My Hero	19,500	32.50
1983 Sippin' Soda	19,500	35.00
Special Moments		
1982 April	10,000	42.50
1982 Rachel	10,000	42.50
Sunday Best		
1982 Stacey	10,000	42.50
1982 Laurie	10,000	42.50
Waterbird Families		
1982 Marsh Venture	10,000	42.50
1982 Afternoon Swim	10,000	42.50
1983 Nesting Wood Ducks	10,000	42.50
1983 Returning Home	10,000	42.50
World of Ozz Franca		
1982 Images	10,000	42.50
1982 Lost and Found	10,000	42.50
1983 Best Friends	10,000	42.50
(Single issue)		
1982 Hog Heaven	15,000	42.50
(Single issue)		
1982 Henry Fonda	10,000	39.50
(Single issue)		
1982 Reggie Jackson	10,000	60.00
(Single issue)		
1982 John Wayne	10,000	39.50
Classic Cars		
1983 '57 Chevy	5,000	39.50
1984 '57 Thunderbird	5,000	39.50
Costume Party		
1983 Belinda	7,500	39.50
Famous Planes of Yesterday		
1983 Spirit of St. Louis	5,000	39.50
1984 Byrd Antarctic	5,000	39.50
Favorite Dreams		
1983 Daddy's Sailor	7,500	39.50
1984 Daddy's Engineer	7,500	39.50
Golfing Greats		
1983 Arnold Palmer	100 Days	45.00
1984 Gary Player	100 Days	45.00
Huggable Moments		
1983 Naptime	10,000	39.50
1983 Playtime	10,000	39.50
Joan Horton Christmas		
1983 Moonlight Sleighride	5,000	39.50
Joys of Christmas		
1983 Toy Shop	5,000	39.50
Jungle Babies		
1983 Baby Bengals	5,000	39.50
Memorable Impressions		
1983 Beachcomber	7,500	39.50
1983 Beach Girl	7,500	39.50
Puzzling Moments		
1983 Problem Solver	7,500	39.50
1983 Practice Makes Perfect	7,500	39.50
Reflections of Sea		
1983 Golden Shores	5,000	42.50
1984 Summer Sands	5,000	39.50
Sadako's Helpers		
1983 Artist's Pal	7,500	39.50
1984 Artist's Helper	7,500	39.50

	Edition Limit	Issue Price (US)
Sensitive Moments		
1983 Sharing Beauty	5,000	$ 39.50
Snow Babies		
1982 Arctic Foxes	7,500	42.50
Summer Fun		
1983 Fishing Together	7,500	39.50
1983 Swinging Together	7,500	39.50
Yesterday's Expressions		
1983 Gloria	5,000	39.50
(Single issue-Set of two)		
1983 Bjorn Borg		
1983 Martina Navratilova	15,000	39.50
(Single issue)		
1983 Frog Heaven	5,000	39.50
(Single issue)		
1983 Hopalong Cassidy	7,500	42.50
(Single issue)		
1983 Laurel and Hardy	15,000	42.50
(Single issue)		
1983 Otter Heaven	5,000	39.50
(Single issue)		
1983 Steve Garvey	10,000	60.00
Billowing Sails		
1984 Flying Cloud	7,500	60.00
Childhood Memories		
1984 Cookie Thief	7,500	29.50
Grandparents		
1984 Grandpa's Delight	10,000	27.50
Little Friends		
1984 Tiny Creatures	5,000	35.00
Moments to Cherish		
1984 Kerry	5,000	29.50
(Single issue)		
1984 Steve Carlton	4,400	45.00
(Single issue)		
1984 Bill Rogers	7,991	42.50
(Single issue)		
1984 Babe	10,000	29.50
(Single issue)		
1984 Owl Heaven	10,000	39.50
(Single issue)		
1984 Forever Yours	15,000	42.50
(Single issue)		
1984 King Remembered	10,000	50.00
(Single issue)		
1984 Nolan Ryan	8,402	42.50
(Single issue)		
1984 Tom Seaver	6,728	42.50
Big Chiefs		
1985 Chief Joseph	5,000	32.50
Joyful Memories		
1985 Chrissy	15,000	39.50
Reggie Jackson's Famous Collector Cars		
1985 Jackson '65 Corvette	10,000	45.00
Hamilton Collection		
Japanese Floral Calendar		
1981 New Year's Day	10 Days	32.50
1982 Early Spring	10 Days	32.50
1982 Spring	10 Days	32.50
1982 Girl's Day	10 Days	32.50
1982 Buddah's Birthday	10 Days	32.50
1983 Heralds of Spring	10 Days	32.50
1983 Boy's Doll Day	10 Days	32.50
1983 Summer	10 Days	32.50
1983 Autumn	10 Days	32.50
1983 Festival of Full Moon	10 Days	32.50
1983 Late Autumn	10 Days	32.50
1983 Winter	10 Days	32.50
Legends of Camelot		
1981 Secret Romance	12,500	62.50
1982 Merlin Magician	12,500	62.50
1982 Sir Lancelot	12,500	62.50
1982 King Arthur	12,500	62.50
1982 Jousting Tournament	12,500	62.50
1982 Sword and Stone	12,500	62.50
1982 Rescued	12,500	62.50
1982 Knights of Round Table	12,500	62.50
Story of Heidi		
1981 Heidi	14,750	45.00
1981 Grandfather	14,750	45.00
1981 Heidi and Peter	14,750	45.00
1981 Grandmother	14,750	45.00
1982 Kittens	14,750	45.00
1982 Mountain Cure	14,750	45.00
Story of Noah's Ark		
1981 Two by Two . . .	12,500	45.00
1982 In Divine Harmony	12,500	45.00
1982 Rainbow	12,500	45.00
1982 Ark Beckons	12,500	45.00
1982 Be Fruitful	12,500	45.00
1982 Journey's End	12,500	45.00

	Edition Limit	Issue Price (US)
Treasures of Chinese Mandarins		
1981 Bird of Paradise	2,500	$ 75.00
1982 Guardians of Heaven	2,500	75.00
1982 Tree of Immortality	2,500	75.00
1982 Dragon of Eternity	2,500	75.00
Tribute to Ballet		
1981 Nutcracker	15,000	62.50
Fairies of Fields and Flowers		
1982 Willow Fairy	NA	45.00
Lewis & Clark Expedition		
1982 In Bitteroots	NA	55.00
1982 Sacajawea at Big Water	NA	55.00
1982 Lewis Crossing	NA	55.00
1982 Buffalo Gangue	NA	55.00
1982 Salt Makers	NA	55.00
1982 Up Jefferson	NA	55.00
1982 Arrival of Sgt. Pryor	NA	55.00
1982 Visitors at Fort Clatsop	NA	55.00
Eternal Wishes of Good Fortune		
1983 Friendship	10 Days	34.95
1983 Love	10 Days	34.95
1983 Fertility	10 Days	34.95
1983 Purity and Perfection	10 Days	34.95
1983 Illustrious Offspring	10 Days	34.95
1983 Peace	10 Days	34.95
1983 Longevity	10 Days	34.95
1983 Immortality	10 Days	34.95
1983 Marital Bliss	10 Days	34.95
1983 Beauty	10 Days	34.95
1983 Fortitude	10 Days	34.95
1983 Youth	10 Days	34.95
Gardens of Orient		
1983 Flowering of Spring	10 Days	19.50
1983 Festival of May	10 Days	19.50
1983 Cherry Blossom Brocade	10 Days	19.50
1983 A Winter's Repose	10 Days	19.50
1983 Garden Sanctuary	10 Days	19.50
1983 Summer's Glory	10 Days	19.50
1983 June's Creation	10 Days	19.50
Majestic Birds of Prey		
1983 Golden Eagle	12,500	55.00
1983 Cooper's Hawk	12,500	55.00
1983 Great Horned Owl	12,500	55.00
1983 Bald Eagle	12,500	55.00
1983 Barred Owl	12,500	55.00
1983 Sparrow Hawk	12,500	55.00
1983 Peregrine Falcon	12,500	55.00
1983 Osprey	12,500	55.00
Utz Mother's Day		
1983 A Gift of Love	Year	27.50
1984 A Helping Hand	Year	27.50
1985 Mother's Angel	Year	27.50
(Single issue)		
1983 Princess Grace	NA	40.00
America at Work		
1984 School Teacher	10 Days	29.50
1984 Piano Workman	10 Days	29.50
1984 Zoo Keeper	10 Days	29.50
1984 Cleaning Women	10 Days	29.50
1984 Hatcheck Girl	10 Days	29.50
1984 Census Taker	10 Days	29.50
1984 Shop Owner	10 Days	29.50
1984 Artist	10 Days	29.50
A Child's Garden of Verses		
1984 Picture Books in Winter	10 Days	24.50
1984 Drops in Water	10 Days	24.50
1984 A Child's Question	10 Days	24.50
1984 Glass River	10 Days	24.50
1984 Busy Bee	10 Days	24.50
1984 At Seaside	10 Days	24.50
1984 Tea Party	10 Days	24.50
1984 Foreign Land	10 Days	24.50
1984 In Hayloft	10 Days	24.50
1984 Among Poppies	10 Days	24.50
1984 5:00 Tea	10 Days	24.50
1984 Love for Kittens	10 Days	24.50
Gamebirds of North America		
1985 Ring-necked Pheasant	15,000	62.50
1985 Bobwhite	15,000	62.50
1985 American Woodcock	15,000	62.50
1985 Wild Turkey	15,000	62.50
1985 California Quail	15,000	62.50
1985 Ruffed Grouse	15,000	62.50
1985 Willow Partridge	15,000	62.50
1985 Prairie Grouse	15,000	62.50
Hamilton Collection (Boehm Studios)		
Rose		
1979 Peace Rose	15,000	45.00
1979 Queen Elizabeth Rose	15,000	45.00
1979 White Masterpiece Rose	15,000	45.00

	Edition Limit	Issue Price (US)
1979 Angel Face Rose	15,000	$ 45.00
1979 Tropicana Rose	15,000	45.00
1979 Elegance Rose	15,000	45.00
1979 Royal Highness Rose	15,000	45.00
1979 Mister Lincoln Rose	15,000	45.00
Boehm Owl		
1980 Snowy Owl	15,000	45.00
1980 Boreal Owl	15,000	45.00
1980 Barn Owl	15,000	45.00
1980 Saw Whet Owl	15,000	45.00
1980 Great Horned Owl	15,000	45.00
1980 Screech Owl	15,000	45.00
1980 Short Eared Owl	15,000	45.00
1980 Barred Owl	15,000	45.00
Hummingbird		
1980 Calliope Hummingbird	15,000	62.50
1980 Broadtail Hummingbird	15,000	62.50
1980 Rufous Flame-Bearer Hummingbird	15,000	62.50
1980 Broad-Billed Hummingbird	15,000	62.50
1980 Streamer-Tail Hummingbird	15,000	62.50
1980 Blue-Throated Hummingbird	15,000	62.50
1980 Crimson-Topaz Hummingbirds	15,000	62.50
1980 Brazilian Ruby	15,000	62.50
Roses of Excellence		
1981 Love Rose	Year	62.50
1982 White Lightnin'	Year	62.50
1983 Brandy	Year	62.50
Water Bird Collection		
1981 Canadian Geese	15,000	55.00
1981 Wood Ducks	15,000	55.00
1981 Common Mallards	15,000	55.00
1981 Green-Winged Teals	15,000	55.00
1981 Ross' Geese	15,000	55.00
1981 Canvas-Backs	15,000	55.00
1981 Hooded Mergansers	15,000	55.00
1981 American Pintails	15,000	55.00
Blossoms and Berries		
1982 Winter Holiday Bouquet	15,000	62.50
1982 Thanksgiving	15,000	62.50
1982 School Days	15,000	62.50
1982 Indian Summer	15,000	62.50
1982 Mid-Summer	15,000	62.50
1982 Autumn	15,000	62.50
1982 Warm Days	15,000	62.50
1982 Summer Majesty	15,000	62.50
1982 Harvest Time	15,000	62.50
1982 Spring Images	15,000	62.50
1982 Mid-Winter	15,000	62.50
1982 Late-Summer	15,000	62.50
Life's Best Wishes		
1982 Longevity	15,000	75.00
1982 Happiness	15,000	75.00
1982 Fertility	15,000	75.00
1982 Prosperity	15,000	75.00
Miniature Roses		
1982 Toy Clown	28 Days	39.50
1982 Rise 'n Shine	28 Days	39.50
1982 Cuddles	28 Days	39.50
1982 Puppy Love	28 Days	39.50
1982 Magic Carousel	28 Days	39.50
1982 Pacesetter	28 Days	39.50
1982 Gloriglo	28 Days	39.50
1982 Beauty Secret	28 Days	39.50
Tribute to Award-Winning Roses		
1983 Irish Gold	15,000	62.50
1983 Handel	15,000	62.50
1983 Queen Elizabeth	15,000	62.50
1983 Elizabeth of Glamis	15,000	62.50
1983 Iceberg	15,000	62.50
1983 Mountbatten	15,000	62.50
1983 Silver Jubilee	15,000	62.50
1983 Peace	15,000	62.50
Hamilton Collection (Hutschenreuther)		
Roses of Redouté		
1983 China Rose	17,500	32.50
Hamilton Collection (Kaiser)		
Summer Days of Childhood		
1983 Mountain Friends	10 Days	29.50
1983 Garden Magic	10 Days	29.50
Hamilton Collection (Porcelaine Ariel)		
A Tribute to Love		
1980 Shaft of Light	17,500	45.00
1980 Jug of Wine	17,500	45.00
1981 Sultan After Sultan	17,500	45.00
1981 Bird Is on Wing	17,500	45.00

	Edition Limit	Issue Price (US)
1982 If Today Be Sweet	17,500	$ 45.00
1982 Flower Once Has Blown	17,500	45.00
Greatest Show on Earth		
1981 Clowns-Heart of Circus	10 Days	30.00
1981 Elephants	10 Days	30.00
1981 Aerialists	10 Days	30.00
1981 Great Parade	10 Days	30.00
1982 Midway	10 Days	30.00
1982 Equestrians	10 Days	30.00
1982 Lion Tamer	10 Days	30.00
1982 Grande Finale	10 Days	30.00
Hamilton Collection (Royal Devon)		
Rockwell Home of Brave		
1981 Reminiscing	18,000	35.00
1981 Hero's Welcome	18,000	35.00
1981 Back to His Old Job	18,000	35.00
1981 War Hero	18,000	35.00
1982 Willie Gillis in Church	18,000	35.00
1982 War Bond	18,000	35.00
1982 Uncle Sam Takes Wings	18,000	35.00
1982 Mother over Top	18,000	35.00
Hamilton Collection (Viletta)		
Coppelia Ballet		
1980 Franz's Fantasy Love	28 Days	25.00
1980 Creation of a Doll	28 Days	25.00
1981 Secret Is Unlocked	28 Days	25.00
1981 Swanhilda's Deception	28 Days	25.00
1981 An Uneasy Sleep	28 Days	25.00
1981 Coppelia Awakens	28 Days	25.00
1982 A Shattered Dream	28 Days	25.00
1982 Wedding	28 Days	25.00
Portraits of Childhood		
1981 Butterfly Magic	28 Days	24.95
1982 Sweet Dreams	28 Days	24.95
1983 Turtle Talk	28 Days	24.95
Waltzes of Johann Strauss		
1981 Emperor's Waltz	28 Days	25.00
1981 Blue Danube	28 Days	25.00
1981 Voices of Spring	28 Days	25.00
1981 Vienna Life	28 Days	25.00
1982 Roses of South	28 Days	25.00
1982 Wine, Women and Song	28 Days	25.00
1982 Artist's Life	28 Days	25.00
1982 Tales of Vienna Woods	28 Days	25.00
Carefree Days		
1982 Autumn Wanderer	10 Days	24.50
1982 Best Friends	10 Days	24.50
1982 Feeding Time	10 Days	24.50
1983 Bathtime Visitor	10 Days	24.50
1983 First Catch	10 Days	24.50
1983 Monkey Business	10 Days	24.50
1984 Touchdown	10 Days	24.50
1984 Nature Hunt	10 Days	24.50
Hamilton Mint		
Picasso		
1972 Le Gourmet	5,000	125.00
1972 Tragedy	5,000	125.00
1973 Lovers	5,000	125.00
Kennedy		
1974 (Gold on Pewter)	Year	40.00
1974 (Pewter)	Year	25.00
Man's Best Friend		
1978 Hobo	9,500	40.00
1978 Doctor	9,500	40.00
1979 Making Friends	9,500	40.00
1979 Gone Fishing	9,500	40.00
1980 Thief	9,500	40.00
1980 Puppy Love	9,500	40.00
Historic Providence Mint		
(Single issue)		
1979 Children's Year	3,000	95.00
Children of Seasons		
1980 Children of Spring	3,000	107.50
America Beautiful		
1981 Spacious Skies	17,500	37.50
1981 Amber Waves of Grain	17,500	37.50
1981 Purple Mountain Majesties	17,500	37.50
1981 God Shed His Grace	17,500	37.50
1981 Crown Good with Brotherhood	17,500	37.50
1981 From Sea to Shining Sea	17,500	37.50
Vanishing American Barn		
1983 Bucks County Barn	14,500	39.50
1983 Victorian Barn	14,500	39.50
1983 New England Barn	14,500	39.50
1983 Southern Tobacco Barn	14,500	39.50

	Edition Limit	Issue Price (US)
1983 Forebay Barn	14,500	$ 39.50
1983 Appalachian Barn	14,500	39.50
1983 Connected Barn	14,500	39.50
1983 Hudson River Barn	14,500	39.50
1983 Log Barn	14,500	39.50
1983 Thatched Barn	14,500	39.50
1983 Lancaster Barn	14,500	39.50
1983 Round Barn	14,500	39.50
Ralph Homan Studios (Viletta)		
Seasons of Oak		
1979 Lazy Days	5,000	55.00
1980 Come Fly with Me	5,000	55.00
Home Plates (Mingolla)		
Christmas (Enamel on Copper)		
1973 Christmas	1,000	95.00
1974 Christmas	1,000	110.00
1975 Christmas	1,000	125.00
1976 Christmas	1,000	125.00
1977 Scene from Childhood	2,000	200.00
Christmas (Porcelain)		
1974 Christmas	5,000	35.00
1975 Christmas	5,000	35.00
1976 Christmas	5,000	35.00
1977 Winter Wonderland	7,000	45.00
Four Seasons (Enamel on Copper)		
1978 Dashing Thru Snow	2,000	150.00
1979 Spring Flowers	2,000	150.00
1980 Beach Fun	2,000	150.00
1981 Balloon Breeze	2,000	150.00
Christmas in Country (Enamel on Copper)		
1979 Dear Santa	1,000	70.00
1980 Country Cousin	1,000	90.00
Hoyle Products		
Clown		
1977 Runaway	7,500	45.00
1978 It's Your Move	7,500	45.00
1979 Understudy	7,500	45.00
1980 Idol	7,500	45.00
Traveling Salesman		
1977 Traveling Salesman	7,500	35.00
1978 Country Pedlar	7,500	40.00
1979 Horse Trader	7,500	40.00
1980 Expert Salesman	7,500	45.00
Wilderness Wings		
1978 Gliding In	5,000	35.00
1979 Taking Off	5,000	40.00
1980 Joining Up	5,000	45.00
1981 Canvasbacks	5,000	47.50
Four Seasons		
1978 Gay Blades	Year	55.00
1979 Boy Meets Dog	Year	55.00
1980 Chilly Reception	Year	65.00
Rockwell Four Seasons (Bronze)		
1979 Adventurers Between Adventures	9,500	55.00
Cowboy		
1977 Sharing an Apple	5,000	35.00
1978 Split Decision	5,000	35.00
1979 Hiding Out	5,000	35.00
1980 In Trouble	5,000	35.00
Family Circus Christmas		
1980 Christmas	5,000	25.00
1981 Christmas	5,000	30.00
Mother's Day		
1980 Mother's Day	5,000	25.00
Rare Rockwells		
1980 Mrs. O'Leary's Cow	7,500	30.00
1981 Come and Get It	7,500	30.00
Hilda		
1981 Toasting Marshmallows	5,000	25.00
Nostalgia		
1981 Pepsi Cola Girl	5,000	25.00
1982 Olympia Girl	5,000	30.00
1982 Savannah Beer Girl	5,000	30.00
1983 Dr. Pepper Girl	5,000	30.00
Remember When		
1982 A Surprise for Kitty	10,000	30.00
1982 Washday	10,000	30.00
1983 Playing Grandmother	10,000	30.00
1983 Physician	10,000	30.00
Wings of Wild		
1982 Cinnamon Teal	5,000	30.00
1982 Moment of Rest	5,000	30.00
1983 Mourning Doves	5,000	30.00
Gothic Romance		
1982 Moonlight Romance	5,000	30.00
By-Gone Days		
1983 Breakfast with Teddy	12,500	35.00
1984 Flower Basket	12,500	35.00

	Edition Limit	Issue Price (US)
Nostalgia–Children		
1983 Pear's Soap Ad	12,500	$ 35.00
1984 Morton Salt Ad	12,500	35.00
Nostalgia–Magazine Covers		
1983 Ladies Home Journal	12,500	35.00
1984 Saturday Evening Post	12,500	35.00
Hudson Pewter		
Bicentennial		
1975 Spirit of '76	10,000	45.00
Mother's Day		
1979 Cherished	10,000	35.00
Songbirds of Four Seasons		
1979 Hummingbird	7,500	35.00
America's Sailing Ships		
1979 U.S.S. Constitution	5,000	35.00
A Child's Christmas		
1979 Littlest Angels	10,000	35.00
1980 Heaven's Christmas Tree	10,000	42.50
Twas Night Before Christmas		
1982 Not a Creature Was Stirring	10,000	47.50
1983 Visions of Sugar Plums	10,000	47.50
Imperial		
America Beautiful		
1969 U.S. Capitol	500	17.50
1970 Mount Rushmore	500	17.50
1971 Statue of Liberty	500	17.50
1972 Monument Valley, Arizona	500	17.50
1973 Liberty Bell	500	17.50
1974 Golden Gate	500	19.95
1975 Mt. Vernon	500	19.95
Christmas		
1970 Partridge (Carnival)	Year	12.00
1970 Partridge (Crystal)	Year	15.00
1971 Two Turtle Doves (Carnival)	Year	12.00
1971 Two Turtle Doves (Crystal)	Year	16.50
1972 Three French Hens (Carnival)	Year	12.00
1972 Three French Hens (Crystal)	Year	16.50
1973 Four Colly Birds (Carnival)	Year	12.00
1973 Four Colly Birds (Crystal)	Year	16.50
1974 Five Golden Rings (Carnival)	Year	12.00
1974 Five Golden Rings (Crystal)	Year	16.50
1975 Six Geese A-Laying (Carnival)	Year	14.00
1975 Six Geese A-Laying (Crystal)	Year	19.00
1976 Seven Swans (Carnival)	Year	16.00
1976 Seven Swans (Crystal)	Year	21.00
1977 Eight Maids A-Milking (Carnival)	Year	18.00
1977 Eight Maids A-Milking (Crystal)	Year	23.00
1978 Nine Ladies Dancing (Carnival)	Year	20.00
1978 Nine Ladies Dancing (Crystal)	Year	25.00
1979 Ten Lords A-Leaping (Carnival)	Year	22.00
1979 Ten Lords A-Leaping (Crystal)	Year	27.00
1980 Eleven Pipers Piping (Carnival)	Year	24.00
1980 Eleven Pipers Piping (Crystal)	Year	29.00
1981 Twelve Drummers Drumming (Carnival)	Year	28.00
1981 Twelve Drummers Drumming (Crystal)	Year	34.00
Coin Crystal		
1971 1964 Kennedy Half Dollar	Year	15.00
1972 Eisenhower Dollar	Year	15.00
(Single issue)		
1976 Bicentennial	Year	20.00
Incolay Studios		
Life's Interludes		
1979 Uncertain Beginning	Year	95.00
1980 Finally Friends	12,000	95.00
Four Elements		
1983 Air	9,170	25.00

OVER-THE-COUNTER ISSUES

	Edition Limit	Issue Price (US)
Enchanted Moments		
1984 Tiffany's World	7,500	$ 95.00
1985 Jennifer's World	7,500	95.00
International Museum		
Christmas Stamp Art		
1979 Gingerbread Santa	9,900	29.00
1980 Madonna and Child	9,900	37.50
1981 Botticelli's Madonna and Child	9,900	45.00
1982 Madonna of Goldfinch	9,900	45.00
Dance, Ballerina, Dance		
1982 First Slippers	14,500	47.50
1982 At Barre	14,500	47.50
1982 Recital	14,500	47.50
1982 Pirouette	14,500	47.50
1982 Swan Lake	14,500	47.50
1982 Opening Night	14,500	47.50
Letter Writers		
1982 Portrait of Michelangelo	15,000	45.00
1982 Mrs. John Douglas	15,000	45.00
1983 Don Antonio de Noriega	15,000	45.00
1983 Lovely Reader	15,000	45.00
1984 Lady Writing Letter	15,000	45.00
1984 Five Feminine Virtues	15,000	45.00
Super Heroes		
1983 Superman	NA	29.50
1983 Wonder Woman	NA	39.50
1983 Batman and Robin	NA	39.50
1984 Shazam	NA	39.50
1984 Aquaman	NA	39.50
1984 Justice League	NA	39.50
International Silver		
We Are One		
1972 Declaration of Independence	7,500	40.00
1973 Midnight Ride of Paul Revere	7,500	40.00
1973 Stand at Concord Bridge	7,500	40.00
1974 Crossing Delaware	7,500	50.00
1974 Battle of Valley Forge	7,500	50.00
1975 Surrender at Yorktown	7,500	50.00
Christmas		
1974 Tiny Tim	7,500	75.00
1975 Caught	7,500	75.00
1976 Bringing Home Tree	7,500	75.00
1977 Fezziwig's Christmas Ball	7,500	75.00
1978 Alleluia	7,500	75.00
1979 Rejoice	7,500	100.00
1980 Adoration	7,500	125.00
Presidential		
1975 Washington	7,500	75.00
1976 Jefferson	7,500	75.00
1976 Lincoln	7,500	75.00
1976 F. Roosevelt	7,500	75.00
1977 Eisenhower	7,500	75.00
1977 Kennedy	7,500	75.00
Seasons American Past		
1976 Autumn	7,500	60.00
1976 Spring	7,500	60.00
1976 Summer	7,500	60.00
1976 Winter	7,500	60.00
See also: American Archives (U.S.A.)		
Interpace		
Modigliani (Single issue)		
1972 Caryatid	10,000	60.00
Architects of Democracy (Set of four)		
1974 George Washington		
1974 John Adams		
1974 Thomas Jefferson		
1974 Alexander Hamilton	1,776	225.00
JM Company		
Competitive Sports		
1979 Downhill Racing Slalom	10,000	25.00
Oriental Birds		
1979 Window at Tiger Spring Temple	10,000	39.00
Love		
1980 Love's Serenade	5,000	50.00
Joys (Viletta)		
Precious Moments		
1979 Friend in Sky	28 Days	21.50
1980 Sand in Her Shoe	28 Days	21.50
1980 Snow Bunny	28 Days	21.50
1980 Seashells	28 Days	21.50
1981 Dawn	28 Days	21.50
1981 My Kitty	28 Days	21.50
Judaic Heritage Society		
Jewish Holidays		
1972 Chanukah (Silver)	2,000	$150.00
1972 Chanukah (Gold)	25	1900.00
1972 Pesach (Silver)	2,000	150.00
1972 Pesach (Gold)	25	1900.00
1972 Purim (Silver)	2,000	150.00
(Single issue)		
1974 Purim (Silver)	1,000	150.00
Great Jewish Women		
1976 Golda Meir	4,000	35.00
1976 Henrietta Szold	4,000	35.00
1976 Emma Lazarus	4,000	35.00
Heritage Plates		
1976 Rabbi	4,000	35.00
1976 Hasidim	4,000	35.00
1976 Shtetl	4,000	35.00
(Single issue)		
1977 Jacob and Angel	5,000	45.00
(Single issue)		
1977 Hatikvah (Copper)	5,000	55.00
(Single issue)		
1977 Hatikvah (Gold Plated)	1,000	75.00
(Single issue)		
1977 Hatikvah (Sterling Silver)	500	180.00
Jewish Holidays		
1979 Chanukah	2,500	50.00
1979 Purim	2,500	50.00
1979 Shavouth	2,500	50.00
1979 Rosh Hashanah	2,500	50.00
1979 Simchat Torah	2,500	50.00
1979 Pesach	2,500	50.00
Jerusalem Wedding		
1979 Bride of Jerusalem	6,000	65.00
1979 Hasidic Dancers	6,000	65.00
Judaic Heritage Society (Avondale)		
(Single issue)		
1980 Shalom–Peace	6,000	95.00
Judaic Heritage Society (Viletta)		
Israel's 30th Anniversary (Single issue)		
1979 L'Chayim to Israel	10,000	59.50
Israel's 30th Anniversary (Single issue)		
1979 Prophecy of Isaiah	4,000	59.50
David Kaplan Studio		
Fiddler's People		
1978 Fiddler on Roof	7,500	60.00
1979 Tevya	7,500	60.00
1980 Miracle of Love	7,500	60.00
1981 Wedding	7,500	60.00
Loveables		
1982 Little Angel	12,500	40.00
Keller & George (Reed & Barton)		
Bicentennial		
1972 Monticello (Damascene)	1,000	75.00
1972 Monticello (Silver Plate)	200	200.00
1973 Mt. Vernon (Damascene)	Year	75.00
Kensington		
Children of Week		
1980 Wednesday's Child	27,500	28.50
Kern Collectibles		
Linda's Little Loveables		
1977 Blessing	7,500	30.00
1978 Appreciation	7,500	37.50
1979 Adopted Burro	7,500	42.50
Runci Mother's Day		
1977 Darcy	5,000	50.00
1978 A Moment to Reflect	5,000	55.00
1979 Fulfillment	5,000	45.00
1980 A Renewal of Faith	5,000	45.00
Christmas of Yesterday		
1978 Christmas Call	5,000	45.00
1979 Woodcutter's Christmas	5,000	50.00
1980 Making Christmas Goodies	5,000	55.00
1981 Singing Christmas Carols	5,000	55.00
Adventures of Old West		
1981 Grizzly Ambush	7,500	65.00
1982 Train Robbers	7,500	65.00
1983 Bank Holdup	7,500	65.00
1984 Nature Strikes	7,500	65.00
My Favorite Pets		
1981 Schnauzers	7,500	$ 39.95
1982 Cocker Spaniels	7,500	39.95
1983 Pointers	7,500	42.50
Horses of Harland Young		
1982 Quarterhorses	10,000	55.00
1983 Arabians	10,000	55.00
1984 Mustangs	10,000	55.00
1985 Thoroughbreds	10,000	55.00
School Days		
1982 Apple for My Teacher	7,500	65.00
1983 Arithmetic Lesson	7,500	65.00
This Little Pig		
1982 Pig Went to Market	9,800	39.95
1983 Pig Stayed Home	9,800	42.50
1984 Pig Had Roast Beef	9,800	45.00
1985 Pig Had None	9,800	45.00
Childhood Innocence		
1983 Sarah	7,500	55.00
1984 Kelly	7,500	55.00
A Child's World		
1983 Kathie	9,800	45.00
1983 Meredith	9,800	45.00
1984 Freddie	9,800	45.00
1984 Jamie	9,800	45.00
1985 Robbie	9,800	45.00
Kitty Cats		
1983 Morrie	7,500	39.00
1984 Tattoo	7,500	39.00
1985 Topsie	7,500	39.00
North American Game Birds		
1983 Canadian Geese	7,500	60.00
1984 Mallards	7,500	60.00
1984 Pheasants	7,500	60.00
Zoological Garden		
1983 Elephants	5,000	55.00
1984 Tigers	5,000	55.00
Children of Southwest		
1984 Navaho Pixie	7,500	36.00
1984 Morning Sun	7,500	36.00
1985 Dark Eyes	7,500	36.00
Country Friends		
1984 Elizabeth	7,500	35.00
Memories of Yesterday		
1984 Patricia	7,500	35.00
Tribal Companions		
1984 My Best Friend	6,000	35.00
(Single issue)		
1984 Champ	7,500	39.50
Birds of Distinction		
1985 New Light, New Life	NA	29.50
Women of Timeless Beauty		
1985 Melinda	5,000	35.00
Kern Collectibles (Haviland & Parlon)		
Patti Canaris Songbird		
1980 Cardinals	5,000	65.00
1981 Blue Birds	5,000	70.00
1982 Orioles	5,000	70.00
1983 Goldfinches	5,000	70.00
Patti Canaris Butterfly		
1984 Monarchs	7,500	75.00
1985 Sonora Blue	7,500	80.00
Kern Collectibles (Pickard)		
Cowboy Artists (Sets of two)		
1976 Out There		
1976 Cutting Out a Stray	3,000	130.00
1977 Broken Cinch		
1977 No Place to Cross	1,000	130.00
Companions		
1977 Cubs	5,000	40.00
1978 Mighty Sioux	5,000	40.00
1979 Nature Girl	5,000	50.00
1980 Buffalo Boy	5,000	50.00
1981 Shepherds	5,000	55.00
Kern Collectibles (Rosenthal)		
John Falter Harvest Time		
1976 Gathering Pumpkins	5,000	70.00
1977 Honest Day's Work	4,000	70.00
Runci Classic		
1977 Summertime	5,000	95.00
1978 Springtime	5,000	95.00
Kern Collectibles (Royal Bayreuth)		
Christmas		
1972 Carriage in Village	4,000	15.00
1973 Snow Scene	5,000	16.50
1974 Old Mill	4,000	24.00
1975 Forest Chalet "Serenity"	4,000	27.50
1976 Christmas in Country	5,000	40.00
1977 Peace on Earth	5,000	40.00
1978 Peaceful Interlude	5,000	$ 45.00
1979 Homeward Bound	5,000	50.00
Sun Bonnet Babies (Set of seven)		
1974 Monday (Washing Day)		
1974 Tuesday (Ironing Day)		
1974 Wednesday (Mending Day)		
1974 Thursday (Scrubbing Day)		
1974 Friday (Sweeping Day)		
1974 Saturday (Baking Day)		
1974 Sunday (Fishing Day)	15,000	120.00
Antique American Art		
1976 Farmyard Tranquility	3,000	50.00
1977 Half Dome	3,000	55.00
1978 Down Memory Lane	3,000	65.00
(Single issue)		
1976 Sun Bonnet Babies Composite	15,000	75.00
L. Henry		
1976 Just Friends	5,000	50.00
1977 Interruption	4,000	55.00
Anniversary		
1980 Young Americans	5,000	125.00
Sun Bonnet Babies Playtime		
1981 Swinging	5,000	60.00
1981 Round Dance	5,000	60.00
1982 Marbles	5,000	60.00
1982 Playing Catch	5,000	60.00
Kern Collectibles (Sango)		
Living American Artist		
1976 Sweethearts (Rockwell)	10,000	30.00
1977 Apache Girl (Perillo)	5,000	35.00
1978 Natural Habitat	5,000	40.00
Great Achievements in Art		
1980 Arabian	3,000	65.00
1981 Texas Longhorns	3,000	70.00
Kilkelly		
St. Patrick's Day		
1975 Pipe and Shamrock	Year	16.50
1976 Third Look in Logan	Year	20.00
Kirk		
DeGrazia		
1972 Heavenly Blessing	200	75.00
Mother's Day		
1972 Mother and Child	3,500	75.00
1973 Mother and Child	2,500	80.00
Bicentennial		
1972 U.S.S. Constellation	825	75.00
1972 Washington	5,000	75.00
Thanksgiving		
1972 Thanksgiving Ways and Means	3,500	150.00
Christmas		
1972 Flight into Egypt	3,500	150.00
Lake Shore Prints		
Rockwell		
1973 Butter Girl	9,433	14.95
1974 Truth about Santa	15,141	19.50
1975 Home from Fields	8,500	24.50
1976 A President's Wife	2,500	70.00
Lapsys		
Crystal Christmas		
1977 Snowflake	5,000	47.50
1978 Peace on Earth	5,000	47.50
Lenox		
Boehm Birds, Young America		
1972 Bird of Peace (Mute Swan)	5,000	150.00
1973 1776	6,000	175.00
Christmas Tree		
1976 Douglas Fir	Year	50.00
1977 Scotch Pine	Year	55.00
1978 Blue Spruce	Year	65.00
1979 Balsam Fir	Year	65.00
1980 Brewer's Spruce	Year	75.00
1981 China Fir	Year	75.00
1982 Aleppo Pine	Year	80.00
Colonial Christmas Wreath		
1981 Virginia	Year	65.00
1982 Massachusetts	Year	65.00
1983 Maryland	Year	70.00
1984 Rhode Island	Year	70.00
1985 Connecticut	Year	70.00
Butterflies and Flowers		
1982 Question Mark and New England Aster	25,000	65.00
1983 Sonoran Blue and Mariposa Lily	25,000	65.00
1983 Malachite and Orchid	25,000	65.00

	Edition Limit	Issue Price (US)
1984 Ruddy Daggerwing and Lantana	25,000	$ 70.00
1984 American Lady and Virginia Rose	25,000	70.00
1985 Buckeye and Bluebells	25,000	75.00
American Wildlife		
1983 Red Foxes	9,500	65.00
1983 Ocelots	9,500	65.00
1983 Sea Lions	9,500	65.00
1983 Raccoons	9,500	65.00
1983 Dall Sheep	9,500	65.00
Nature's Nursery		
1983 Snow Leopards	15,000	65.00
1983 Koalas	15,000	65.00
1984 Llamas	15,000	70.00
1984 Bengal Tigers	15,000	70.00
1985 Emperor Penguins	15,000	75.00
1985 Polar Bears	15,000	75.00
See also: American Express (U.S.A.)		
Lincoln Mint		
Great Artists (Dali)		
1971 Unicorn Dyonisiaque (Gold)	100	1500.00
1971 Unicorn Dyonisiaque (Silver)	5,000	100.00
1972 Dyonisiaque et Pallas Athens (Gold)	300	2000.00
1972 Dyonisiaque et Pallas Athens (Gold Plate)	2,500	150.00
1972 Dyonisiaque et Pallas Athens (Silver)	7,500	125.00
Easter		
1972 Christ (Silver)	20,000	150.00
1972 Christ (Gold Plate)	10,000	200.00
1974 Christ (Pewter)	Year	45.00
Mother's Day		
1972 Collies (Silver)	3,000	125.00
Christmas		
1972 Madonna Della Seggiola (Gold Plate)	125	150.00
1972 Madonna Della Seggiola (Silver)	3,000	125.00
Dali Cross Plate		
1977 Gold Cross	5,000	225.00
1977 Silver Cross	10,000	175.00
Lincoln Mint (Gorham)		
Christmas		
1978 Santa Belongs to All Children	7,500	29.50
Litt		
Christmas		
1978 Madonna & Child	1,000	200.00
1979 O Holy Night	1,000	200.00
Annual		
1979 Apache Sunset	1,250	275.00
Lynell Studios		
Little Traveler		
1978 On His Way	4,000	45.00
1979 On Her Way	4,000	45.00
American Adventure		
1979 Whaler	7,500	50.00
1979 Trapper	7,500	50.00
1980 Forty-Niner	7,500	50.00
1981 Pioneer Woman	7,500	50.00
1981 Wagon Master	7,500	50.00
1982 Wagon Ho!	7,500	50.00
All-American Soap Box Derby		
1979 Last Minute Changes	Year	24.50
1980 At Gate	Year	24.50
1981 In Stretch	Year	29.50
Rockwell Legendary Art Christmas		
1979 Snow Queen	60 Days	29.50
1980 Surprises for All	60 Days	29.50
1981 Grandpop and Me	60 Days	29.50
1982 Santa's Secret	10,000	35.00
1983 Looking for Santa	10,000	35.00
John Wayne		
1979 Man of Golden West	Year	45.00
RCA Victor Nipper Plate		
1980 His Master's Voice	NA	24.50
Rockwell Legendary Art Annual		
1980 Artist's Daughter	Year	65.00
Rockwell Legendary Art Mother's Day		
1980 Cradle of Love	60 Days	29.50
1981 A Mother's Blessing	60 Days	29.50
1982 Memories	60 Days	29.50
1983 Dear Mother	60 Days	29.50
1984 First Mother's Day	60 Days	29.50
Rockwell Legendary Art Rare Rockwell Paintings		
1980 Poor Richard	17,500	45.00
Popeye's 50th Anniversary (Single issue)		
1980 Happy Birthday Popeye	Year	$ 22.50
Great Chiefs of Canada		
1980 Chief Joseph Brant	7,500	65.00
1981 Crowfoot	7,500	65.00
1982 Tecumseh	7,500	65.00
Betsey Bates Christmas		
1979 Olde Country Inn	7,500	38.50
1980 Village School House	7,500	38.50
1981 Village Blacksmith	7,500	38.50
1982 Christmas Village	7,500	38.50
Children's World		
1981 Official Babysitter	15,000	24.50
1981 Cowboy Capers	15,000	29.50
1982 Nurse Nancy	15,000	29.50
1982 Pet Shop	15,000	29.50
Eyes of Seasons		
1981 Winter	19,500	38.50
1981 Spring	19,500	38.50
1981 Summer	19,500	38.50
1981 Autumn	19,500	38.50
Hagel Christmas		
1981 Shhh!	17,500	29.50
1982 Kiss for Santa	10,000	35.00
How West Was Won		
1981 Pony Express	19,500	38.50
1982 Oregon Trail	19,500	38.50
1982 California Gold Rush	19,500	38.50
1982 Cattle Drive	19,500	38.50
1983 Peace Pipe	19,500	38.50
1983 Driving Golden Spike	19,500	38.50
North American Wildlife		
1981 Snuggling Cougars	7,500	65.00
Oriental Dreams		
1981 Tranquility	15,000	55.00
Rockwell's Scotty		
1981 Scotty Stowaway	17,500	45.00
1982 Scotty Strikes Bargain	17,500	35.00
(Single issue)		
1981 Reagan-Bush Inaugural	17,500	45.00
Best of Times		
1982 Candy Shop	15,000	38.50
Circus Dreams		
1982 Two for Show	19,500	24.50
Greatest Clowns of Circus		
1982 Emmett Kelly	NA	38.50
1982 Lou Jacobs	NA	38.50
1982 Felix Adler	NA	38.50
1982 Otto Griebling	NA	38.50
Hagel Mother's Day		
1982 Once Upon a Time	60 Days	29.50
Hobo Joe		
1982 Hold Onions	10,000	50.00
1982 Do Not Disturb	10,000	50.00
1983 No Camping or Fishing	10,000	50.00
1983 Traveling in Style	10,000	50.00
Little House on Prairie		
1982 Welcome to Walnut Creek	19,500	45.00
1982 Country Girls	19,500	45.00
1982 Women at Harvestime	19,500	45.00
1982 Sweethearts Tree	19,500	45.00
1983 School Marm	19,500	45.00
1983 Bell for Grove	19,500	45.00
1983 Mary's Gift	19,500	45.00
1983 Caroline's Eggs	19,500	45.00
(Single issue)		
1982 Betty Boop	15,000	24.50
(Single issue)		
1982 I Love Lucy	100 Days	45.00
(Single issue)		
1982 Norman Rockwell Tribute	5,000	55.00
(Single issue)		
1982 Thanks for Memories	100 Days	45.00
(Single issue)		
1982 Young at Heart	100 Days	45.00
Lionel Barrymore		
1983 Nantucket	7,500	45.00
(Single issue)		
1984 Wayne Gretzky	Year	39.95
Mallek Studios		
Navajo Christmas		
1971 Indian Wise Men	1,000	15.00
1972 On Reservation	2,000	17.00
1973 Hoke Denetsosie	2,000	17.00
1974 Monument Valley	2,000	18.00
1975 Coming Home for Christmas	2,000	18.00
1976 Deer with Rainbow	2,000	20.00
1977 Goat Herders	2,000	$ 20.00
1978 Hogan Christmas	2,000	20.00
1979 Navajo Madonna	3,000	25.00
1980 Children's Playmates	3,500	25.00
Chinese Lunar Calendar		
1972 Year of Rat	1,000	15.00
1973 Year of Ox	1,000	15.00
1974 Year of Rabbit	1,000	15.00
Christmas Game Birds		
1972 Gambel Quail	1,000	15.00
1973 Partridge	1,000	15.00
1974 Owl and Cactus	1,000	15.00
1975 Chinese Wood Duck	1,000	15.00
1976 Wild Turkey	1,000	15.00
1977 Mallard	1,000	15.00
1978 Canadian Geese	1,000	15.00
1979 American Woodcock	1,000	15.00
Mexican Christmas		
1972 Manger	1,000	15.00
1973 Madonna	1,000	15.00
1974 Corona	1,000	18.00
1975 Pinata	1,000	18.00
1976 Procession	1,000	20.00
1977 Wisemen	1,000	20.00
Navidad (Single issue)		
1972 Navidad en Mexico	500	15.00
(Single issue)		
1972 Amish Harvest	1,000	17.00
A.B.C.'s		
1974 A.B.C. Rabbit	1,000	15.00
1975 A.B.C. Mice	1,000	15.00
1976 A.B.C. Ducklings	1,000	15.00
1977 A.B.C. Elephant	1,000	15.00
1978 A.B.C. Owls	1,000	15.00
(Single issue)		
1976 Kewpie Doll	1,000	15.00
(Single issue)		
1982 Barnyard Serenade	5,000	25.00
(Single issue)		
1982 Beep, Beep	2,000	25.00
Marigold		
Super Stars		
1983 Mickey Mantle	10,000	60.00
1984 Joe DiMaggio	10,000	60.00
1984 Willie Mays	10,000	60.00
Master Engravers of America		
Indian Dancers		
1979 Eagle Dancer	2,500	300.00
1980 Hoop Dancer	2,500	300.00
McCalla Enterprises (Viletta)		
Making Friends		
1978 Feeding Neighbor's Pony	5,000	45.00
1979 Cowboys 'n' Indians	5,000	47.50
1980 Surprise for Christy	5,000	47.50
Love Letters		
1980 Mail Order Bride	5,000	60.00
Metal Arts		
America's First Family (Single issue)		
1977 Carters	9,500	40.00
Freedom (Single issue)		
1977 Washington at Valley Forge (Sterling)	500	225.00
Freedom (Single issue)		
1977 Washington at Valley Forge (Pewter)	1,000	95.00
Winslow Homer's Sea		
1977 Breezing Up	9,500	29.95
Rockwell Copper Christmas		
1978 Christmas Gift	Year	48.00
1979 Big Moment	Year	48.00
Metlox Potteries		
See: Vernonware (U.S.A.)		
Metropolitan Museum of Art		
Treasures of Tutankhamun		
1977 King Tut	2,500	150.00
Mingolla		
See: Home Plates (U.S.A.)		
Mistwood Designs (Fairmont)		
American Wildlife		
1981 Desperado at Waterhole	5,000	45.00
1981 Bayou Bunnies	5,000	50.00
Woodland Game Birds		
1981 After Flight	5,000	60.00
Modern Concepts		
Special Moments		
1982 David's Dilemma	12,500	$ 35.00
1983 Secrets	12,500	35.00
1983 Enough for Two	12,500	38.50
1984 Chatterbox	12,500	38.50
Magic of Sea		
1983 Future Miss	NA	25.00
1984 One, Two, Three!	NA	26.50
Signs of Love		
1983 When Hearts Touch	17,500	39.00
1984 My Very Own	17,500	39.00
Nursery Rhyme Favorites		
1984 Sugar & Spice	7,500	35.00
1985 Snips & Snails	7,500	35.00
Modern Masters		
Through Eyes of Love		
1981 Enchanted Eyes	9,500	55.00
1982 Summer Secrets	9,500	55.00
1983 Garden Gathering	9,500	55.00
Babes in Woods		
1982 Newborn Fawn	9,500	45.00
1983 First Outing	9,500	45.00
1983 Baby Bandit	9,500	50.00
1984 Moment's Rest	9,500	50.00
Floral Felines		
1982 Baron	9,500	55.00
1983 Her Majesty	9,500	55.00
1984 Duchess	9,500	55.00
1984 His Lordship	9,500	55.00
Will Moses America		
1982 September Fair	7,500	45.00
1983 Spring Recess	7,500	45.00
Litter Basket		
1983 Last of Litter	15 Days	35.00
1984 Double Delight	15 Days	35.00
1984 Tender Trio	15 Days	35.00
1985 Litter Bug	15 Days	35.00
1985 Hide and Seek	15 Days	35.00
1985 Poodle Picnic	15 Days	35.00
Little Ladies		
1983 When Mommy's Away	15 Days	29.50
1984 Before Show Begins	15 Days	29.50
(Single issue)		
1983 Twelve Days of Christmas	12 Days	45.00
Childhood Revisited		
1984 Young Virtuoso	9,500	39.50
1985 Fantasy and Fairy Tales	9,500	39.50
1985 Petit Fleur	9,500	39.50
Wings of Nobility		
1984 American Bald Eagle	7,500	49.50
1984 Peregrine Falcon	7,500	49.50
1984 Red-Shouldered Hawk	7,500	49.50
Modern Masters/GBS		
Horses of Fred Stone		
1981 Patience	9,500	55.00
1982 Arabian Mare and Foal	9,500	55.00
1982 Safe and Sound	9,500	55.00
1983 Contentment	9,500	55.00
A Child's Best Friend		
1982 Christi's Kitty	15 Days	29.50
1982 Patrick's Puppy	15 Days	29.50
Moussalli		
Birds of Four Seasons		
1978 Cardinal (Winter)	1,000	375.00
1979 Indigo Bunting (Fall)	1,000	375.00
1979 Hummingbird (Summer)	1,000	375.00
1980 Wren (Spring)	1,000	375.00
Mother's Day		
1979 Chickadee	500	450.00
Museum Editions (Ridgewood)		
Colonial Heritage		
1974 Tidewater, Virginia	9,900	40.00
1975 Pennsbury Manor	9,900	40.00
1975 Old New York	9,900	40.00
1976 Hammond-Harwood House	9,900	40.00
1976 Joseph Webb House	9,900	40.00
1977 Old Court House	9,900	40.00
1977 Mulberry Plantation	9,900	40.00
Museum Editions (Viletta)		
Christmas Annual		
1978 Expression of Faith	7,400	49.95
1979 Skating Lesson	7,400	49.95
Colonial Heritage		
1978 Moffatt-Ladd House	9,900	40.00
1978 Trent House	9,900	40.00
1979 Cupola House	9,900	40.00

OVER-THE-COUNTER ISSUES

	Edition Limit	Issue Price (US)
1979 Nicholas House	9,900	$ 40.00
1980 Derby House	9,900	40.00
1980 Davenport House	9,900	40.00
Nostalgia Collectibles		
Shirley Temple		
1982 Baby Take a Bow	25,000	75.00
1983 Curly Top	25,000	75.00
1983 Stand Up and Cheer	25,000	75.00
Shirley Temple Classics		
1983 Captain January	25,000	35.00
1984 Heidi	25,000	35.00
1984 Little Miss Marker	25,000	35.00
1984 Bright Eyes	25,000	35.00
1985 Little Colonel	25,000	35.00
1985 Rebecca of Sunnybrook Farm	25,000	35.00
(Single issue)		
1985 Elvis—Once and Forever King	25,000	40.00
(Single issue)		
1985 James Dean—America's Rebel	25,000	45.00
Ohio Arts		
Norman Rockwell		
1979 Looking Out to Sea	20,000	19.50
OK Collectibles		
Fantasy Farm		
1984 Lowena	3,000	39.95
Meadow		
1984 Chester	5,000	55.00
Pacific Art		
Just Like Daddy's Hats		
1983 Jessica	10,000	29.00
(Single issue)		
1983 Guardian Angel	7,500	29.50
Paramount Classics (Pickard)		
(Single issue)		
1977 Coronation Plate	5,000	95.00
(Single issue)		
1977 Queen Victoria	5,000	95.00
(Single issue)		
1977 King George III	5,000	95.00
Pemberton & Oakes (Viletta)		
Moments Alone		
1980 Dreamer	15 Days	28.80
1981 Reverie	15 Days	28.80
1982 Gentle Thoughts	15 Days	28.80
1983 Wheat Field	4,800	28.80
Nutcracker II		
1981 Nutcracker Grand Finale	28 Days	24.40
1982 Arabian Dancers	28 Days	24.40
1983 Dewdrop Fairy	28 Days	24.40
1984 Clara's Delight	28 Days	24.40
Swan Lake		
1983 Swan Queen	15,000	35.00
Pickard		
Presidential		
1971 Truman	3,000	35.00
1973 Lincoln	5,000	35.00
(Single issue)		
1982 Great Seal of United States	10,000	95.00
Children of Christmas Past		
1983 Sledding on Christmas Day	7,500	60.00
Children of Mary Cassatt		
1983 Simone in a White Bonnet	7,500	60.00
1983 Children Playing on Beach	7,500	60.00
1984 Child in a Straw Hat	7,500	60.00
Let's Pretend		
1984 Cleopatra	5,000	80.00
1984 Mark Antony	5,000	80.00
1985 Robin Hood	5,000	80.00
1985 Maid Marian	5,000	80.00
(Single Issue)		
1984 Statue of Liberty	10,000	150.00
Wings of Freedom		
1985 Courtship Flight	2,500	250.00
See also:		
Kern Collectibles (U.S.A.)		
Paramount Classics (U.S.A.)		
Porcelain Limited		
Children of Seasons		
1982 Spring Joy	9,800	49.95
1982 Summer Love	9,800	49.95

	Edition Limit	Issue Price (US)
1982 Fall's Adventure	9,800	$ 49.95
1982 Winter's Dreamer	9,800	49.95
Ram		
Boston 500		
1973 Easter	500	30.00
1973 Mother's Day	500	30.00
1973 Father's Day	500	30.00
1973 Christmas	500	30.00
Great Bird Heroes		
1973 Cher Ami	1,000	7.95
1973 Mocker	1,000	7.95
Reco International		
Americana (Single issue)		
1972 Gaspee	1,000	130.00
Four Seasons (Set of four)		
1973 Fall		
1973 Spring		
1973 Summer		
1973 Winter	2,500	200.00
Western (Single issue)		
1974 Mountain Man	1,000	165.00
Christmas (Single issue)		
1977 Old Mill in Valley	5,000	28.00
Games Children Play		
1979 Me First	10,000	45.00
1980 Forever Bubbles	10,000	45.00
1981 Skating Pals	10,000	45.00
1982 Join Me	10,000	45.00
Grandparents		
1981 Grandma's Cookie Jar	Year	37.50
1981 Grandpa and Doll House	Year	37.50
Arabelle and Friends		
1982 Ice Delight	15,000	35.00
1983 First Love	15,000	35.00
Little Professionals		
1982 All Is Well	10,000	39.50
1983 T.L.C.	10,000	39.50
1984 Lost and Found	10,000	39.50
1985 Reading, Writing and ...	10,000	39.50
A Childhood Almanac		
1984 School Days	14 Days	29.50
1984 Fireside Dreams	14 Days	29.50
1984 Be Mine	14 Days	29.50
1985 Easter Morning	14 Days	29.50
1985 For Mom	14 Days	29.50
1985 Summer Secrets	14 Days	29.50
1985 Daydreaming	14 Days	29.50
Mother's Day		
1985 Once Upon a Time	Year	29.50
Sophisticated Ladies		
1985 Felicia	NA	29.50
Springtime of Life		
1985 Teddy's Bathtime	14 Days	29.50
Reed & Barton		
Audubon		
1970 Pine Siskin	5,000	60.00
1971 Red-Shouldered Hawk	5,000	60.00
1972 Stilt Sandpiper	5,000	60.00
1973 Red Cardinal	5,000	60.00
1974 Boreal Chickadee	5,000	60.00
1975 Yellow-Breasted Chat	5,000	65.00
1976 Bay-Breasted Warbler	5,000	65.00
1977 Purple Finch	5,000	65.00
(Single issue)		
1970 Zodiac	1,500	75.00
California Missions		
1971 San Diego	1,500	75.00
1972 Carmel	1,500	75.00
1973 Santa Barbara	1,500	60.00
1974 Santa Clara	1,500	60.00
1976 San Gabriel	1,500	65.00
Annual		
1972 Free Trapper	2,500	65.00
1973 Outpost	2,500	65.00
1974 Toll Collector	2,500	65.00
1975 Indians Discovering Lewis & Clark	2,500	65.00
Currier & Ives		
1972 Village Blacksmith	1,500	85.00
1972 Western Migration	1,500	85.00
1973 Oaken Bucket	1,500	85.00
1973 Winter in Country	1,500	85.00
1974 Preparing for Market	1,500	85.00
Kentucky Derby		
1972 Nearing Finish	1,000	75.00
1973 Riva Ridge	1,500	75.00
1974 100th Running	1,500	75.00
(Single issue)		
1972 Delta Queen	2,500	75.00

	Edition Limit	Issue Price (US)
(Single issue)		
1972 Road Runner	1,500	$ 65.00
Founding Father		
1973 Ben Franklin	2,500	65.00
1974 George Washington	2,500	65.00
1975 Thomas Jefferson	2,500	65.00
1976 Patrick Henry	2,500	65.00
1976 John Hancock	2,500	65.00
1976 John Adams	2,500	65.00
(Single issue)		
1975 Chicago Fire	Year	60.00
(Single issue)		
1975 Mississippi Queen	2,500	75.00
See also:		
Collector Creations (U.S.A.)		
Keller & George (U.S.A.)		
Ridgewood		
Bicentennial		
1974 First in War	12,500	40.00
Tom Sawyer (Set of four)		
1974 Trying a Pipe		
1974 Lost in Cave		
1974 Painting Fence		
1974 Taking Medicine	3,000	39.95
Wild West (Set of four)		
1975 Discovery of Last Chance Gulch		
1975 Doubtful Visitor		
1975 Bad One		
1975 Cattleman	15,000	65.00
Leyendecker Christmas		
1975 Christmas Morning	10,000	24.50
1976 Christmas Surprise	10,000	24.50
Leyendecker Mother's Day		
1976 Grandma's Apple Pie	5,000	24.50
1977 Tenderness	10,000	35.00
Little Women		
1976 Sweet Long Ago	5,000	45.00
1976 Song of Spring	5,000	45.00
1977 Joy in Morning	5,000	45.00
See also: Museum Editions (U.S.A.)		
River Shore		
Baby Animals		
1979 Akiku	20,000	65.00
1980 Roosevelt	20,000	65.00
1981 Clover	20,000	65.00
1982 Zuela	20,000	65.00
Della Robbia Annual		
1979 Adoration	5,000	550.00
1980 Virgin and Child	5,000	450.00
Remington Bronze		
1977 Bronco Buster	15,000	55.00
1978 Coming Thru Rye	15,000	60.00
1979 Cheyenne	15,000	60.00
1980 Mountain Man	15,000	60.00
(Single issue)		
1979 Spring Flowers	17,000	75.00
(Single issue)		
1980 Looking Out to Sea	17,000	75.00
Grant Wood		
1981 American Gothic	17,000	80.00
Rockwell's Four Freedoms		
1981 Freedom of Speech	17,000	65.00
Vignette		
1981 Broken Window	22,500	19.50
1982 Sunday Best	22,500	19.50
(Single issue)		
1981 Grandpa's Guardian	17,000	80.00
Christmas After Christmas		
1982 Kay's Doll	9,500	75.00
Rockwell Collectors Club		
Christmas		
1978 Christmas Story	15,000	24.50
Rockwell Museum		
American Family		
1978 Baby's First Step	9,900	28.50
1978 Happy Birthday Dear Mother	9,900	28.50
1978 Sweet Sixteen	9,900	28.50
1978 First Haircut	9,900	28.50
1979 First Prom	9,900	28.50
1979 Student	9,900	28.50
1979 Wrapping Christmas Presents	9,900	28.50
1979 Birthday Party	9,900	28.50
1979 Little Mother	9,900	28.50
1980 Washing Our Dog	9,900	28.50
1980 Mother's Little Helper	9,900	28.50
1980 Bride & Groom	9,900	28.50

	Edition Limit	Issue Price (US)
Christmas		
1979 Day After Christmas	25,000	$ 75.00
1980 Checking His List	Year	75.00
1981 Ringing in Good Cheer	Year	75.00
1982 Waiting for Santa	Year	75.00
1983 High Hopes	Year	75.00
1984 Space Age Santa	Year	55.00
(Single issue)		
1979 Norman Rockwell Remembered	Year	45.00
American Family II		
1980 New Arrival	22,500	35.00
1980 Sweet Dreams	22,500	35.00
1980 Little Shaver	22,500	35.00
1980 We Missed You Daddy	22,500	35.00
1980 Home Run Slugger	22,500	35.00
1980 Giving Thanks	22,500	35.00
1980 Space Pioneers	22,500	35.00
1980 Little Salesman	22,500	35.00
1980 Almost Grown Up	22,500	35.00
1980 Courageous Hero	22,500	35.00
1980 At Circus	22,500	35.00
1980 Good Food, Good Friends	22,500	35.00
Classic		
1981 Puppy Love	60 Days	24.50
1981 While Audience Waits	60 Days	24.50
1981 Off to School	60 Days	24.50
1982 Country Doctor	60 Days	24.50
1982 Spring Fever	60 Days	24.50
1982 Dollhouse for Sis	60 Days	24.50
Mother's Day		
1982 A Tender Moment	5,000	70.00
World of Children		
1982 Downhill Racer	15,000	45.00
1982 Vacation's Over	15,000	45.00
1982 Little Patient	15,000	45.00
1982 Bicycle Boys	15,000	45.00
(Single issue)		
1983 A Tribute to J.F.K.	NA	39.50
(Single issue)		
1983 With This Ring	NA	45.00
A Touch of Rockwell		
1984 Songs of Praise	NA	14.95
1984 Bedtime Prayers	NA	14.95
1984 First Day of School	NA	14.95
1984 Surprise Treat	NA	14.95
1984 Runaway	NA	14.95
Roman		
Child's World		
1982 Baby Blossoms	15,000	24.95
1982 I Wish, I Wish	15,000	24.95
1982 Trees So Tall	15,000	24.95
1982 Daisy Dreamer	15,000	24.95
1983 Caught it Myself	15,000	24.95
1983 Winter Wrappings	15,000	24.95
1983 So Cuddley	15,000	24.95
1983 Can I Keep Him?	15,000	24.95
Ice Capades Clown		
1983 Presenting Freddie Trenkler	30 Days	24.50
Petty Girls of Ice Capades		
1983 Ice Princess	30 Days	24.50
Cats		
1984 Grizabella	30 Days	29.50
1984 Mr. Mistoffelees	30 Days	29.50
1984 Rum Tum Tugger	30 Days	29.50
1985 Growltiger	30 Days	29.50
1985 Skimbleshanks	30 Days	29.50
1985 Mungojerrie and Rumpelteazer	30 Days	29.50
Magic of Childhood		
1984 Special Friends	10 Days	24.50
(Single issue)		
1984 Carpenter	NA	100.00
Royal Cornwall		
Bethlehem Christmas		
1977 First Christmas Eve	10,000	29.95
1978 Glad Tidings	10,000	34.50
1979 Gift Bearers	10,000	34.50
1980 Great Joy	10,000	39.95
Creation		
1977 In Beginning	19,500	45.00
1977 In His Image	19,500	45.00
1977 Adam's Rib	19,500	45.00
1977 Banished from Eden	19,500	45.00
1977 Noah and Ark	19,500	45.00
1977 Tower of Babel	19,500	45.00
1978 Sodom & Gomorrah	19,500	45.00
1978 Jacob's Wedding	19,500	45.00
1978 Rebekah at Well	19,500	45.00
1978 Jacob's Ladder	19,500	45.00

	Edition Limit	Issue Price (US)
1978 Joseph's Coat of Many Colors	19,500	$ 45.00
1978 Joseph Interprets Pharaoh's Dream	19,500	45.00
Classic Christmas		
1978 Child of Peace	17,500	55.00
1978 Silent Night	17,500	55.00
1978 Most Precious Gift	17,500	55.00
1978 We Three Kings	17,500	55.00
Four Seasons		
1978 Warmth	17,500	60.00
1978 Voices of Spring	17,500	60.00
1978 Fledgling	17,500	60.00
1978 We Survive	17,500	60.00
Golden Age of Cinema		
1978 King & His Ladies	22,500	45.00
1978 Fred & Ginger	22,500	45.00
1978 Judy & Mickey	22,500	45.00
1979 Philadelphia Story	22,500	45.00
1979 Thin Man	22,500	45.00
1979 Gigi	22,500	45.00
Mother's Day		
1978 God Bless Mommy	10,000	35.00
Alice in Wonderland		
1979 Alice and White Rabbit	27,500	45.00
1979 Advice from a Caterpillar	27,500	45.00
1979 Cheshire Cat's Grin	27,500	45.00
1979 Mad Hatter's Tea Party		
1979 Queen's Croquet Match	27,500	45.00
1979 Who Stole Tarts?	27,500	45.00
Kitten's World		
1979 Just Curious	27,500	45.00
1979 Hello, World	27,500	45.00
1979 Are You a Flower?	27,500	45.00
1979 Talk to Me	27,500	45.00
1979 My Favorite Toy	27,500	45.00
1979 Purr-Fect Pleasure	27,500	45.00
Promised Land		
1979 Pharaoh's Daughter Finds Moses	24,500	45.00
1979 Burning Bush	24,500	45.00
1979 Let My People Go	24,500	45.00
1979 Parting of Red Sea	24,500	45.00
1979 Miriam's Song of Thanksgiving	24,500	45.00
1979 Manna from Heaven	24,500	45.00
1979 Water from Rock	24,500	45.00
1979 Battle of Amalek	24,500	45.00
1979 Ten Commandments	24,500	45.00
1979 Golden Calf	24,500	45.00
1979 Moses Smashes Tablets	24,500	45.00
1979 Glorious Tabernacle	24,500	45.00
Treasures of Childhood		
1979 My Cuddlies Collection	19,500	45.00
1979 My Coin Collection	19,500	45.00
1979 My Shell Collection	19,500	45.00
1979 My Stamp Collection	19,500	45.00
1979 My Doll Collection	19,500	45.00
1979 My Rock Collection	19,500	45.00
Beauty of Bouguereau		
1980 Lucie	19,500	35.00
1980 Madelaine	19,500	35.00
1980 Frere et Soeur	19,500	35.00
1980 Solange et Enfant	19,500	35.00
1980 Colette	19,500	35.00
1980 Jean et Jeanette	19,500	35.00
Four Faces of Love		
1980 Romeo & Juliet	17,500	55.00
1980 Young Galahad	17,500	55.00
1980 At Locksley Hall	17,500	55.00
1980 St. Agnes Eve	17,500	55.00
Dorothy's Day		
1980 Brand New Day	15,000	55.00
1980 All by Myself	15,000	55.00
1981 Off to School	15,000	55.00
1981 Best Friends	15,000	55.00
1981 Helping Mommy	15,000	55.00
1981 Bless Me Too	15,000	55.00
Legendary Ships of Seas		
1980 Flying Dutchman	19,500	49.50
1981 Refanu	19,500	49.50
1981 Gaspé Bay	19,500	49.50
1981 Rescue	19,500	49.50
1980 Copenhagen	19,500	49.50
1982 Palatine	19,500	49.50
1982 Pride	19,500	49.50
1982 Foochow Sea Junk	19,500	49.50
1982 Roth Ramhach	19,500	49.50
1982 Frigorifique	19,500	49.50

	Edition Limit	Issue Price (US)
Little People		
1980 Off to Picnic	19,500	$ 34.50
1981 Decorating Tree	19,500	34.50
1981 Cruising Down River	19,500	34.50
1981 Sweetest Harvest	19,500	34.50
1981 Happy Chorus	19,500	34.50
1981 Painting Leaves	19,500	34.50
Memories of America		
1980 Bringing in Maple Sugar	5,000	120.00
1980 Old Automobile	5,000	120.00
1981 Halloween	5,000	120.00
1981 Rainbow	5,000	120.00
Windows on World		
1980 Golden Gate of San Francisco	19,500	45.00
1981 Snow Village/Madulain	19,500	45.00
1981 Rainy Day in London	19,500	45.00
1981 Water Festival/Venice	19,500	45.00
1981 Harvesting in Ukraine	19,500	45.00
1981 Serengeti Plain	19,500	45.00
1982 Springtime in Paris	19,500	45.00
1982 Lunch in Michelstadt	19,500	45.00
1982 Flamenca of Madrid	19,500	45.00
1982 Tokyo at Cherry Time	19,500	45.00
1982 Palace of Winds, Jaipur	19,500	45.00
1982 Carnival Time in Rio	19,500	45.00
Exotic Birds of Tropique		
1981 Scarlet Macaws	19,500	49.50
1981 Toco Toucan	19,500	49.50
1981 Rosy Flamingos	19,500	49.50
1982 Greater Cockatoo	19,500	49.50
1982 Ultramarine King	19,500	49.50
1982 Red Fan Parrot	19,500	49.50
1982 Bird of Paradise	19,500	49.50
1982 Mariqua Sunbird	19,500	49.50
1982 Andean Cock-of-Rock	19,500	49.50
1983 Rufous Hornbill	19,500	49.50
1983 Seven-colored Tanager	19,500	49.50
1983 Ivory-billed Aracari	19,500	49.50
Love's Precious Moments		
1981 Love's Sweet Vow	17,500	55.00
1981 Love's Sweet Verse	17,500	55.00
1981 Love's Sweet Offering	17,500	55.00
1981 Love's Sweet Embrace	17,500	55.00
1981 Love's Sweet Melody	17,500	55.00
1981 Love's Sweet Kiss	17,500	55.00
Most Precious Gifts of Shen-Lung		
1981 Fire	19,500	49.50
1981 Water	19,500	49.50
1981 Sun	19,500	49.50
1982 Moon	19,500	49.50
1982 Earth	19,500	49.50
1982 Sky	19,500	49.50
Puppy's World		
1981 1st Birthday	19,500	49.50
1981 Beware of Dog	19,500	49.50
1981 Top Dog	19,500	49.50
1981 Need a Friend?	19,500	49.50
1981 Double Trouble	19,500	49.50
1981 Just Clowning	19,500	49.50
1981 Guest for Dinner	19,500	49.50
1981 Gift Wrapped	19,500	49.50
Courageous Few		
1982 Fall of Jericho	24,500	59.50
1982 Gideon's Three Hundred	24,500	59.50
1982 Strength of Samson	24,500	59.50
1982 Ruth	24,500	59.50
1982 David and Goliath	24,500	59.50
1982 Solomon's Wisdom	24,500	59.50
1983 Building of Temple	24,500	59.50
1983 Elijah	24,500	59.50
1983 Job	24,500	59.50
1983 A Psalm of David	24,500	59.50
1983 Daniel and Lions	24,500	59.50
1983 Jonah and Whale	24,500	59.50
Impressions of Yesteryear		
1982 Moon Mist	19,500	59.50
1982 Fall Flowers	19,500	59.50
1982 Wishing Well	19,500	59.50
1982 Letter	19,500	59.50
1982 Sledding	19,500	59.50
1982 Swans	19,500	59.50
1983 Winter Park	19,500	59.50
1983 Seashore	19,500	59.50
1983 Red Tree	19,500	59.50
1983 Sailboat	19,500	59.50
1983 Red Balloon	19,500	59.50
1983 Snowman	19,500	59.50

	Edition Limit	Issue Price (US)
Legend of Peacock Maidens		
1982 Dance of Peacock Maiden	19,500	$ 69.50
1982 Promise of Love	19,500	69.50
1982 Betrayal	19,500	69.50
1982 Prince and Python	19,500	69.50
Noble Flower Maidens		
1982 Iris Maiden	19,500	65.00
1982 Plum Blossom Maiden	19,500	65.00
1982 Quince Maiden	19,500	65.00
1982 Cherry Blossom Maiden	19,500	65.00
1982 Crysanthemum Maiden	19,500	65.00
1982 August Lily Maiden	19,500	65.00
2000 Years of Sailing Ships		
1982 USS Constitution	NA	39.50
1982 Santa Maria	NA	39.50
1983 Mayflower	NA	39.50
1983 Drakar	NA	39.50
1983 Cutty Sark Thermopylae	NA	39.50
1983 HMS Royal Sovereign	NA	39.50
1983 Vasa	NA	39.50
1983 Bounty	NA	39.50
1983 HMS Victory	NA	39.50
1983 Royal Barge	NA	39.50
1984 America	NA	39.50
1984 Golden Hind	NA	39.50
America's Golden Years		
1983 County Fair	19,000	49.50
1983 Sunday Picnic	19,500	49.50
1983 Barnstorming	19,500	49.50
1983 Amusement Park	19,500	49.50
1983 Fourth of July	19,500	49.50
1983 County Fair	19,500	49.50
1983 Big Top	19,500	49.50
1983 Old Boardwalk	19,500	49.50
1983 On Bay	19,500	49.50
1983 Harvest Dance	19,500	49.50
1983 Whistle Stop	19,500	49.50
1983 Halloween	19,500	49.50
1983 Christmas Eve	19,500	49.50
Memories of Western Prairies		
1983 Picking Daisies	Year	49.50
1984 Feeding Colt	Year	49.50
Joyful World of Children		
1984 China Doll	NA	29.50
Royal Devon		
See: Hamilton Collection (U.S.A.)		
Royal Oaks Limited		
Love's Labor		
1982 Intruder	15,000	50.00
1982 It's My Turn!	15,000	50.00
1983 Look! I Can Fly!	15,000	50.00
1983 Just Like Your Own!	15,000	50.00
Royal Orleans		
Pink Panther Christmas		
1982 Sleigh Ride	13,000	25.00
1983 Happy Landings	13,000	18.50
1984 Down Chimney	13,000	18.50
(Single issue)		
1982 M*A*S*H	Year	25.00
In Trompe L'Oeil		
1984 Up to Mischief	10,000	25.00
Yorkshire Brontës		
1984 Wuthering Heights	30 Days	35.00
1985 Jane Eyre	30 Days	35.00
Coca-Cola Classic Santa		
1983 Good Boys and Girls	15,000	55.00
1983 Gift to Santa	15,000	65.00
1985 Santa, Pause Here	15,000	65.00
Marilyn—An American Classic		
1983 Seven Year Itch	20,000	35.00
1984 Gentlemen Prefer Blondes	20,000	35.00
1985 Niagara	20,000	35.00
Elvis in Concert		
1984 Aloha in Hawaii	20,000	35.00
1985 Las Vegas	20,000	35.00
(Single issue)		
1984 Buddy Holly	Year	25.00
Famous Movies		
1985 Cat on Hot Tin Roof	20,000	35.00
(Single issue)		
1985 Dynasty	20,000	35.00
Royal Worcester		
Birth of a Nation		
1972 Boston Tea Party	10,000	45.00
1973 Ride of Paul Revere	10,000	45.00

	Edition Limit	Issue Price (US)
1974 Incident at Concord Bridge	10,000	$ 50.00
1975 Declaration of Independence	10,000	65.00
1976 Washington Crossing Delaware	10,000	65.00
Currier & Ives		
1974 Road-Winter	10,000	59.50
1975 Old Grist Mill	10,000	59.50
1976 Winter Pastime	10,000	59.50
American History		
1977 Washington's Inauguration	1,250	65.00
Annual		
1977 Home to Thanksgiving	500	59.50
Royalwood		
(Single issue)		
1977 Doctor and Doll	Year	21.50
Leyendecker		
1978 Cornflake Boy	10,000	25.00
1978 Cornflake Girl	10,000	25.00
John A. Ruthven		
Moments of Nature		
1977 Screech Owls	5,000	37.50
1979 Chickadees	5,000	39.50
1980 California Quail	5,000	39.50
Sebastian		
America's Favorite Scenes		
1978 Motif #1	10,000	75.00
1979 Grand Canyon	10,000	75.00
Seeley's Doll Plates		
Antique French Dolls		
1979 Bru	5,000	39.00
1979 E.J.	5,000	39.00
1979 A.T.	5,000	39.00
1980 Alexandre	5,000	39.00
1980 Schmitt	5,000	39.00
1980 Marque	5,000	39.00
Old German Dolls		
1981 Lucy	7,500	39.00
1981 Whistler	7,500	39.00
1982 April	7,500	39.00
1982 Elise	7,500	39.00
(Single issue)		
1981 Dear Googly	7,500	39.00
Old Baby Dolls		
1982 Hilda	9,500	43.00
1982 Goldie	9,500	43.00
1982 Lori	9,500	43.00
1982 Bye-Lo	9,500	43.00
1982 Laughing Baby	9,500	43.00
French Dolls II		
1983 Snow Angel	5,000	39.00
1983 "H's" Bébé Halo	5,000	39.00
1983 Bru's Faith	5,000	39.00
1984 Steiner's Easter	5,000	39.00
1984 Marque's Alyce	5,000	39.00
1984 Jumeau's Gaynell	5,000	39.00
Seven Seas		
Historical Event		
1969 Moon Landing, No Flag	2,000	13.50
1969 Moon Landing, with Flag	25,000	13.50
1970 Year of Crisis	4,000	15.00
1971 First Vehicular Travel	3,000	15.00
1972 Last Moon Journey	2,000	15.00
1973 Peace	3,000	15.00
Mother's Day		
1970 Girl of All Nations	5,000	15.00
1971 Sharing Confidence	1,400	15.00
1972 Scandinavian Girl	1,600	15.00
1973 All-American Girl	1,500	15.00
Christmas Carols		
1970 I Heard Bells	4,000	15.00
1971 Oh Tannenbaum	4,000	15.00
1972 Deck Halls	1,500	18.00
1973 O Holy Night	2,000	18.00
1974 Jingle Bells	1,200	25.00
1975 Winter Wonderland	1,500	25.00
1976 Twelve Days of Christmas	1,200	25.00
1977 Up on Housetop	1,500	25.00
1978 Little Town of Bethlehem	1,500	25.00
1979 Santa Claus Is Coming to Town	1,500	25.00
1980 Frosty Snowman	1,500	25.00

OVER-THE-COUNTER ISSUES

	Edition Limit	Issue Price (US)
New World		
1970 Holy Family	3,500	$ 15.00
1971 Three Wise Men	1,500	15.00
1972 Shepherds Watched	1,500	18.00
Passion Play (Single issue)		
1970 Oberammergau	2,500	18.00
Shenango		
See: Castleton China (U.S.A.)		
Sierra Productions		
My Favorite Puppy		
1984 Caught	7,500	30.00
War Parties		
1984 Sioux	5,000	30.00
Signature Collection		
Carnival		
1982 Knock 'em Down	19,500	39.95
1982 Carousel	19,500	39.95
1983 Fortune Teller	19,500	39.95
1983 Ring Bell	19,500	39.95
How Do I Love Thee . . .		
1982 Alaina	24,000	39.95
1982 Taylor	24,000	39.95
1983 Rendezvous	24,000	39.95
1983 Embrace	24,000	39.95
Legends		
1982 Paul Bunyan	10,000	45.00
1983 Rip Van Winkle	10,000	45.00
Melodies of Childhood		
1982 Twinkle, Twinkle	25,000	35.00
1983 Row Your Boat	25,000	39.95
1984 Mary Had a Lamb	19,500	35.00
Angler's Dream		
1983 Brook Trout	9,800	55.00
1983 Striped Bass	9,800	55.00
1984 Largemouth Bass	,9,800	55.00
1984 Chinook Salmon	9,800	55.00
Baker Street Duo		
1983 Sherlock Holmes	9,800	55.00
1983 Watson	9,800	55.00
Childhood Delights		
1983 Amanda	10,000	45.00
Grandma's Scrapbook		
1983 Courting	12,500	45.00
1983 Sunday Drive	12,500	45.00
Unicorn Magic		
1983 Morning Encounter	10,000	50.00
1983 Afternoon Outing	10,000	50.00
Songs of Stephen Foster		
1984 Oh! Susannah	3,500	60.00
1984 Jeanie/Light Brown Hair	3,500	60.00
Silver Creations		
Churchillian Heritage		
1972 Hour of Decision	NA	150.00
1973 Yalta Conference	NA	150.00
1973 Clydesdales	NA	150.00
Smith Glass		
Americana		
1971 Morgan Silver Dollar	5,000	10.00
Christmas		
1971 Family at Christmas	NA	10.00
1972 Flying Angel	NA	10.00
1973 St. Mary's in Mountains	NA	10.00
Famous Americans		
1971 Kennedy	2,500	10.00
1971 Lincoln	2,500	10.00
1972 Jefferson Davis	5,000	11.00
1972 Robert E. Lee	5,000	11.00
Southern Living Gallery		
Wildflowers of South		
1981 Wild Honeysuckle	19,500	49.50
1981 Flowering Dogwood	19,500	49.50
1981 Buttercup	19,500	49.50
1981 Regal Lily	19,500	49.50
1981 Queen Anne's Lace	19,500	49.50
1981 Bluebonnet	19,500	49.50
1981 Southern Magnolia	19,500	49.50
1981 Bee Balm	19,500	49.50
1981 Lady Slipper Orchid	19,500	49.50
1981 Birdsfoot Violet	19,500	49.50
1981 Frost Aster	19,500	49.50
1981 Black-Eyed Susan	19,500	49.50
Game Birds of South		
1982 Bobwhite Quail	19,500	39.95
1982 Wild Turkey	19,500	39.95
1982 Mourning Dove	19,500	39.95
1982 Mallard Duck	19,500	39.95
1982 Wood Duck	19,500	39.95
1982 Ruffed Grouse	19,500	39.95

	Edition Limit	Issue Price (US)
1982 Pintail Duck	19,500	$ 39.95
1982 Ring-necked Pheasant	19,500	39.95
1982 American Woodcock	19,500	39.95
1982 American Coot	19,500	39.95
1982 Canada Goose	19,500	39.95
1982 Green-winged Teal	19,500	39.95
Southern Forest Families		
1984 Eastern Cottontail	19,500	39.50
1984 Raccoon	19,500	39.50
1984 Whitetail Deer	19,500	39.50
1984 Oppossum	19,500	39.50
1984 Striped Skunk	19,500	39.50
1984 Bobcat	19,500	39.50
1984 Fox Squirrel	19,500	39.50
1984 Chipmunk	19,500	39.50
1984 Flying Squirrel	19,500	39.50
1984 Beaver	19,500	39.50
1984 Muskrat	19,500	39.50
Sterling America		
Christmas Customs		
1970 England	2,500	18.00
1971 Holland	2,500	18.00
1972 Norway	2,500	18.00
1973 Germany	2,500	20.00
1974 Mexico	2,500	24.00
Twelve Days of Christmas		
1970 Partridge	2,500	18.00
1971 Turtle Doves	2,500	18.00
1972 French Hens	2,500	18.00
1973 Colly Birds	2,500	18.00
1974 Five Rings	2,500	24.00
1975 Six Geese	2,500	24.00
1976 Seven Swans	2,500	24.00
1977 Eight Maids	2,500	28.00
Mother's Day		
1971 Mare & Foal	2,500	18.00
1972 Horned Owl	2,500	18.00
1973 Raccoons	2,500	20.00
1974 Deer	2,500	24.00
1975 Quail	2,500	24.00
Stieff		
Bicentennial		
1972 Declaration of Independence	10,000	50.00
1974 Betsy Ross	10,000	50.00
1975 Crossing Delaware	10,000	50.00
1976 Serapio & Bon Homme	10,000	50.00
Stratford Collection		
Famous Clowns		
1982 Emmett Looking Out	10,000	35.00
1982 Jack Thum and Child	10,000	35.00
Real Children		
1982 Michael's Miracle	24,500	45.00
1983 Susan's World	24,500	45.00
Young Wildlife		
1982 Siberian Cub at Play	15,000	35.00
1982 Curious Raccoon	15,000	35.00
Stuart International		
Childhood Secrets		
1983 Billy's Treasure	19,500	39.50
American Road		
1984 Farmer Takes a Ride	9,800	22.50
1984 Henry's First Ride	9,800	22.50
Spring Flowers		
1984 Megan	5,500	55.00
1985 Danielle	5,500	55.00
Syracuse China		
Grandma Moses (Sets of four)		
1972 Old Checkered House in Winter		
1972 Mary and Little Lamb		
1972 In Harvest Time		
1972 Sugaring Off	NA	80.00
1972 Hoosick Valley from Window		
1972 Taking in Laundry		
1972 It Snows, Oh it Snows		
1972 Joy Ride	NA	80.00
Towle Silversmiths		
Valentines		
1972 Single Heart	Year	10.00
1973 Entwined Hearts	Year	10.00
Christmas		
1972 Three Wise Men	2,500	250.00
U.S. Historical Society		
Annual Historical		
1977 Great Events	5,000	60.00
1978 Great Events	10,000	75.00

	Edition Limit	Issue Price (US)
Stained Glass Cathedral Christmas		
1978 Canterbury Cathedral	10,000	$ 87.00
1979 Flight into Egypt (St. John Divine)	10,000	97.00
1980 Madonna and Child	10,000	125.00
1981 Magi	10,000	150.00
1982 Flight into Egypt	10,000	150.00
1983 Shepherds at Bethlehem	10,000	150.00
1984 O Come Let Us Adore Him	10,000	150.00
American Christmas Carols		
1982 Deck Halls	10,000	55.00
1983 O Christmas Tree	10,000	55.00
1984 Winter Wonderland	10,000	55.00
1985 Here We Come a Caroling	10,000	65.00
Great American Sailing Ships		
1983 Old Ironsides–U.S.S. Constitution	10,000	135.00
1984 Charles W. Morgan	10,000	135.00
Stained Glass Flowers		
1983 Spring Flowers	10,000	135.00
200 Years of Flight		
1983 Man's First Flight	5,000	85.00
1983 Miracle at Kitty Hawk	5,000	85.00
1984 China Clipper	5,000	85.00
1984 Man in Space	5,000	85.00
Buffalo Bill's Wild West		
1984 Pony Express	5,000	55.00
1984 Annie Oakley	5,000	55.00
1984 Sitting Bull	5,000	55.00
1984 Buffalo Hunter	5,000	55.00
1984 Farewell Appearance	5,000	55.00
1984 Deadwood Stage	5,000	55.00
1984 Rough Riders	5,000	55.00
1984 Royal Visit	5,000	55.00
(Single issue)		
1984 Robert E. Lee	10,000	150.00
Great American Sailing Ships		
1985 Flying Cloud	10,000	150.00
Vague Shadows		
Plainsmen		
1979 Buffalo Hunt	2,500	300.00
1979 Proud One	2,500	300.00
Professionals		
1979 Big Leaguer	15,000	29.95
1980 Ballerina's Dilemma	15,000	32.50
1981 Quarterback	15,000	32.50
1982 Rodeo Joe	15,000	35.00
1983 Major Leaguer	15,000	35.00
1983 Hockey Player	15,000	35.00
Santa		
1980 Santa's Joy	Year	29.95
1981 Santa's Bundle	Year	29.95
Storybook Collection		
1980 Little Red Riding Hood	18 Days	29.95
1981 Cinderella	18 Days	29.95
1981 Hansel and Gretel	18 Days	29.95
1982 Goldilocks and Three Bears	18 Days	29.95
Arctic Friends (Set of two)		
1981 Siberian Love		
1981 Snow Pals	7,500	100.00
Four Princesses		
1981 Lily of Mohawks	7,500	50.00
1981 Pocahontas	7,500	50.00
1982 Minnehaha	7,500	50.00
1982 Sacajawea	7,500	50.00
(Single issue)		
1981 Apache Boy	5,000	95.00
Child Life		
1982 Siesta	12,500	45.00
1983 Sweet Dreams	3,500	45.00
Legends of West		
1982 Daniel Boone	10,000	65.00
1982 Davy Crockett	10,000	65.00
1983 Kit Carson	10,000	65.00
1983 Buffalo Bill	10,000	65.00
Nature's Harmony		
1982 Peaceable Kingdom	12,500	100.00
1982 Zebra	12,500	50.00
1982 Tiger	12,500	50.00
1983 Black Panther	12,500	50.00
1983 Elephant	12,500	50.00
War Ponies		
1982 Sioux War Pony	7,500	60.00
1983 Nez Perce War Pony	7,500	60.00
1983 Apache War Pony	7,500	60.00
Chieftains II		
1983 Chief Pontiac	7,500	70.00
1984 Chief Victorio	7,500	70.00

	Edition Limit	Issue Price (US)
1984 Chief Tecumseh	7,500	$ 70.00
1984 Chief Cochise	7,500	70.00
1985 Chief Black Kettle	7,500	70.00
Indian Nations		
1983 Blackfoot	7,500	35.00
1983 Cheyenne	7,500	35.00
1983 Apache	7,500	35.00
1983 Sioux	7,500	35.00
Motherhood		
1983 Madre	12,500	50.00
1984 Madonna of Plains	3,500	50.00
1985 Abuela	3,500	50.00
Perillo Masterpiece		
1983 Papoose	3,000	100.00
Thoroughbreds		
1984 Whirlaway	9,500	50.00
1984 Secretariat	9,500	50.00
1984 Seabiscuit	9,500	50.00
1984 Man O'War	9,500	50.00
Tribal Ponies		
1984 Arapaho	3,500	65.00
1984 Comanche	3,500	65.00
1984 Crow	3,500	65.00
(Single issue)		
1984 Lovers	NA	50.00
(Single issue)		
1984 Navajo Girl	3,000	95.00
Vernonware (Metlox Potteries)		
Songs of Christmas		
1971 Twelve Days	9,000	15.00
1972 Jingle Bells	9,000	17.50
1973 First Noel	9,000	20.00
1974 Upon a Midnight Clear	9,000	20.00
1975 O Holy Night	10,000	20.00
1976 Hark! Herald Angels	10,000	20.00
1977 Away in Manger	10,000	30.00
1978 White Christmas	10,000	30.00
1979 Little Drummer Boy	10,000	30.00
Viletta		
Disneyland		
1976 Betsy Ross	3,000	15.00
1976 Crossing Delaware	3,000	15.00
1976 Signing Declaration	3,000	15.00
1976 Spirit of '76	3,000	15.00
Bicentennial		
1977 Patriots	15,000	37.00
In Tribute to America's Great Artists		
1978 DeGrazia by Don Marco	5,000	65.00
Days of West		
1978 Cowboy Christmas	5,000	55.00
Alice in Wonderland		
1980 Alice and White Rabbit	28 Days	25.00
1981 Mad Hatter's Tea Party	28 Days	25.00
1981 Alice and Cheshire Cat	28 Days	25.00
1981 Alice and Croquet Match	28 Days	25.00
1982 Advice to Caterpillar	28 Days	25.00
1982 End of a Dream	28 Days	25.00
Down Home Memories		
1984 Watermelon Party	19,500	39.95
1984 Cleaning off Cemetery	19,500	39.95
1984 Waiting for Bedtime	19,500	39.95
1984 Hunting Blackberries	19,500	39.95
1984 Opossum Hunt	19,500	39.95
1984 Weighing up Cotton	19,500	39.95
1984 Hilly Town	19,500	39.95
1984 April Plowing	19,500	39.95
1984 Churning on Front Porch	19,500	39.95
1984 Summer Rain	19,500	39.95
1984 Sunning Quilts	19,500	39.95
1984 Summer Baptism	19,500	39.95

See also:
Abbey Press (U.S.A.)
American Arts Services (U.S.A.)
Carson Mint (U.S.A.)
Collector's Heirlooms (U.S.A.)
R. J. Ernst Enterprises (U.S.A.)
Ghent Collection (U.S.A.)
Hamilton Collection (U.S.A.)
Ralph Homan Studios (U.S.A.)
Joys (U.S.A.)
Judaic Heritage Society (U.S.A.)
McCalla Enterprises (U.S.A.)
Museum Editions (U.S.A.)
Pemberton & Oakes (U.S.A.)
Warwick (U.S.A.)
Westbury (U.S.A.)
Edward Weston Editions (U.S.A.)

Volair (Gorham)

Audubon American Wildlife Heritage

	Edition Limit	Issue Price (US)
1977 House Mouse	2,500	$ 90.00
1977 Royal Louisiana Heron	2,500	90.00
1977 Virginia Deer	2,500	90.00
1977 Snowy Owl	2,500	90.00

Warwick (Viletta)

Great Comedians

	Edition Limit	Issue Price (US)
1978 Little Tramp	7,500	35.00
1978 Outrageous Groucho	7,500	35.00

George Washington Mint

American Indian

	Edition Limit	Issue Price (US)
1972 Curley (Gold)	100	2000.00
1972 Curley (Proof)	100	1000.00
1972 Curley (Sterling)	7,300	150.00
1973 Two Moons (Gold)	100	2000.00
1973 Two Moons (Proof)	100	1000.00
1973 Two Moons (Sterling)	7,300	150.00

Mother's Day

	Edition Limit	Issue Price (US)
1972 Whistler's Mother (Sterling)	9,800	150.00
1972 Whistler's Mother (Proof)	100	1000.00
1972 Whistler's Mother (Gold)	100	2000.00
1974 Motherhood (Gold)	100	2000.00
1974 Motherhood (Proof)	100	1000.00
1974 Motherhood (Sterling)	2,300	175.00

Picasso

	Edition Limit	Issue Price (US)
1972 Don Quixote (Gold)	100	2000.00
1972 Don Quixote (Proof)	100	1000.00
1972 Don Quixote (Sterling)	9,800	125.00

Remington

	Edition Limit	Issue Price (US)
1972 Rattlesnake (Gold)	100	2000.00
1972 Rattlesnake (Proof)	100	1000.00
1972 Rattlesnake (Sterling)	800	250.00

Da Vinci

	Edition Limit	Issue Price (US)
1972 Last Supper	NA	125.00

N. C. Wyeth

	Edition Limit	Issue Price (US)
1972 Uncle Sam's America (Gold)	100	$2000.00
1972 Uncle Sam's America (Proof)	100	1000.00
1972 Uncle Sam's America (Sterling)	9,800	150.00
1973 Massed Flags (Gold)	100	2000.00
1973 Massed Flags (Proof)	100	1000.00
1973 Massed Flags (Sterling)	2,300	150.00

Israel Anniversary (Single issue)

	Edition Limit	Issue Price (US)
1973 Struggle	10,000	300.00

Picasso (Single issue)

	Edition Limit	Issue Price (US)
1974 Rites of Spring (Sterling)	9,800	125.00

Remington (Single issue)

	Edition Limit	Issue Price (US)
1974 Coming Through Rye (Sterling)	2,500	300.00

Wendell August Forge

Great Americans

	Edition Limit	Issue Price (US)
1971 J.F.K. (Pewter)	5,000	40.00
1971 J.F.K. (Silver)	500	200.00
1972 Lincoln (Pewter)	5,000	40.00
1972 Lincoln (Silver)	500	200.00

Great Moments

	Edition Limit	Issue Price (US)
1971 Columbus (Pewter)	5,000	40.00
1971 Columbus (Silver)	500	200.00
1972 Landing of Pilgrims (Pewter)	5,000	40.00
1972 Landing of Pilgrims (Silver)	500	200.00
1973 First Thanksgiving (Pewter)	5,000	40.00
1973 First Thanksgiving (Silver)	500	200.00
1974 Patrick Henry (Pewter)	5,000	40.00
1974 Patrick Henry (Silver)	500	200.00
1975 Paul Revere (Pewter)	5,000	45.00
1975 Paul Revere (Silver)	500	200.00
1976 Signing of Declaration (Pewter)	5,000	50.00
1976 Signing of Declaration (Silver)	500	200.00

Wings of Man

	Edition Limit	Issue Price (US)
1971 Columbus' Ships (Pewter)	5,000	$ 40.00
1971 Columbus' Ships (Silver)	500	200.00
1972 Conestoga Wagon (Pewter)	5,000	40.00
1972 Conestoga Wagon (Silver)	500	200.00

Peace (Single issue)

	Edition Limit	Issue Price (US)
1973 Facing Doves (Silver)	2,500	250.00

Christmas

	Edition Limit	Issue Price (US)
1974 Caroler (Bronze)	2,500	25.00
1974 Caroler (Pewter)	2,500	30.00
1975 Christmas in Country (Bronze)	2,500	30.00
1975 Christmas in Country (Pewter)	2,500	35.00
1976 Lamplighter (Bronze)	2,500	35.00
1976 Lamplighter (Pewter)	2,500	40.00
1977 Covered Bridge (Bronze)	2,500	40.00
1977 Covered Bridge (Pewter)	2,500	45.00

Wildlife

	Edition Limit	Issue Price (US)
1977 On Guard (Aluminum)	1,900	35.00
1977 On Guard (Bronze)	1,500	45.00
1977 On Guard (Pewter)	1,500	55.00
1977 On Guard (Silver)	100	250.00
1978 Thunderbird (Aluminum)	1,900	40.00
1978 Thunderbird (Bronze)	1,500	50.00
1978 Thunderbird (Pewter)	1,500	60.00
1978 Thunderbird (Silver)	100	250.00

Westbury (Viletta)

Tender Moments

	Edition Limit	Issue Price (US)
1978 Old Fashioned Persuasion	7,500	40.00
1979 Dandelions	7,500	45.00

Westminster Collectibles

Holidays

	Edition Limit	Issue Price (US)
1976 All Hallows Eve	5,000	$ 38.50
1977 Christmas	5,000	38.50

Westmoreland

Christmas

	Edition Limit	Issue Price (US)
1972 Holy Birth	2,500	35.00
1973 Manger Scene	3,500	35.00
1974 Gethsemane	1,500	35.00
1975 Christ Is Risen	1,500	45.00

Edward Weston Editions (Viletta)

Unicorn Fantasies

	Edition Limit	Issue Price (US)
1979 Follower of Dreams	5,000	55.00
1980 Twice Upon a Time	5,000	55.00
1981 Familiar Spirit	5,000	60.00
1982 Noble Gathering	5,000	65.00

Weddings Around World

	Edition Limit	Issue Price (US)
1979 Hawaiian Wedding	5,000	75.00
1980 Dutch Wedding	5,000	75.00

Wheaton

Presidential

	Edition Limit	Issue Price (US)
1971 Adams	9,648	5.00
1971 Eisenhower	8,856	5.00
1971 Hoover	10,152	5.00
1971 Kennedy	11,160	5.00
1971 Lincoln	9,648	5.00
1971 Madison	9,504	5.00
1971 Monroe	9,792	5.00
1971 F. D. Roosevelt	9,432	5.00
1971 Taft	9,648	5.00
1971 Van Buren	9,576	5.00
1971 Washington	10,800	5.00
1971 Wilson	8,712	5.00

Whitehall China

Raphael Soyer

	Edition Limit	Issue Price (US)
1979 Model on Bed	10,000	39.95

Wildlife Internationale

Water Fowl

	Edition Limit	Issue Price (US)
1983 Wood Ducks	5,000	65.00

INDEX OF BRADEX-LISTED
PLATE MAKERS AND SPONSORS

NOTE: "Maker" is a general term for the name under which a plate is issued and is not necessarily the actual "manufacturer."
A Maker can be a distributor, manufacturer, or occasionally a "sponsor." See GLOSSARY OF COMMONLY USED TERMS.

INDEX OF PLATE TITLES AND SERIES BY TYPE

NOTE: Plate titles listed in alphabetical order and enclosed in quotation marks:
"Aabenraa Marketplace".......... **Pg. 58**

Types of series are listed in bold face with individual makers indented and listed below:
Anniversary
Goebel (*Hummel*)......... **Pg. 115**

A

INDEX OF PLATE TITLES AND SERIES BY TYPE

INDEX OF PLATE TITLES AND SERIES BY TYPE

INDEX OF PLATE TITLES AND SERIES BY TYPE

INDEX OF PLATE TITLES AND SERIES BY TYPE

INDEX OF PLATE ARTISTS

INDEX OF PLATE ARTISTS

GLOSSARY OF COMMONLY USED TERMS

A

Aftermarket. See *Market*.

Alabaster. A dense, fine-grained form of gypsum (calcium sulfate) stone, usually white to pink and slightly translucent. Alabaster stone can be carved in fine detail for ornamental objects and hardened by intense heat. Italian alabaster is also called Florentine marble. Ivory alabaster is composed of alabaster but is non-translucent and acquires a patina with age like that of old ivory.

Allotment. A number of plates, all alike and usually at issue, allocated by a maker to a distributor or dealer. See *Lot*.

Alloy. Two or more metals combined while molten. Alloying is done to achieve hardness, toughness, or luster. See *Pewter*.

Annual. A plate issued once each year as part of a series. The term is most often used when a plate does not commemorate a specific holiday.

Annular kiln. A round oven made from brick used to fire ceramic plates.

Art Deco, Art Décoratif. A style of decoration popular in Europe and America from 1920 to 1945. The Art Deco movement sought to glorify progress and the future by using as motifs such shapes as the cylinder, circle, rectangle, and cone.

Art Nouveau. A style of decoration in Europe and America from 1890 to 1920. The Art Nouveau movement used twining floral patterns as its primary decorative motifs.

Asked Price, Ask. The offering price posted for a plate by a seller on the Exchange.

At Issue. A plate being offered for sale at the time of its manufacture and at the original price set by the maker.

B

Back Issue. See *Issue*.

Backstamp. The information on the back of a plate, usually including the maker's signature, name, or trademark (logo-type). It may also record serial number, title, artist's signature, edition limit, explanation of the plate, sponsor, production techniques, awards, or release initials. It may be hand-applied, stamped, incised (cut or pressed), or applied as a decalcomania.

Banding. A method for hand-application of precious metals, such as gold, silver, or platinum, to the edge or other parts of a glazed plate. The decorator uses a camel's hair brush to apply a liquid metal suspended in special oils. The plate is then fired to adhere the metal to the glaze.

Baroque. An elaborate style of decoration developed in Europe in the seventeenth and eighteenth centuries and noted for exaggerated gesture and line. Example: Dresden **(22-D68-0.0)**.

Bas-relief. See *Relief Sculpture*.

Bavaria (Bayern). A province in the southwest corner of Germany long known as a center for porcelain factories. The region contains large deposits of kaolin, the key porcelain component.

Bearish. Marked by declining prices, either actual or expected. A bear market is one of declining prices.

Bedroom Dealer. A trade term for a small dealer who usually operates from his home, buys discounted plates, and resells them for a small profit.

Bid Price, Bid. The amount a prospective buyer offers to pay for a plate on the Exchange.

Bisque, Biscuit. A plate that has been fired but not glazed, leaving it with a matte texture. So called because of the biscuit-like appearance. Example: Lladró **(72-L41-0.0)**.

Blue Chip. An established series by a well-known maker in which nearly every issue shows a steady sequence of price rises above issue price, usually over an extended period of time.

Body. 1. The formula or combination of substances that make up potter's clay, generally referring to stoneware and earthenware. **2.** The basic plate form to which ornamentation is applied.

Bone Ash. Calcium phosphate, a component of bone china, added to give whiteness and translucency. It is obtained by calcinating (reducing to powder by heat) animal bones, usually those of oxen.

Bone China (Bone Porcelain). A type of china developed by Josiah Spode in England in the 1790s. By replacing part of the kaolin in the china formula with bone ash, greater translucency and whiteness is obtained at lower firing temperatures. The finest bone china contains up to 50% bone ash. It is the most commonly made china in England. Example: Royal Doulton **(26-R62-0.0).**

Bradex. Common term for the *Bradford Exchange Current Quotations,* a periodic listing of the current market prices of collector's plates now listed on the Exchange. See *Listed Plate, Exchange.*

Broker. A representative of the Bradford Exchange Trading Floor who enters bids and asks of all traders and confirms all transactions.

Bullish. Marked by rising prices, either actual or expected, and optimistic atmosphere. A bull market is one of rising prices.

Buy Order. An offer by an individual or dealer to purchase one or more plates on the secondary market. See *Bid Price, Exchange.*

C

Cameo Effect. Ornamentations in relief on a background of contrasting color to resemble a cameo. Examples: Wedgwood Jasper ware **(26-W90-0.0)** and Incolay Studios **(84-I31-0.0).**

Carnelian. A hard translucent quartz that has a reddish color.

Celsius, Centigrade. The thermometric scale in which 0° represents the freezing point of water and 100° the boiling point. Celsius temperature is denoted by "C" after the number.

Ceramic. A general term applying to all of the various plates made from clay and hardened by firing.

Certificate. An attestation of authenticity which may accompany each plate in an edition. A certificate authenticates a plate as being part of an issue and usually confirms the plate's individual number within the edition.

China, Chinaware. A hard, vitreous ceramic whose main components are kaolin and china stone fired at high temperature. Originally the term was used for those ceramics which only came from China. Later it was applied to all "hard" and "soft" porcelain. China is often used as a generic term which includes porcelain, but is properly distinguished from it by a high bisque firing temperature and a lower glaze firing temperature. The main firing (bisque) of china is approximately 7% lower than the main firing (glaze) of porcelain. In china production, the glaze is applied after the main firing and fixed with a second lower-temperature firing. A typical china formula is 40% kaolin, 10% ball clay, and varying proportions of china stone, feldspar, and flint. See *Porcelain.*

China Clay. See *Kaolin.*

China Stone, Petuntse. A feldspathic material in china formulas. China stone acts as a flux which helps dissolve and fuse the other components into a vitreous mass.

Christmas Plates, Christmas Series. Annual plates issued to commemorate Christmas, usually as part of a series. Plate names for Christmas include Noël (French), Weihnachten (German), Jul (Danish), Navidad (Spanish and Portuguese), and Natale (Italian). The oldest Christmas series is that of Bing & Grøndahl, produced continuously since 1895 **(14-B36-1.0).**

Clay. Any of various plastic, viscous earths used to make plates. It is formed by the decomposition, due to weathering, of igneous rocks such as granite, feldspar, and pegmatite.

Close. Last traded price on the Exchange.

Closed-End Series. A series of plates with a predetermined number of issues. Example: D'Arceau-Limoges *Douze Sites Parisiens de Louis Dali (Twelve Parisian Places)* **(18-D15-6.0).**

Cobalt Blue. Cobalt oxide in the form of a dark black powder which, when fired, turns a deep blue. It was the first known and is still the most commonly used ceramic underglaze color because of its ability to withstand high firing temperatures. It can produce a variety of shades. Examples: Kaiser cobalt blue **(22-K4-0.0),** Bing & Grøndahl Copenhagen blue **(14-B36-0.0),** Royal Copenhagen Danish Blue **(14-R59-0.0),** and Rörstrand Scandia blue **(76-R54-0.0).**

Collector's Plate. A decorative plate produced in a limited edition for the purpose of being collected. Although the earliest plates were not produced with this objective, they have since acquired the name by virtue of being collected and are now produced for this purpose.

Commemorative Plate. A plate produced in remembrance of an event. Example: Wedgwood *Bicentennial of American Independence.* **(26-W90-3.0).**

Coterie Plate. A collector's plate with a limited following which is traded too infrequently to be listed on the Exchange.

Crystal. See *Lead Crystal.*

Cut Glass. Glass decorated by the cutting of grooves and facets, usually done with a copper engraver's wheel.

D

Damascene. An electroplating effect, created and patented by Reed & Barton **(84-R18-0.0),** of etching and then depositing layers of gold, copper, and silver on bronze. Originally the term referred to the art, developed in Damascus, of ornamenting iron or steel with inlaid precious metals.

Dealer. A marketer of plates who buys primarily from makers or distributors and sells primarily to the public.

Dealer-Broker. A dealer who acts as an agent of the Bradford Exchange to transact secondary market purchases and sales for his customers via the Instaquote Trading System. See *Broker, Instaquote Trading System, Market.*

Decalcomania. The printed reproduction of original artwork which is produced by individual color separations, either in offset lithography, silk-screen printing, or a combination of both.

Delftware. Earthenware covered with an opaque white glaze made of stannic oxide, and oxide of tin. Originally developed in Delft, Holland, in the sixteenth century, Delftware has the appearance of being covered with a thick white paint. Similar ware is the majolica of Italy and faience of France and Germany. See *Faience, Majolica, Tin Glaze.*

GLOSSARY OF COMMONLY USED TERMS

Dilute Colors. Solutions of metallic salts which are absorbed by the bisque body of a plate when it is glazed and fired, producing soft, impressionistic tones. Perfected in Copenhagen in about 1883. Examples: Royal Copenhagen **(14-R59-0.0)**, Bing & Grøndahl **(14-B36-0.0)**, and Grande Copenhagen **(14-G65-0.0)**.

Distributor. A marketer of plates who buys from manufacturers and sells to dealers. Some distributors also act as makers and as dealers.

Dresden, Meissen. Neighboring cities now in East Germany where the first hard-paste porcelain outside of China was produced by Johann Friedrich Böttger in 1708.

Dresden China. Term used in England beginning in the eighteenth century to describe true hard-paste porcelain. See *Dresden, Porcelain.*

E

Earthenware. A term for any ceramics which are not vitrified. Typical components of earthenware are 43% ball clay, 24% kaolin, 23% flint, and 10% pegmatite. Fired earthenware is normally covered with either a transparent or opaque glaze. High-fired earthenware is fired at a higher temperature to produce a harder ware. Example: Royal Doulton *Beswick Christmas* series **(26-R62-1.0)**.

Edition. The total number of plates, all with the same decoration, produced by a maker. Editions of collector's plates are normally limited to a fixed number and are not repeated. To do so would constitute a violation of the edition limit.

Electroplating. A process by which metal plates are coated with another metal by electrical charges.

Embossed Design. Raised ornamentation produced by the plate mold or by stamping a design into the body of the plate. Example: Belleek **(26-B18-0.0)**.

Enamel. A glaze material colored with suspended mineral oxides for decorating plates.

Engraved Design. Decoration produced by cutting into the surface of metal, glass, or china plates with either a tool or acid, as in etching. See *Intaglio.*

Etched Design. Decoration produced by cutting into the surface of a plate with acid. The plate is first covered with an acid-resistant paint or wax, and the design is carved through this coating. When the plate is immersed in acid, the acid "bites" into the plate surface in the shape of the design. Example: Franklin Mint silver plates **(84-F64-0.0)**. See *Intaglio.*

Exchange. A place where plates are traded, most commonly the Bradford Exchange, the world's largest trading center in limited-edition collector's plates. Incorporated in 1962, it was formerly known as Bradford Galleries Exchange. See *Trading Floor.*

F

Faience. Tin-enameled earthenware from France, Germany, or Spain developed in the seventeenth century and named for the Italian town of Faenza, a center for majolica, another name for this ware. See *Delftware.*

Feldspar. A mineral composed of aluminum silicates with either potassium, sodium, calcium, or barium. Feldspar decomposes to form kaolin, the key ingredient of china and porcelain. The addition of undecomposed feldspar to china formulas gives the ware greater hardness.

Fine China. A designation of quality which is made after firing; those plates which do not merit the designation are simply called "china."

Fire. The heating process which hardens ceramic plates in a kiln. Ceramic clay begins to undergo chemical change at 500° C and vitrifies at around 1300° C.

First Edition. The first, and presumably the only, edition of a collector's plate. The term (or its abbreviation, "FE") is sometimes used for the edition which is the first issue in a series of collector's plates. However, since no edition is normally ever reopened and therefore no "second edition" is possible, all issues of collector's plates are properly termed first editions.

First Issue. Chronologically, the first plate in a series, i.e., the plates issued in the first year of an annual series.

Flint Glass. See *Lead Crystal.*

Flux. Finely ground material added to porcelain formulas which lowers the vitrification temperature and helps fuse the components. See *Feldspar.*

Foot Rim. A slightly projected ring on the convex side of a plate. The foot rim raises the plate in the kiln during firing.

G

Glaze. Glassy, hard surface coating on plates made of silicates (glass-forming compounds) and mineral oxides. Glaze is put on ceramic ware to make it wear-resistant, waterproof, decorative, and to seal the pores. Glaze material suspended in water is applied after the first firing and is heated to the glaze's vitrification point when it fuses to the plate body. Glaze is applied by dipping, spraying, or painting. Decorating is added under, over, or with the glaze layer. See *Underglaze Decoration, Overglaze Decoration.*

I

Incised Design. Ornamentation cut into the body of the plate. Example: Veneto Flair **(38-V22-0.0)**.

Incolay Stone. The material from which the cameo-like plates produced by Incolay Studios are made. Incolay stone may contain, among other minerals, semi-precious carnelian and crystal or topaz quartz. Example: Incolay Studios **(84-I31-0.0)**.

Inlaid. Decoration on a plate created by etching, incising, or engraving a design on the surface and filling with another material.

Instaquote Trading System.™ The computerized auction market for collector's plates that is an exclusive service of The Bradford Exchange Trading Floor. Both individual collectors and dealers may trade on the system.

Intaglio. Decoration created by cutting beneath the surface of the plate. Example: Morgantown Crystal **(84-M58-0.0)**. See *Engraved Design, Etched Design.*

Iridescence. A rainbow effect on a plate's surface caused by the diffraction of light. True iridescent color effects are readily distinguished from a plate's inherent color because the pattern will change as the plate is moved. Example: Belleek **(26-B18-0.0).**

Issue. 1. The release for sale of an edition of plates by a maker. **2.** A plate in an edition. **3.** An edition within a series. A new issue is the release of the most recent plate in a continuing series. A back issue is a plate other than the most recently-issued plate in a series. Back issue usually denotes a plate that has sold out at issue price and is available only on the secondary market. See *Market.*

Issue Price. Original or first price of the plate established by the maker at the time the plate is released for sale.

J

Jasper Ware. Hard, fine-grained, unglazed stoneware made by adding barium sulfate to clay, developed by Josiah Wedgwood in the 1770s. The term "jasper" does not indicate the presence of jasper stone but most likely denotes the variety of colors in which Jasper ware can be produced. Though white in its original form, Jasper ware can be stained in blue, green, lilac, yellow, maroon, pink, taupe, or black to serve as a background for embossments of white Jasper relief for a cameo effect. When stained throughout, the body of it is called solid Jasper ware. Example: Wedgwood **(26-W90-0.0).**

Jigger. A machine with a revolving mold on which plates are formed. Semi-malleable clay is thrown on the revolving mold forming the top of the plate. The bottom of the plate is formed by a metal blade which is fastened to a pivotal arm.

K

Kaolin. The only clay which yields a white material when fired and the indispensable element of porcelain and china plates. Also called true clay or china clay, it is formed by the complete decomposition by weathering of feldspar. Kaolin is a refractory clay which can be fired at high temperatures without deforming. It produces a vitreous, translucent ceramic when fired with fluxes (fusible rocks) such as feldspar. The components of kaolin clay are 50% silica, 33% alumina, 2% oxides, 1% magnesia, 2% alkali, and 12% water.

KPM. The trademark on plates from Königliche Porzellan-Manufaktur, Berlin, Germany. Plates made by this manufacturer date from as early as 1763.

L

Lead Crystal. Extremely transparent fine quality glass, also called flint glass and lead glass, which contains a high proportion of lead oxide to give extra weight, better refractiveness and a clear ringing tone when tapped. Full lead crystal is the term used to identify glass with a 24% or greater lead content. Example: Lalique **(18-L3-0.0).**

Lead Glass. See *Lead Crystal.*

Limited-Edition Plates. Plates produced in a fixed quantity, either predetermined by number or determined by a specific period of issue or by a period of production. All true collector's plates are limited-editions.

Limoges. A town in south central France famous for its porcelain production since the discovery of kaolin deposits nearby in 1768. Limoges porcelain manufacturers have joined together to enforce quality standards. Examples: D'Arceau-Limoges **(18-D15-0.0),** Haviland **(18-H6-0.0),** Haviland & Parlon **(18-H8-0.0),** and Limoges-Turgot **(18-L52-0.0).**

Listed Plate. A plate listed and regularly quoted on the *Bradford Exchange Current Quotations.* Such a plate is often referred to as being "Bradex-listed." See *Bradex, Exchange, Over-The-Counter Plate.*

Lot. A number of plates, all in the same edition and represented by a sell order on the Exchange, usually on the secondary market and not at issue. See *Allotment.*

Luster. Decoration applied to a plate surface by application of metallic oxides such as gold, silver, platinum, or copper over the glaze. When gently fired, this leaves a thin metallic film.

M

Majolica, Maiolica. Earthenware finished with opaque white enamel, similar to faience and Delftware, but first made in the Spanish island of Majorca. See *Delftware.*

Maker. The name by which a plate is known or under which it is issued, e.g., manufacturer, distributor, or sponsor. In most cases the "maker" is the actual manufacturer, e.g., Bing & Grøndahl **(14-B36-0.0).** However, it can also be a commissioner or distributor, e.g., Schmid **(22-S12-0.0),** using a trade name, while the physical production is in fact done by a sub-contractor.

Market. The structure within which plates are bought and sold. The primary market consists of new issues which are sold by the makers or their sales representatives to dealers and distributors. Dealers and distributors in turn normally sell the new issues to the public at issue price. Secondary market or aftermarket refers to the buying and selling of plates previously sold, and usually sold out, on the primary market. In many cases secondary market prices are higher than those of the primary market.

Market Bradex. A kind of "Dow Jones" index of the overall collector's plate market expressed as a percentage, based on the current price/issue price ratio of twelve key indicator series.

Market Price. The price at which a plate is currently traded, regardless of its issue price. See *Issue Price.*

Market Price Order. An open bid posted on the Exchange to purchase an issue at the price the market demands. Only over-the-counter plates are currently traded in this way on the Exchange. See *Over-The-Counter Plate.*

Meissen. See *Dresden.*

Mint Condition. A plate in new or like-new condition (free of manufacturer defects and damage) accompanied by any original certificates and packing materials included at issue.

Modeling. The process of making the original pattern from which the master mold is made for a sculptured plate.

Mold. A general term for the form which gives a plate its shape. Clay, metal or glass is pressed into a mold to form a blank (without ornamentation). Intaglio decoration or raised ornamentation may also be formed in the mold. China or porcelain slipcasting is done in plaster-of-paris molds. Slip (diluted clay formula) is poured into the mold, and the excess water is absorbed into the plaster-of-paris. When the plate is jiggered, the mold forms the back and a tool forms the front using a moist clay mixture. See *Slip*.

N

New Issue. See *Issue*.

O

Open-End Series. A continuing series of annual plates with no established termination. Example: Royal Copenhagen *Christmas* series **(14-R59-1.0).**

Open Stock. Plates available in or produced in unlimited numbers or for an unlimited time period (and therefore not considered collector's plates).

Overglaze Decoration. A decoration consisting of precious metals such as gold, platinum, or silver and/or lithographic patterns in up to twenty-five colors, applied by hand to a porcelain piece after it has been glazed and fired a second time (glost fired). Hand-applied lithographic decoration—the most widely used form of overglaze decoration—can also be used underglaze. See *Glaze, Underglaze Decoration*.

Over-The-Counter Plate. A collector's plate not traded in sufficient volume to be *listed* on the Exchange. The majority of such plates, however, are *traded* on the Exchange and can be obtained, when available, at the prevailing market prices. See *Listed Plate*.

P

Parian China. A highly vitrified, translucent china characterized by an iridescent luster and rich, creamy tint much like that of parian marble, for which it is named. The process for making parian ware was invented by the Copeland and Garrett firm in England in the mid-nineteenth century. Example: Belleek **(26-B18-0.0).**

Paste. The combination of substances that make up potter's clay, generally that for porcelain or china.

Pewter. An alloy of tin with copper and antimony as hardeners. The greater the amount of copper and antimony, the harder the ware. Fine pewter is composed of 80% tin and 20% antimony and brass or copper. See *Alloy*.

Plate, Exchange. See *Swap'n'Sell*.

Point, Bradex Point. One percentage point of the Market Bradex.

Porcelain. The hardest vitreous ceramic fired at the highest temperatures. Although the term porcelain is often interchanged with china, true porcelain, as the term is used in the field, is distinguished from china by its very high glaze firing and low bisque firing temperature compared with the high bisque firing and lower glaze firing of china. The main firing (glaze) of porcelain is approximately 7% higher than the main firing (bisque) of china. The glaze fuses with the porcelain plate body and produces an extremely hard surface. Hard-paste or true porcelain is made from a formula whose primary components are kaolin and china stone (petuntse). When fired, the china stone vitrifies, producing a hard, glassy ceramic. True porcelain is translucent when thin, white unless colored, impervious to scratching, and transmits a ringing tone when struck. A typical porcelain formula is 50% kaolin, 25% quartz and 25% feldspar. Soft-paste porcelain was developed in Renaissance Europe in an attempt to imitate the true porcelain of China. Soft-paste porcelain was a mixture of white sand, gypsum, soda, alum, salt, and niter, fired until it vitrified. It had a soft texture, great sensitivity to sudden temperature changes, was warmer to the touch than true porcelain, and could be scratched with a file. The terms "hard" and "soft" porcelain refer to the "hard" firing temperature (around 1450°C) required for true porcelain and the "soft" firing temperature (around 1150°C) used for soft-paste porcelain. See *China*.

Pottery. 1. A general term used for all ceramic ware, but in fact properly applied only to earthenware and non-vitrified ceramics. 2. The place where ceramic objects are made and fired.

Primary Market. See *Market*.

Q

Queen's Ware. An earthenware of ivory or cream color developed by Josiah Wedgwood. The name "Queen's Ware" was adopted by other potters for similar stoneware; also often referred to as "white ware."

Quote. The Exchange's best estimate of market price at the close of the current bi-monthly trading period.

R

Relief Sculpture. Sculpture in which the design or figure is not freestanding but is raised from a background. There are three degrees of relief sculpture: Alto-relievo or high relief, where the design is almost detached from the background; Basso-relievo or bas-relief, where the design is raised somewhat; and Relievostiacciato, where the design is scarcely more than scratched. Relief designs on plates may be formed in the plate mold or formed separately and applied to the plate body. Examples: Davenport Pottery *Toby Plate Collection* **(26-D8-1.0)** and Edwin M. Knowles *Biblical Mothers Collection* **(84-K41-6.0).**

S

Saggers. Boxes of fire-clay into which objects to be glost fired are put for protection against direct contact with the flames.

Second, Second Sorting. A plate judged to be a grade below first quality, usually indicated by a scratch or gouge through the glaze over the backstamp on the back.

Secondary Market. See *Market*.

Sell Order. An offer at an asked price given by an individual or dealer to sell one or more plates on the secondary market. See *Asked Price, Exchange*.

Slip. Ceramic paste or body diluted with water to a smooth, creamy consistency used for slip-casting. See *Mold.*

Sponsor. Authoritative body (prestigious organization, museum, or person) which attests to the authenticity of the artwork depicted on a plate.

Steatite, Soapstone. A natural rock whose primary component is talc. Steatite is used in porcelain formulas as a flux.

Sterling Silver. An alloy which, by United States law, must have the minimum fineness of 92.5% by weight of pure silver and a maximum of 7.5% by weight of a base metal, usually copper. Example: Franklin Mint *Christmas* **(84-F64-1.0).**

Stoneware. A hard ceramic fired to vitrification but not to translucency. Typical components of stoneware are 30% ball clay, 32% kaolin, 15% flint, and 23% cornish stone. Example: Wedgwood's Jasper Ware **(26-W90-0.0).**

Supermarket Plate. Common term for a plate edition of dubious limitations, cheaply produced and not considered a true collector's plate.

Swap 'n' Sell Event. An open buy and sell auction for the trading of plates from one collector to another. Swap 'n' Sell events have been organized at major plate conventions, traveling shopping mall shows, and between collector's clubs. A registration fee is normally charged for those plates offered by sellers.

T

Terra Cotta. A general term for any kind of fired clay. Strictly speaking, terra cotta is an earthenware produced from a clay which fires to a dull ochre or red color. The ware, left unglazed is coarse and porous. Example: Veneto Flair **(38-V22-0.0).**

Tin Glaze. A glaze, colored white by oxide of tin, which produces a heavy opaque surface when fired. See *Delftware.*

Toriart. The process by which wood shavings and resin are combined to form a wood material which is then molded and carved into three-dimensional forms. Example: Anri **(38-A54-0.0).**

Trader. An individual or a dealer who buys, sells, or bids on plates through the Exchange. See *Trading Floor, Exchange.*

Trading Floor. The physical area of The Bradford Exchange where the trading of plates takes place. All secondary market trading on the Exchange originates here, and it is the daily market activity on the Trading Floor that determines the prices quoted on the Exchange. See *Broker, Bradex, Quote.*

Transfer-Printing. Method by which an engraved design may be transferred from an engraver's plate or lithographer's block to the surface of a plate. Originally, thin papers were inked with a mixture of metallic oxide in an oily medium, or sometimes used with a greasy substance onto which metallic oxide could be dusted. Transfer-printing may be overglaze or underglaze.

Translucency. The quality of transmitting light without transperance. In a plate, translucency depends on the quality of the china or porcelain, thickness of the plate, and firing temperature. Underfired porcelain is not translucent.

Triptych. A set of three panels hinged side by side, bearing paintings or carvings, usually on a religious theme and originally used as a portable altarpiece. Example: Anna-Perenna **(22-A3-3.0).**

True Clay. See *Kaolin.*

U

Underglaze Decoration. Decoration applied after a plate has been fired once (bisque fired) but before it is glazed and fired a second time. Underglaze painting is most commonly done in cobalt blue pigment (although other colors can be used) because this is the most stable color and can withstand high firing temperatures. True underglaze technique indicates that such painting was done by hand. See *Glaze, Overglaze Decoration.*

V

Vitrification. A fusion of potters clay at temperatures between 1250°C and 1450°C to form a glassy, nonporous substance. With continued heating, the substance will become translucent.